TRANSISTOR

CIRCUIT ANALYSIS

AND DESIGN

PRENTICE-HALL INTERNATIONAL, INC., *London*
PRENTICE-HALL OF AUSTRALIA, PTY., LTD., *Sydney*
PRENTICE-HALL OF CANADA, LTD., *Toronto*
PRENTICE-HALL OF INDIA (PRIVATE) LTD., *New Delhi*
PRENTICE-HALL OF JAPAN, INC., *Tokyo*

TRANSISTOR

CIRCUIT ANALYSIS

AND DESIGN

John J. Corning   Manager,
Monolithic Circuit Packaging Engineering
International Business Machines Corporation

Prentice-Hall, Inc.   Englewood Cliffs, New Jersey

Library of Congress Catalog Number 65-21179
Printed in the United States of America
93005c

To my wife, Marie

PREFACE

This text is intended as a thorough and comprehensive yet easy-to-read discourse on transistor circuit analysis and design. It will be useful in the curricula of technical institutions and engineering colleges, and as a reference work for technicians and practicing circuit design engineers. The material is presented logically and meaningfully, starting with an exposure to semiconductor theory and carrying on through transistor parameters and characteristics and techniques for circuit analysis and design. A highly mathematical approach is not used. The entire work is based on the premise that the reader needs background only in algebra and basic electrical circuits.

The material falls generally into four blocks. The first is an introduction to semiconductor physics and its relation to junction behavior in diodes and transistors (Chapters 1–3). The second block (Chapters 4–7) is a concentrated coverage of transistors from the device viewpoint; this includes parameters, characteristics, biasing techniques, and equivalent circuits. The major portion of the book (Chapters 8–15) deals with the analysis and design of transistor circuits, including low- and high-frequency amplifiers, oscillators, pulse circuits, and power-supply circuits. The text concludes (Chapter 16) with a series of lab experiments.

The explanation of semiconductor theory is largely qualitative and easily understood. This material is confined generally to discussions of charge behavior, which serve as the basis for understanding current directions and junction phenomena in diodes and transistors.

The discussions of devices emphasize the real attributes of transistors, such as leakage currents and parameter distributions. This approach, of course, is vital to meaningful circuit design work. A treatment of d-c bias techniques is the first consideration of the device as a circuit element. The aim here is an ability to design circuits to achieve any desired operating point and stability. The a-c analysis of transistors exploits graphical interrelations, and yields equivalent-circuit concepts that provide a practical relation between theory and application.

vii

The material on circuit analysis and design is presented with actual circuit problems in mind. Thus the manner in which d-c bias circuitry effects a-c performance is discussed as routine. The compromises between performance variables are discussed. Examples emphasize the use of parameters as they appear on device specification sheets. The material presented here on *RC* circuits, cascade stages, and frequency response is not presented elsewhere in such breadth or with so direct a link to real-case circuit design. In like fashion the material on oscillators and pulse circuits emphasizes the use of both tunnel diodes and unijunction devices. In every circuit discussion there is an attempt to describe logically and qualitatively the operation of the given circuit and the design criteria involved. We then consider the design of circuits to achieve prescribed performance goals. Every major section of the text has illustrative examples to demonstrate the implementation of the relevant analytical or design philosophy. These can also serve as a ready reference and refresher media from which an engineer or technician can extrapolate solutions to problems that he encounters in his working environment.

As a supplement to the text material it is beneficial for the student to establish confidence in working physically with semiconductors and semiconductor circuits. To this end a series of laboratory experiments is suggested. These experiments are designed to provide an understanding of the *basic* concepts of circuit operation; hence they are relatively simple. Approached with the proper attitude, they will provide not only an understanding of the variables in circuit operation, but also stimulation and incentive for the experimenter to design and study circuits of his own choice.

I have developed the material presented here over a period of years while teaching those people for whom the book is intended. When certain topics proved especially difficult for the student to comprehend, I developed presentation methods and sequences that minimized the comprehension problem. Knowing also the inherent desire of the student to apply knowledge to a field of his interest, I have included a large scope of circuit applications. Circuit analysis must be simple yet thorough. A great number of specific design procedures are itemized. This text, then, provides not only knowledge, but understanding of how to apply it in many areas.

I am deeply grateful to the many people who provided competent secretarial assistance in the typing of the manuscript. Special thanks are directed to Miss Diane Goodwin.

I wish also to express my sincere and lasting appreciation to David De Witt, Robert A. Henle, and Dr. Paul R. Low of International Business Machines Corporation for their technical counsel and for their many constructive comments in the technical review of this book.

JOHN J. CORNING

Poughkeepsie, New York

CONTENTS

1

SEMICONDUCTOR

MATERIALS

To properly design a given circuit using semiconductor diodes and transistors, we must have a complete knowledge of the electrical properties of these devices, including an awareness of certain limitations such as the maximum allowed values of current, voltage, and power. We must also know how performance properties such as power gain and terminal impedances vary with temperature, frequency, and operating point either individually or in combination. These limitations and attributes, to be discussed in later chapters, are best understood in terms of the properties of semiconductor materials.

The complexity of semiconductors stems from the nature of the materials used to make them. As simple as the concepts of current flow seem to be for passive devices, special knowledge is necessary in order to understand the total aspects of current flow in semiconductor devices. Once this basic knowledge is acquired, the understanding of performance properties and applications is relatively simple. The steppingstones that relate the nature of the material to the final device are: (1) the nature of the semiconductor material determines the device geometry, and (2) that the device geometry in turn establishes the values of the dynamic performance attributes and the electrical limitations.

The beginnings of our study lie logically in a knowledge of the materials used in semiconductors. The easiest way to understand them is to compare them with other known materials—namely, conductors and insulators.

1.1. Review of electron theory. Our study of conductors, insulators, and semiconductors will be mainly an analysis of current flow in these materials. To begin this analysis, we must review the electron theory of matter. We should know, for example, that every material, whether a solid, liquid, or gas, is composed of some combination of basic elements, such as oxygen, copper, sodium, or sulphur. Over one hundred elements have been discovered and each one is different from every other one, as we shall see.

The smallest piece of any element that retains its physical and chemical properties is called an *atom*. Notice that this generalization applies to all elements. Thus, an atom of copper is the smallest piece of the element copper, an atom of gold is the smallest piece of the element gold, and so on for all the elements. All of the atoms that go together to make a given element are the same. The atoms of different elements are different. In fact, the reasons for the differences between elements are the differences in the atoms of the elements.

Classically, an atom is described as a miniature solar system, the equilibrium of which depends on the laws of charged particles. These laws state that unlike electric charges attract each other, whereas like charges repel each other. Hence, just as gravitational forces keep the planets traveling in orderly paths around the sun, electrostatic forces control the motion of negatively charged electrons traveling in orbits around a positively charged center. The center of the atom and center of electrostatic attraction is called the *nucleus*. Besides containing all the positive charge in an atom, it also has practically all the mass or weight of the atom.

The simplest of atomic configurations is that of the hydrogen atom as shown in Fig. 1.1. In this instance the nucleus contains one unit of positive charge, called a *proton*. A single electron is held, traveling in an orbit or shell around the nucleus, by its electrostatic attraction to an equal and opposite charge. This example not only establishes the appearance of the simplest of atoms, but also demonstrates another key attribute of atoms: they are electrically neutral systems.

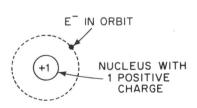

E⁻ IN ORBIT

NUCLEUS WITH
1 POSITIVE
CHARGE

Fig. 1.1 Hydrogen atom.

Any periodic table of the chemical elements lists all the elements sequentially from 1 to 103. This serial number or *atomic number* indicates the number of protons in the nucleus. Since the atoms of a given element are electrically neutral, the atomic number also indicates the number of orbital electrons that exist in each atom of each element. For aluminum the atomic number is 13; therefore the protons in the nucleus and the orbital electrons number 13 respectively. Lead has atomic number 82; there are 82 protons in the nucleus and 82 electrons traveling in the shells of the atom.

The periodic table also lists the *atomic weight* or atomic mass for each element. Here there is apt to be some concern. The mass of a proton has been quite accurately measured by work with the hydrogen atom. A review of the periodic table reveals that almost every atom has an atomic weight greater than the weight provided by it protons. This suggests that particles having mass but no charge must exist in the nucleus. Such charges are called *neutrons*. Table 1.1 gives the proton and neutron count in the nuclei of atoms of selected elements.

TABLE 1.1   Resumé of the atomic structure of selected elements.

ELEMENT	ATOMIC #	ATOMIC WT.	PROTONS	NEUTRONS	A	B	C	D	E	F
					ORBIT OCCUPANCY					
H	1	1	1	0	1					
He	2	4	2	2	2					
Li	3	7	3	4	2	1				
Ar	18	40	18	22	2	8	8			
Ge	32	72	32	40	2	8	18	4		

Some of the more complicated atomic structures—those of helium, neon, and silicon—are shown in Fig. 1.2. The sum total aspects of the atoms are indicated by showing both protons and neutrons in the nucleus. Electrons equaling the number of protons are traveling in shells around each nucleus. The fact of atomic neutrality is one to be remembered, as it is a basis for the charge analysis of materials encountered later on.

Let us develop further the reasons for the distribution of electrons in separate shells, traveling around a nucleus. The "classical" model for an atom is shown in Fig. 1.3(a). As this figure suggests, it is unlikely that we will

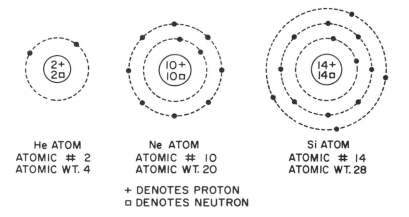

He ATOM
ATOMIC # 2
ATOMIC WT. 4

Ne ATOM
ATOMIC # 10
ATOMIC WT. 20

Si ATOM
ATOMIC # 14
ATOMIC WT. 28

+ DENOTES PROTON
□ DENOTES NEUTRON

Fig. 1.2   Forms of the helium, neon, and silicon atoms.

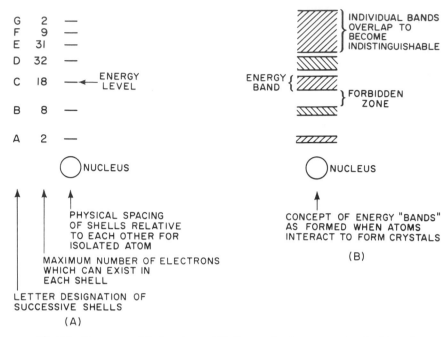

Fig. 1.3 Energy models for atoms. (A) Energy levels are associated with each shell of an isolated atom. (B) Energy bands occur when isolated atoms are brought together so that shells interact.

ever encounter an atom with more than seven shells of electrons. As may be seen, the shells have different radii, and the distances between shells get smaller as we proceed away from the nucleus. The most significant aspect of the shells is that they represent the energy states of the electrons. What does this mean? We know electrons are in motion about the nucleus. Thus, they have energy—in particular, kinetic energy or energy of motion. They also have potential energy due to their position relative to the nucleus. It is reasonable to expect, however, that all electrons do not have the same energy. Consider this analogy. Fifty people gather for a meeting. Each by the most basic of descriptive generalities is a human being, yet each has a different weight. Conceivably there might be 50 separate weights varying between 160 and 208 pounds. As a convenience, however, it could be reported that three people had weights close to 165 pounds, seven people had weights close to 175 pounds, 20 people had weights close to 185 pounds, 15 people had weights close to 195 pounds, and five people had weights close to 205 pounds. We know that all people in each group are not of identical weight; yet, using a tolerance of several pounds, we can lump the weights around a central average number. So, too, our electrons are related to the energy levels or shells.

Each shell is said to embrace or contain a specific number of allowed energy states or levels. Therefore, one can expect to find electrons with their particular energy levels in the appropriate and corresponding shell which contains an allowed state equal to the energy level of the particular electron. That is, electrons with energies at or near value A associate with the shell A energy level of Fig. 1.3(a), and this pattern continues for each successive shell.

Low-energy electrons travel in the orbits or shells close to the nucleus, while electrons with high energy travel in orbits or shells far from the nucleus. Thus as we proceed from shell A out from the nucleus of any atom, the energy levels of the electrons in each shell increase. As the brief resume of atomic structures in Table 1.1 indicates, each inner shell of an atom is filled completely before the next shell has electron occupancy. This generality applies to all elements.

A fundamental law of charge behavior is that unlike charges are attracted towards each other. The low-energy electrons in innermost orbits experience a large amount of attractive force towards the nucleus. Such innermost electrons are called *bound electrons* as they are rarely if ever removed from the control of the parent nucleus. The high-energy electrons in the outer shells experience relatively little attractive force to the nucleus because of their large separation from the nucleus. Under certain conditions which are discussed later, we will observe how such outer electrons are displaced easily from the control of the parent nucleus.

When individual atoms are placed close together to form homogeneous masses or crystals of the solid state, there is interaction between corresponding shells or energy levels in the individual atoms. The interaction causes the electrons of corresponding shells to change their energy levels. Whereas each shell of an isolated atom had very few allowed energy levels, the so-called "shell" of an atom in a crystal is more appropriately thought of as a *band* of a larger number of discrete energy levels. Each allowed energy band in the crystalline atom is separated by an energy increment. Since the electrons can group only in the allowed bands and never between bands, the increments of energy separating the allowed bands can be referred to as *forbidden zones* or *forbidden bands*. The spread of energy levels into energy bands as we take a single atom and join it with others to form a crystal is shown in Fig. 1.3(b).

The precise number of individual energy levels included in each band of energies is established by the principles of quantum mechanics, a subject not included in the scope of this text. It should be expected, however, that as we proceed farther from the nucleus, and encounter more electrons in the successive shells, there is greater complexity to the interaction of electrons. It will be found that the greatest number of discrete levels are created near the outer shells. It will be found also that the separation between these discrete levels within the allowed energy band is the smallest for outer-shell interaction. It will also be found that the forbidden zone between successive bands gets smaller and smaller. It is even permissible to conceive of the forbidden zone disappearing completely, with the result that successive bands merge to become overlapping. The condition of the last energy band will be seen to be the determining factor in the classification of an element as an insulator, conductor, or semiconductor.

Let us consider the term *valence state*. When an atom is in its normal electrically neutral state; that is, when it has a balanced number of protons and electrons, the outermost electrons are called *valence electrons*. The implication is that the *valence shell* is the highest energy level associated with the atom in its normal state. Thus, for aluminum with an atomic number of 13, the valence shell is shell C, and for copper with an atomic number of 29, the valence shell is shell D. When atoms are brought together to form crystals, the energy band created by the interaction of the valence shells is called the *valence band*.

1.2. Conductors and insulators.   Having reviewed the basics of electron theory, we will apply these first to a study of current flow in highly conductive materials. A perusal of the physical properties of metals will reveal that silver, copper and gold, in that order, are the best metallic conductors of all the elements. The most general comment possible is that these elements have but few electrons in their valence shells, and that the valence shells are in fact outer rather than inner shells. Typically, the valence band of a conducting element is only partially filled. This means that within the confines of the valence band there are *available, unfilled* energy states. The presence of these unfilled states permits the valence electrons to be relatively free to move randomly between unfilled states in the valence band. This condition exists because we view the existence of these free valence electrons only with respect to their existence in proximity to the unfilled states which are available within the valence band. We no longer associate these free electrons with any given atom. The valence electron follows a random path as the particle moves from state to state in the valence band; this random condition is partialy due to the collisions which occur between the moving valence electron and the atomic lattice itself (for example, atoms and/or other electrons). The random path of a valence electron might be as shown in Figure 1.4(a). When we now apply an electric field across our material, each random increment of path is bent slightly in response to the electrostatic force of the field. The applied field causes then the valence electron to experience a specific direction of drift through the conductor. This is shown in Fig. 1.4(b). The drift of charge in a specifically controlled direction provides a measureable current flow. Note that the greater the magnitude of the applied field the more pronounced the control of the drift of the valence particles. The simultaneous existence of loosely bound valence electrons and empty available states in the same band is the dominant characteristic of the class of elements known as *conductors*.

In our discussion of conductors, we have thus far cited only the case of an unfilled valence band. Conduction is easy because available states exist right within the valence band itself. Another situation is apt to occur in the valence state of conductors. We have mentioned that the forbidden zone between energy bands diminishes to zero if we get far enough

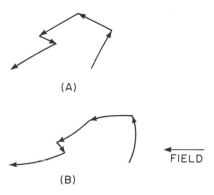

(A)

(B)

FIELD

Fig. 1.4 Motion of valence electron in a conductor. (A) Random motion occurs when no field is applied. (B) Direction of drift results when field is applied.

away from the nucleus. It could happen then for elements with many electrons that a completely filled valence band overlaps a completely empty band. We are again in a situation where unoccupied energy levels are readily available to the electrons in the valence band of the metal. We can expect that such an element behaves as the conductor previously described.

Let us now consider the situation of elements either singly or in combination that have lower atomic numbers. The valence shells we have in mind are A, B, and C. The resultant valence bands are usually *completely filled*. The only available unoccupied energy levels exist in the *next* energy band. For low-level valence bands, however, the forbidden zone increment to the next higher energy band is a significant amount of energy. In addition, electrons in the lower shells tend to be tightly bound to the nucleus. Since the valence electrons do not move in response to an applied potential, and since no available states are really available, such an element is known as an *insulator*.

The basic difference between insulators and conductors can be depicted pictorially by an *energy diagram*. We have established that unoccupied energy states *must* be readily available to valence electrons if conduction is to occur. The band of unoccupied energy states may be defined as a *conduction band*. This is reasonable because any valence electron existing in proximity to an unoccupied state moves readily to the unoccupied state. Using an energy diagram, we can pictorially show the relative positions of the valence bands and the nearest conduction band to distinguish between conductors and insulators. These are shown in Fig. 1.5. In the diagram which applies to a conductor, we note a broad valence band overlapping the conduction band. The former band exists typically in elements with shells D, E, and

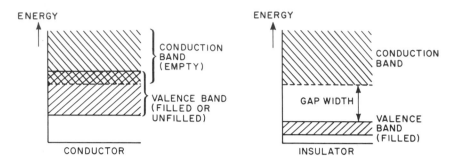

Fig. 1.5 Energy diagrams for conductors and insulators.

F as valence shells. The valence band as shown may be filled or unfilled, because in either instance, valence electrons move easily to empty, available energy states in the conduction band. In the diagram that applies to an insulator, we notice first, a narrow valence band, and, secondly, a significant energy difference *between* the top of the valence band and the bottom of the conduction band. Such a narrow valence band exists if the elements have as typical valence shells, shells A, B, and C. The energy difference between the valence and conduction bands is noted as a *gap width* or a *forbidden zone*.

To summarize, we note that any element with valence electrons having energy greater than the minimum energy of the conduction band is considered a *conductor*. Any element or substance whose valence electrons have energy less than the minimum of the conduction band will not conduct electricity easily, and categorically will be an *insulator*. Most elements with valence electrons in the lower shells A, B, and C do not conduct electricity as well as most elements with valence electrons in the higher shells D, E, and F. It should be understood that with insulators no high voltage (within reason) will cause the tightly bound valence electrons to break away from their parent nuclei.

One final comment of importance is that materials formed from elements classed as conductors have a positive temperature coefficient of resistance. Thus as temperature increases the resistance of the material increases. The dominating factor in this phenomenon is the vibration of the atoms in their crystalline array or lattice. As temperature increases, the thermal energy causes increases in the vibrational displacement of atoms in their crystalline array. This atom motion impedes the ability of conduction electrons to move as far as they otherwise would in the presence of a given field at lower temperatures. Since the displacement distance of electrons decreases as temperature increases, the effective current is less. This, of course, corresponds to an increase in material resistance.

1.3. Intrinsic semiconductors. Having established a basis for understanding the relative ease or difficulty of current flow in conductors and insulators, we proceed to consider a class of elements known as *semiconductors*. As we might infer from the name, these are elements that *do* exhibit conductive characteristics, but to a limited degree. The major attribute distinguishing semiconductors from all other elements, is that semiconductors have a negative temperature coefficient of resistance. Such a phenomenon exists because of a uniquely small gap width (as compared to insulators) existing between the valence band and the conduction band. At low temperatures all valence electrons retain association with the valence band, and the semiconductor behaves like an insulator. At higher temperatures, valence electrons are energized to the conduction band and the semiconductor starts to behave like a conductor. These facts explain the negative temperature coefficient that semiconductors exhibit. Since the conductivities are never very high except for very high temperatures we can properly consider a semiconductor to be a special class of insulator.

Of all the existing elements some thirteen possess negative coefficients of resistance. These elements are called *elemental semiconductors* and are listed in Table 1.2. When reduced to their pure form, these elements are called *intrinsic semiconductors*. The more common and useful semiconductor materials are those which appear in column IV of the periodic table. These elements are unique in having four electrons in the valence shell. The shells that contain the four valence electrons are as follows: for carbon, the second shell; for silicon, the third shell; for germanium, the fourth shell; and for tin, the fifth shell. These elements serve as the classical examples in explaining an energy-band situation that can lead to a negative temperature coefficient of resistance.

We can begin with the physical picture of the column IV elements. The presence of the four valence electrons results in a very uniform and orderly meshing of the atoms when they join to form crystals of the solid state.

TABLE 1.2 Elements in the periodic table considered elemental semiconductors. Group number indicates number of E^- in outer shell. Period number indicates identity of valence shell.

GROUP	IIIA	IVA	VA	VIA	VIIA
PERIOD 2	B	C			
PERIOD 3		Si	P	S	
PERIOD 4		Ge	As	Se	
PERIOD 5		Sn	Sb	Te	I
PERIOD 6			Bi		

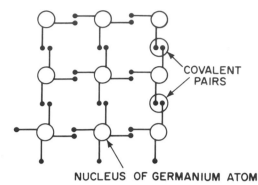

COVALENT
PAIRS

NUCLEUS OF GERMANIUM ATOM

Fig. 1.6 Two-dimensional picture of column or group IV bonding.

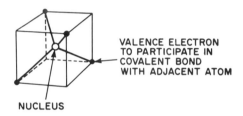

VALENCE ELECTRON
TO PARTICIPATE IN
COVALENT BOND
WITH ADJACENT ATOM

NUCLEUS

Fig. 1.7 Three-dimensional picture of column IV bonding. Each corner electron becomes a covalent bond. Repetitious buildup of arrays such as this constitutes the three-dimensional crystal.

Figure 1.6 is a two-dimensional presentation of the meshing of a number of atoms. The actual three-dimensional arrangement of the atoms is shown in Fig. 1.7. The centermost atom in Figs. 1.6 and 1.7 has its valence shell overlapping the valence shells of four surrounding atoms. One electron in each of these surrounding atoms seems to pair up with an electron in our centermost atom. Each of these pairs of electrons is equidistant between the two nuclei. This unique form of electron sharing is called *covalent* sharing. A special type of force exists between the electrons in the individual electron pairs. This force is called a *covalent bond*. The band structure that results for the crystalline state is shown in Fig. 1.8. Here we notice a relatively wide valence band separated from the conduction band by a relatively narrow gap width.

At very low temperatures, all the covalently-bonded electron pairs are intact, and no conduction would be observed if a field were applied. As the

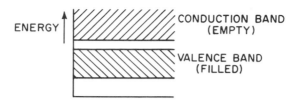

Fig. 1.8 Energy diagram and band conditions in an intrinsic material at low temperature.

ambient temperature of such materials is increased, the covalent electrons are given more and more energy. Ultimately, we might expect one of the electrons of a covalent pair to get enough energy to overcome the covalent bonding force. When enough energy is given to the system, covalent electrons will be energized all the way to the energy levels of the conduction band. Such an electron can then be thought of as actually moving away permanently from the covalent bond. Once this happens, the electrical balance or the neutrality of the atom from whence it came is disturbed, and the atom becomes a positive ion. For convenience, we can assume this unit of positive charge to exist at the spot formerly occupied by the electron that has been energized away. Such a unit of positive charge is called a *hole*, and is demonstrated in Fig. 1.9.

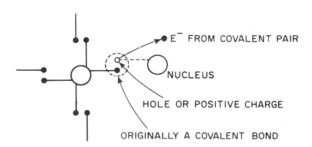

Fig. 1.9 Nature of a covalent bond.

The energy gap between the valence and conduction bands in an intrinsic semiconductor can be represented by the symbol ΔE. It is important to realize that particles *cannot* and *do not* exist in this zone. They must associate with either the conduction or the valence bands since an electron can associate with only one allowed state.

The energy diagram for an intrinsic semiconductor at room temperature is shown in Fig. 1.10. Here we show two electrons in the conduction band

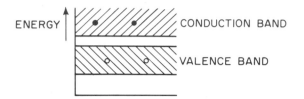

Fig. 1.10   Energy diagram of an intrinsic material at room temperature.

and two holes in the valence state. The two holes are the former locations in the valence state of the electrons now shown in the conduction state. Figure 1.10 illustrates an important fact about an intrinsic semiconductor: the number of excess electrons in the conduction state equals the number of holes (positive ions) in the valence state.

In passing, we should note that for silicon the gap width or forbidden zone is 1.1 electron volts of energy and that the actual number of intrinsic electrons in the conduction state at room temperature is 1.5×10^{10} e/cc of material. The gap width for germanium is 0.7 electron volts and there are 2.4×10^{13} e/cc of material in the conduction state at room temperature. Germanium has its valence electrons in shell D whereas silicon has its valence electrons in shell C. Thus, the energy concept presentation is justified with the knowledge that the energy difference between the two valence levels and the fixed conduction reference is more for silicon than for germanium.

Quite frequently in the literature a concept known as the *Fermi level* is used to supplement the understanding of the temperature-dependent energy distribution of electrons in a crystal. We have seen, for example, that in an intrinsic semiconductor all covalent bonds were intact at low temperature. At higher temperature covalent bonds break, creating excess electrons in the higher energy states associated with the conduction band. Holes or unoccupied energy states are made available, then, in the valence band. From a mathematical viewpoint there is interest in the probabilities of specific energy states being occupied by electrons. Such a probability function is given by the so-called *Fermi-Dirac distribution function*, which is

$$f(E) = \frac{1}{1 + e^{(E - E_r)/kT}} \qquad (1.1)$$

where $f(E) =$ the probability that a specific energy level E is occupied at a specific temperature T

$E =$ the specific energy level

$T =$ temperature in degrees absolute

$k =$ Boltzmann's constant $= 1.38 \times 10^{-23}$ joule/°K

$E_F =$ the energy known as *Fermi level*

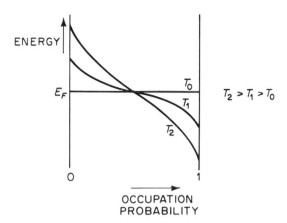

Fig. 1.11 Fermi distribution function of occupation probability for various temperatures.

The *Fermi level* E_F has double significance. From a strict mathematical viewpoint, it is the energy level for which the probability of occupancy is 1/2. Extending the mathematical to obtain a physical interpretation, we can induce that most energy states higher than E_F are unoccupied whereas most energy states below E_F are occupied. The Fermi-Dirac distribution function can be shown graphically as in Fig. 1.11. When the curve is drawn for an absolute temperature of zero, we can see that the probability of finding an occupied state at energies higher than E_F is zero. Thus, all the energy levels below E_F are filled whereas all energy states above E_F are empty. For temperatures other than absolute zero, we note that the distribution function is symmetrical about the Fermi level E_F. Thus, as the probability of finding occupied states above E_F increases, the probability of finding unoccupied states below E_F increases. The primary interpretation of Fermi level is that it is the specific energy level for which the occupation probability is 1/2. The actual energy *value* for the Fermi level will depend on the crystal being analyzed and the temperature at which the analysis is being made. No matter what the temperature or excess-electron condition, the Fermi level will always adjust to a value indicating an occupation probability of 1/2.

Let us now apply the concept of Fermi level to an intrinsic semiconductor. At room temperature and beyond, excess electrons exist in the high-energy states associated with the conduction band. For every excess electron in the conduction band, there is a hole or unoccupied state in the valence band. The holes exist because of broken covalent bonds and are at the top of the valence state. The excess electrons in all likelihood exist near the bottom of the conduction band. We should expect, then, that the Fermi level for an intrinsic semiconductor lies in the vicinity of the halfway point between the

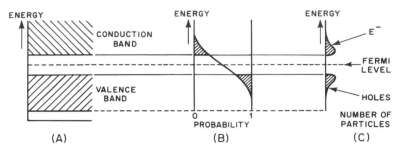

Fig. 1.12 Summary for intrinsic semiconductor: (A) Fermi-level position on energy diagram. (B) Distribution function for a given band gap. (C) Distribution of E^- occupancy and E^- nonoccupancy (hole).

top of the valence and the bottom of the conduction bands. The positioning of the Fermi level in an intrinsic semiconductor is shown in Fig. 1.12(a) at an arbitrary temperature. The complete plot of the distribution function is shown in Fig. 1.12b. Here we see that the tails overlap the conduction and valence bands. There are then predictable probabilities that electrons exist in the conduction state and holes exist in the valence state. In Fig. 1.12(c) we show the possible distributions of unoccupied energy levels (holes) in the valence band and occupied energy levels (excess electrons) in the conduction band. As mentioned earlier, the greatest part of these distributions lie near the respective band edges.

When a potential is applied across the intrinsic semiconductor material, there are two specific components of current. One current component is composed of electrons already in the conduction state. This, of course, is something we should have anticipated. The second component of current involves the holes in the valence state. *Hole current* in the valence state is explained with the help of Fig. 1.13. Here we illustrate a material at a temperature such that three electrons have been elevated to the conduction band. There are then three corresponding holes shown in the valence state. When a potential is applied as shown, the behavior of the excess or high-energy electrons in the conduction state is quite predictable—they drift to the right. The holes in the valence band are always able to be filled to reform a covalent bond if an electron were spatially available. In the presence of a field, neighboring atoms contribute thermally-excited valence electrons which drift to fill the specific holes of interest. When an electron fills a hole, a new hole is created at the spot formerly occupied by the electron. Valence action then, is merely an orderly rearrangement of charges in the valence state. For convenience, we call the ionic charge "motion" in the valence state a *hole current*. This distinguishes the valence contribution from the

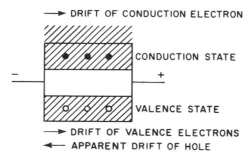

Fig. 1.13 Conduction in an intrinsic semiconductor. Note that the applied field causes both conduction and valence electrons to drift in the same direction.

conduction band contribution, which is termed an *electron current*. Even though the number of electrons comprising the electron current equals the number of holes comprising the hole current, the magnitudes of the two currents are not equal. For germanium, the electron current is approximately twice the magnitude of the hole current. In silicon the electron current is approximately three times the hole current. This phenomenon of unequal current magnitudes can be explained in terms of a particle property known as *drift mobility*.

Basically, the *mobility factor* is a numerical indication of how well, or how poorly, charged particles will move through a material when a potential is applied across the material. The effective drift velocity of the particle involves a given time and a given linear distance d through the material. Both valence and conduction electrons encounter the impediment of crystal or lattice imperfections as they travel through a semiconductor. Because the conduction band electrons have higher energy than the valence electrons, they experience less diversions in the presence of crystal imperfections than do valence band electrons. Thus, in a given time, they are less opposed in progressing through the material than are the valence electrons. An idealized view of conduction and valence electron displacement through a material in a given time is shown in Figure 1.14. Valence electron displacement is less than conduction electron displacement. This is analogous to saying that the mobility factor of conduction band electrons is greater than the mobility factor of valence band holes. This is why the electron current exceeds the hole current in both silicon and germanium. The actual values of the drift mobility factors at room temperature are as follows: for electrons in silicon,

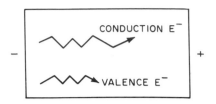

CONDUCTION E⁻

−   +

VALENCE E⁻

Fig. 1.14 Displacement distances of conduction and valence electrons in an intrinsic semiconductor for a specific time interval and a given field.

1500 cm/sec/v/cm; for holes in silicon, 500 cm/sec/v/cm; for electrons in germanium, 3900 cm/sec/v/cm; for holes in germanium, 1900 cm/sec/v/cm. These values are not constant. There is a generally decreasing value for mobility as temperature increases. The exact function depends on the concentration of the particles, but, in general, can be said to decrease because of the increased agitation of the atomic-lattice vibration which causes lower effective drift motion.

Certain mathematical expressions describing current flow and other electrical properties of a semiconductor are of interest. In the most basic form, the calculation of current flow in any material requires a knowledge of how many carriers are passing a certain point per unit of time. That is to say

$$I = \frac{\Delta Q}{\Delta T} \qquad (1.2)$$

where I = current, in amperes
ΔQ = quantity of charge, in coulombs
ΔT = time interval, in seconds

More specifically, Eq. 1.2 could be rewritten as

$$I = NevA \qquad (1.3)$$

where I = current, in amperes
N = density of conduction carriers, number/cm³
e = electron charge = 1.6×10^{-19} coulombs
v = velocity of carriers, cm/sec
A = cross sectional area, in cm²

Notice that the units of Eq. (1.3) reduce to coulombs/second just as in Eq. (1.2). The velocity of the carriers is related to the mobility factor as follows:

$$v = \frac{\mu V}{L} \qquad (1.4)$$

where v = velocity of carriers, cm/sec
μ = mobility, cm²/volt-sec
V = applied voltage, volts
L = length of material, cm

Combining Eqs. (1.3) and (1.4), we get

$$I = \frac{Ne\mu VA}{L} \tag{1.5}$$

Equation (1.5) is a general equation, useful in determining the current in any material. It relates the physical properties of the material (N, μ, L, A) and the applied voltage, V. As far as an intrinsic semiconductor is concerned, we have established that the total current is the sum of an electron current and a hole current. That is,

$$I_{\text{net}} = I_n + I_p \tag{1.6}$$

where I_{net} = net or total current
       I_n = electron current
       I_p = hole current

Substituting the appropriate physical values, we might observe for an intrinsic semiconductor that

$$I_n = \frac{n_i e \mu_n VA}{L} \tag{1.7}$$

$$I_p = \frac{p_i e \mu_p VA}{L} \tag{1.8}$$

where n_i = concentration of intrinsic electrons in the conduction band
       p_i = concentration of intrinsic holes in the valence band
       μ_n = electron mobility
       μ_p = hole mobility

Since, for an intrinsic material, $n_i = p_i = n$,

$$I_{\text{net}} = ne \frac{V}{L} A(\mu_n + \mu_p) \tag{1.9}$$

The conductivity, σ, of the material is given by

$$\sigma = ne(\mu_n + \mu_p) \tag{1.10}$$

where σ = conductivity in (ohm-cm)$^{-1}$. In spite of the decrease in mobility with temperature, the increase in the number of carriers, n, is very rapid as temperature increases. Thus, we see that for semiconductor materials the conductivity improves as temperature is increased.

One final comment about intrinsic materials. The numbers chosen (Fig. 1.13) for excess electrons and bound holes were merely to clarify the principles of current flow. At room temperature intrinsic germanium has 2.4×10^{13} electrons/cm^3 in the conduction band and intrinsic silicon has 1.5×10^{10} electrons/cm^3 in the conduction band.

Semiconductor materials in the intrinsic state, such as those discussed, are not especially useful. Certain types of impurities, when introduced into intrinsic materials, increase the semiconductor's usefulness and versatility. When such impurities are added to an intrinsic semiconductor, the new composite is called an *extrinsic semiconductor*. Generally speaking, the conductivity of an extrinsic material is never less than the conductivity of the parent intrinsic material.

1.4. N-Type semiconductors.   The N-type impurities are such elements as arsenic, antimony, and phosphorus. These elements have five electrons in the valence shell. When one of these impurity atoms is placed into intrinsic germanium, four of the five valence electrons bond covalently to valence electrons in surrounding germanium atoms. The fifth electron, however, stands alone. Such a material is called a "negative" or *N-type* semiconductor. This situation is depicted in Fig. 1.15.

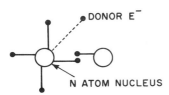

Fig. 1.15   Localized N atom in an intrinsic semiconductor.

Relatively speaking, the fifth electron assumes an energy level higher than any other electron in the system. There are several reasons for assigning it this level. The most obvious factor is that the fifth electron does not experience any covalent bonding force. Another reason is the presence of significant screening interferences between the fifth electron and its parent nucleus by virtue of the other atoms present in the system. This tends to reduce the force of attraction between the fifth electron and its parent nucleus. Thus, with the application of only a small amount of heat energy to the system, the fifth electron would be observed, energywise, to have been elevated to the conduction band. Continued application of heat energy would cause electrons from the intrinsic material to appear in the conduction state.

Because the fifth electrons appear so easily in the conduction state, they are called *donor* electrons. Figure 1.16(a) shows the positioning of the donor energy level with respect to the valence and conduction bands. The valence band shown is that of the parent intrinsic material. It is clearly seen that the energy increment $\Delta E'$ between the donor level and conduction band is much less than the energy increment ΔE between the valence band of the intrinsic material and the conduction band. It is generally agreed that the energy increment $\Delta E'$ is approximately .05 electron volts for N-type silicon and approximately .04 electron volts for N-type germanium. These are much smaller increments than the ΔE values of 1.1 and 0.7 electron volts for intrinsic silicon and germanium respectively, as mentioned earlier. Figure 1.16(a) also shows that the Fermi level shifts towards the conduction band side of the energy gap. As is shown in Fig. 1.16(b) the presence of donor electrons increases the probability of finding electrons in the conduction band. The greater the number of donor electrons the greater the distribution

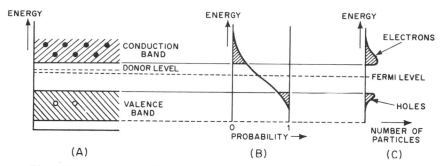

Fig. 1.16 Summary for N-type semiconductor: (A) Energy diagram showing donor and Fermi levels at room temperature. (B) Fermi distribution (C) Distribution of electrons and holes in the N-type material.

of electrons in the conduction band. This is shown in Figure 1.16(c). For an N-type semiconductor at room temperature, all the donor electrons are in the conduction band. If enough donor impurities have been added to the intrinsic material, the number of electrons in the conduction band will become very much greater than the number of holes in the valence band. The number of holes in the valence band of an N material is considerably less than the number of holes in the valence band of an intrinsic material. This situation exists due to the replacement of intrinsic atoms by donor atoms. In an N material, the total current is essentially an electron current.

The specific charge densities of interest in an N-type material are N_d, n_1 and p_1

where N_d = density of donor electrons

n_1 = density of electrons from the intrinsic material in the conduction band

p_1 = density of holes from the intrinsic material in the valence band

The N_d and n_1 charges are associated with the conduction band. The p_1 charges are associated with the valence band. As for an intrinsic material, n_1 equals p_1, and is a function of temperature. As mentioned, however, with a typical N-type material the sum of N_d plus n_1 is very much greater than p_1. For convenience, in an N-type material, we introduce the entities N_n and P_n—where N_n represents the total density of electrons available in the conduction band, and P_n represents the total density of holes available in the valence band. At any temperature,

$$N_n P_n = n_i p_i = n^2 \qquad (1.11)$$

This is the *law of mass action*, which says that the product of the total-electron and total-hole densities in an N-type material is the same as the product of the electron density and the hole density in a piece of the parent *intrinsic* material at the same temperature. For an N-type material we would find

$$N_n \gg P_n$$

$$\sigma_n = N_n e \mu_n \tag{1.12}$$

$$I_{\text{net}} = N_n e \mu_n V \frac{A}{L} \tag{1.13}$$

where σ_n = conductivity of the N material

1.5. P-Type semiconductors. Elements such as indium, gallium, and aluminum are called P-type impurities. These elements have only three electrons in their valence shells. If an atom of indium were placed in intrinsic germanium, we would obtain the situation shown in Fig. 1.17. Here we observe the formation of three covalent bonds, and the presence of an incomplete covalent bond. The spot, or void where a covalent bond could exist if another electron were present is called an *acceptor hole*, hence the name "positive" or *P-type*. Figure 1.18(a) shows that there is a discrete energy level associated with the acceptor holes. We notice that the energy increment $\Delta E''$ separating the acceptor level and the valence band, is much less than the energy increment ΔE of the intrinsic material. The acceptor holes, with an energy level just above the valence band are very useful.

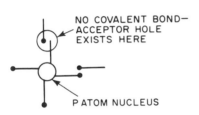

NO COVALENT BOND—
ACCEPTOR HOLE
EXISTS HERE

P ATOM NUCLEUS

Fig. 1.17 Localized P-atom in an intrinsic material.

Recall that in an intrinsic material, electrons had to receive the full energy increment ΔE to associate with the conduction band. Even if the actual energy of the electron was just less than the conduction minimum, or even if it were just enough to break a covalent bond, the electron has to associate with the valence band. In our P-type material, the intrinsic electrons need only receive an energy increment $\Delta E''$ before useful results are observed. The acceptor holes which were added to the material will then attract and trap the free intrinsic electrons leaving true holes in the valence band. This could be restated as follows: if an increment of energy equal to $\Delta E''$ is added to the system, the acceptor holes are made available for interaction with free electrons from the intrinsic material. The value of the energy increment $\Delta E''$ is about 0.08 electron volts for P-type silicon and about 0.04 electron volts for P-type germanium. Figure 1.18(a) shows also the suppression of the Fermi level towards the valence band side of the gap width. As is shown in Fig. 1.18(b) the presence of the acceptor voids increases the probability of finding holes in the valence band. The greater the number of acceptor voids, the greater the distribution of holes in the valence band. This is shown in Fig. 1.18(c). Figure 1.18(a) also shows the situation in P-type material at room temperature. All the acceptor holes are activated in association with the valence band. Some small number of electrons from the intrinsic material are in the conduction band, with a corresponding, equiva-

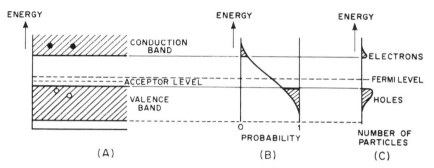

Fig. 1.18 Summary for P-type material. (A) Energy diagram showing acceptor and Fermi levels. (B) Fermi distribution. (C) Distribution of electrons and holes in the P-type material.

lent number of holes in the valence band. If enough acceptor impurities have been added to an intrinsic material, the number of holes in association with the valence band will become very much greater than the number of electrons in the conduction band. The number of electrons in the conduction band of a P material is considerably less than the number of electrons in the conduction band of an intrinsic material. This situation exists due to the replacement of intrinsic atoms by acceptor atoms. In a P material, the total current is essentially a hole current.

The specific charge densities which are of interest to us in a P-type material are P_a, n_2 and p_2

where P_a = density of acceptor holes

   n_2 = density of electrons from the intrinsic material in the conduction band

   p_2 = density of holes from the intrinsic material in the valence band.

For a P-type material, the P_a and p_2 charges are associated with the valence band. The n_2 charges are associated with the conduction band. As might have been anticipated, the densities n_2 and p_2 are equal, and are a function of temperature. For any P-type material, the quantity P_a plus p_2 is very much greater than n_2. For convenience in a P-type material we introduce the quantities P_p and N_p where P_p represents the total density of holes available in the valence band, and N_p represents the total density of electrons available in the conduction band. In the same manner that the law of mass action applied to an N-type material, we observe that for a P-type material

$$P_p N_p = n_i p_i = n^2 \tag{1.14}$$

Here we are observing that the product of the total-hole and total-electron densities in the P-type material is the same as the product of the electron density and the hole density in a piece of the parent intrinsic material at the same temperature. For a P-type material

$$P_p \gg N_p$$

$$\sigma_p = P_p e \mu_p \tag{1.15}$$

$$I_{\text{net}} = P_p e \mu_p V \frac{A}{L} \tag{1.16}$$

where $\sigma_p =$ conductivity of the P material

One final point deserves mention. We have seen that, at room temperature, both N-type and P-type semiconductors have intrinsic electrons in the conduction state. When we increase the temperature above room temperature, the number of free intrinsic electrons in the conduction state increases also. No matter what the initial density of impurity charges, every N- and P-type semiconductor becomes intrinsic in nature at very high temperatures. The presence of the minority particles in an N or P material, that is particles from the intrinsic material, at room temperature plays an important role in the behavior of diodes and transistors.

SUGGESTED READING

1. T. L. Martin, Jr., *Physical Basis for Electrical Engineering*, Englewood Cliffs, N. J.: Prentice-Hall, Inc., 1957.

2. A. Van der Ziel, *Solid State Physical Electronics*, Englewood Cliffs, N. J.: Prentice-Hall, Inc., 1957.

3. Lo, Endres, *et al*, *Transistor Electronics*, Englewood Cliffs, N. J.: Prentice-Hall, Inc., 1955.

4. A. Nussbaum, *Semiconductor Device Physics*, Englewood Cliffs, N. J.: Prentice-Hall, Inc., 1962.

5. Riddle & Ristenbatt, *Transistor Physics and Circuits*, Englewood Cliffs, N. J.: Prentice-Hall, Inc., 1958.

6. W. Gartner, *Transistors: Principles, Design and Applications*. Princeton, N. J.: D. Van Nostrand Co., Inc., 1960.

7. Dewitt and Rossoff, *Transistor Electronics*, New York: McGraw-Hill Book Company, 1957.

8. L. Hunter, *Handbook of Semiconductor Electronics*, New York: McGraw-Hill Book Company, 1962.

9. A. Dekker, *Electrical Engineering Materials*, Englewood Cliffs, N. J.: Prentice-Hall, Inc., 1959.

10. W. Shockley, *Electrons and Holes in Semiconductors*, Princeton, N. J.: D. Van Nostrand Co., Inc., 1950.

PROBLEMS

1. What is the significance of shells in an atom?

2. Explain the evolution of energy bands for crystalline atoms.

3. What is the definition of an insulator? Draw the energy diagram for such a material.

4. What is the definition of a conductor? Draw the energy diagram for such an element.

5. What is the major attribute of a semiconductor?

6. What is a covalent bond?

7. What is the significance of the gap width for a semiconductor?

8. Are there more holes numerically in the valence band of an intrinsic semiconductor than there are electrons in the conduction state? Explain.

9. A piece of intrinsic germanium and an equal volume piece of intrinsic silicon are available. The silicon measures lower resistivity than the germanium. Which material is at the higher temperature?

10. Does the Fermi level in an intrinsic material vary with temperature? Explain completely.

11. What is a donor energy level?

12. Explain the positioning of the Fermi level in N-type material.

13. What is an acceptor energy level?

14. Explain the concept of hole current.

15. Calculate the resistivity of intrinsic germanium at room temperature. Calculate the current in a specimen .1 cm × .1 cm × 2 cm when 80 volts is applied across the 2-cm length.

16. The resistivity of N-type germanium measures 4 Ω-cm at room temperature. Calculate the carrier concentrations N_n and P_n. Calculate the current in a specimen .1 cm × .1 cm × 2 cm when 80 volts is applied across the 2-cm length.

17. Calculate the density P_p to make a P-type germanium material have a resistivity of 4 Ω-cm.

2

JUNCTION

PHENOMENA

Chapter 1 established the nature of semiconductor materials. In particular we considered the unique charge condition in these materials, and the way current is conducted through them. Let us now observe the unusual reaction when we place N- and P-type materials together to form a single crystal composite. This PN combination constitutes a semiconductor junction. The semiconductor junction is a *rectifying* junction in that electrons flow easier through the junction in one direction than in the opposite direction. This chapter deals with the nature of a semiconductor junction, including its electrical characteristics and its electrical limitations.

2.1. The basic PN junction. The N- and P-type materials shown separately in Fig. 2.1 form a semiconductor rectifying junction only if they are formed together in the same crystal structure. This is *not* a mechanical joining, but is one where N and P materials are essentially melted together to permit formation of a single crystalline phase. The actual junction is formed at the boundary or transition between the N and P regions. It is worthwhile to recall certain basic facts about each material as shown individually. First, both the N-type and the P-type materials are electrically neutral systems. Secondly, the N-type material has far more electrons than positive holes. Since the abundance of electrons was introduced by the addition of neutral impurity atoms with five valence electrons, however, the statement about system neutrality is not contradicted.

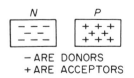

− ARE DONORS
+ ARE ACCEPTORS

Fig. 2.1 N and P materials.

Thirdly, the P-type material has far more holes than electrons. Since the abundance of holes was introduced by the addition of neutral impurity atoms with three valence electrons, our picture of a neutral system still applies. In Fig. 2.1 the minus signs in the N-type material indicate donor electrons. In the P-type material the plus signs indicate acceptor holes. Let us assume just for the present, that the concentration of donor electrons N_d equals the concentration of acceptor holes P_a.

Any NP junction is already in a state of equilibrium when we take it physically to study it. Consider the hypothetical possibility of placing discrete N and P materials together to achieve the true-life single crystal composite. When we actually place the materials together, there is an immediate interaction between the extrinsic particles N_d and P_a in the immediate vicinity of the junction. Donor electrons diffuse from the N material into the P material, and acceptor holes diffuse from the P material into the N material. No external motivation is necessary for the motion exhibited by these particles. The situation here is explained by the *law of diffusion*. This law stipulates that when two isolated and unequal concentrations of charges exist in a system, particles from the denser area will diffuse towards the less dense area in an effort to make the density of charge uniform for the whole system. It is important to note that the charge action in the diffusion mechanism is not at all the same as the drift mechanism discussed earlier in relation to conductors or to the electron and hole currents in an intrinsic material. *Diffusion current* is the motion of charge from a dense to a less dense charge location. *Drift current* is the controlled motion of charge through a material because of the forces on the charges due to an applied field. Thinking only of our N material for the moment, we certainly can recognize that the N material has a higher density of electrons than does the P material. Thus as the diffusion concept would dictate, the donor electrons diffuse, or are injected into the P material. These donor electrons are the majority carrier in the N-type material since they outnumber the other charges present. The electrons which diffuse into the P-type material from the N-type material are called *injected minority carriers*. The acceptor holes are truly the majority carrier in the P-type material. When a donor electron leaves its parent atom in the N material permanently, as happens when the donor is injected into the P-type material, the parent donor atom becomes a positive ion. Thus, in the vicinity of the junction in the N material, there is a *positive* charge. Even as the donor electrons diffuse into the P-type material, so also holes from the P-type material diffuse or are injected into the N-type material. When a hole leaves its parent atom permanently, the parent acceptor atom becomes a negative ion. Thus, in the vicinity of the junction in the P material there is a *negative* charge.

Over a finite distance, then, on either side of the junction, the dominant charge condition is that of ionized impurity atoms. Since this condition is caused indirectly by the *absence* of the impurity carriers originally associated with the impurity atoms, we call this finite region the *depletion region*. The stock of impurity carriers built into this region has truly been used up or reduced by the diffusion mechanism. The difference in charge which exists across the junction in the depletion region may be looked on as a potential difference between the two materials. Figure 2.2 shows the appearance of the charge and potential conditions in the vicinity of an NP junction at equilibrium. The entire N material is separated from the entire P material by the potential barrier which exists across the depletion region.

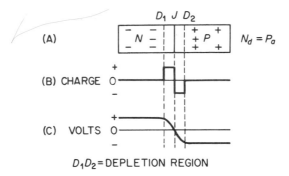

D_1D_2 = DEPLETION REGION

Fig. 2.2 NP junction at equilibrium. (A) Depletion region contribution of each material is void of majority carriers. (B) Charge condition in the depletion region. (C) Junction potential curve caused by charge unbalance in the depletion region.

The presence of the junction potential barrier prevents the injection of carriers from continuing indefinitely. Once this potential hill is established, a donor electron sees a domain in the P material which is negative. Likewise, a hole in the P material sees a domain in the N material which is positive. An electron does not naturally want to go to a more negative region, unless it has sufficient energy to overcome the work barrier which the potential hill presents. A similar state is experienced by acceptor holes in the P material with regard to the more positive domain of the N material. Ultimately an equilibrium situation is attained. At such time, the potential hill serves to check unlimited exchange of majority carriers across the junction.

The concept of charge equilibrium and the potential barrier at the junction of N and P materials is described quantitively by Boltzmann's law. This law indicates the value of voltage for given charge densities at which a charge equilibrium will be attained. For materials at equilibrium we find

$$P_n = P_p e^{-q\phi/kT} \tag{2.1}$$

$$N_p = N_n e^{-q\phi/kT} \tag{2.2}$$

where P_n = hole density in N material = p_1
   P_p = hole density in P material $\cong P_a$
   N_p = electron density in P material = n_2
   N_n = electron density in N material $\cong N_d$
   q = electron charge = 1.6×10^{-19} coulombs
   k = Boltzmann's constant = 1.38×10^{-23} joule/°K
   T = degrees absolute = °K
   ϕ — equilibrium potential voltage of N region relative to P region
     in volts.

By the law of mass action cited in Section 1.4, we have by Eqs. (1.11) and (1.13) that

$$N_n P_n = P_p N_p = n^2 \tag{2.3}$$

$$\frac{P_n}{P_p} = \frac{N_p}{N_n} = n^2 \tag{2.4}$$

Substituting the appropriate equality of eq. (2.4) into eq. (2.1) or (2.2) and solving for ϕ, we get

$$\phi = \frac{kT}{q} \ln \frac{N_n P_p}{n^2} \tag{2.5}$$

Equation (2.5) indicates for a given N and P material, and a given temper-

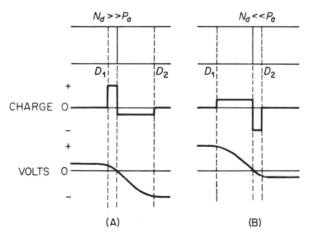

Fig. 2.3 Depletion width conditions for two possible unequal impurity concentration ratios. (A) $N_d \gg P_a$ potential exists mainly in the P region. (B) $N_d \ll P_a$ potential exists mainly in the N region.

ature, the actual magnitude of the potential barrier between the N and P materials at equilibrium.

In passing, it is interesting to note the depletion width phenomena when junctions are formed with materials having unequal impurity concentrations. The interaction of impurity charges on either side of the junction necessarily involves unequal distances or volumes of materials before equilibrium is attained. Figure 2.3 shows the possible situations. For either situation, $N_d \gg P_a$ or $P_a \gg N_d$, the bulk of the depletion width is in the material with the lowest doping (that is, the material with the lowest concentration of impurity atoms). We note also that the greatest portion of the junction potential lies in the material with the greatest resistivity.

2.2. Equilibrium junction currents. During the time when equilibrium is being reached, and after equilibrium itself is reached, the total-charge situation in a PN junction is as shown in Fig. 2.4. There must be a balancing of all carrier motion across the junction. Thus, for every donor electron

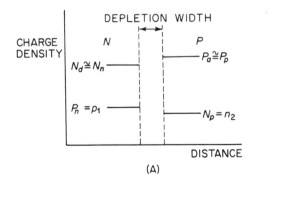

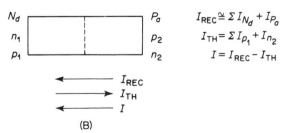

Fig. 2.4 (A) Charge density distributions in neutral regions of a PN junction at equilibrium. (B) Current components across NP junction at equilibrium.

N_d which goes from the N material to the P material, there is an intrinsic electron n_2 which goes from the P material to the N material. Likewise, for every acceptor hole P_a which goes from the P material to the N material, there is an intrinsic hole p_1 which goes from the N material to the P material. This cancelling effect must exist. There is no external potential to sustain a net current from either N-to-P or P-to-N materials. The current which is the sum of the individual currents due to N_d and P_a is called the *recombination* current. The current which is the sum of the individual currents due to n_2 and p_1 is called the *thermal* current. Mathematically, in terms of conventional current directions,

$$I_{\text{REC}} = I_{P_a} + I_{N_d} \tag{2.6}$$

$$I_{TH} = I_{p_1} + I_{n_2} \tag{2.7}$$

$$I = I_{\text{REC}} - I_{\text{TH}} \tag{2.8}$$

where I = net junction current

      I_{REC} = recombination current

      I_{TH} = thermal current

At equilibrium, the recombination current equals the thermal current in magnitude, and the net current equals zero.

It is of interest to note at this time the effects of temperature on a PN junction at equilibrium. An increase in temperature does raise the energy level of donors and acceptors, but most important, it will increase the number

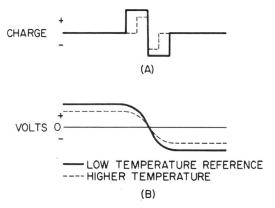

Fig. 2.5 Temperature effects on an NP junction at equilibrium. (A) Charge condition—increased number of carriers from intrinsic source at higher temperature causes equilibrium with less charge exchange. (B) Potential curve—actual barrier height is less at higher temperature.

of particles from the intrinsic source, n_1, p_1, n_2, and p_2. The increase in the number of particles from the intrinsic source suggests that less particle activity occurs in the attainment of charge equilibrium between materials in the depletion width. If less charge activity is involved, the equilibrium potential barrier decreases. This might also have been extracted from the statement of the Boltzmann law in Eq. (2-5). That is

$$\phi = \frac{kT}{q} \ln \frac{N_n P_p}{n^2} \qquad (2.9)$$

As temperature increases, the quantity n^2 increases in a dominant way. Thus the magnitude of the barrier potential decreases. Figure 2.5 depicts the situation. Where equilibrium currents are concerned we find that regardless of the reduced magnitude of the barrier potential, this potential aids the flow of thermal carriers p_1 and n_2. Since the number of these carriers has increased due to temperature, the component of current I_{TH} increases. The total current is still zero at equilibrium, however, because the reduced potential barrier permits an increased and compensating component of I_{REC} to flow and cancel I_{TH}.

2.3. The forward-biased junction. The application of voltage externally to the N and P materials drastically affects the equilibrium situation just described. Let us first consider the application of a voltage in the *forward-bias* direction. This, by definition, is a voltage applied so as to make the P material positive in relation to the N material. Figure 2.6(a) shows how such a voltage is applied. The direction of the applied forward voltage is such that the equilibrium barrier potential is reduced in height. This is shown in Fig. 2.6(b). As the height of the potential hill is reduced from the equilibrium value, the restriction on the N_d and P_a carriers climbing the hill is lessened. Thus, the recombination component of current increases. The thermally-generated carriers from each region will continue to traverse the hill since the P side is still negative in relation to the N side at forward biasing.

Under conditions of biasing, the Boltzmann equations assume the form

$$P'_n = P'_p e^{-q(\phi - V_{PN})/kT} \qquad (2.10)$$

$$N'_p = N'_n e^{-q(\phi - V_{PN})/kT} \qquad (2.11)$$

where P'_n = concentration of injected holes at edge of depletion width in N material

P'_p = concentration of holes at edge of depletion width in the P material

N'_p = concentration of injected electrons at edge of depletion width in P material

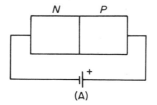

(A)

POLARITY OF APPLIED VOLTAGE TO FORWARD-BIAS A JUNCTION

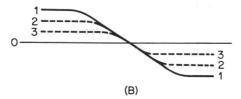

(B)

JUNCTION BARRIER VOLTAGE FOR VARIOUS MAGNITUDES OF APPLIED
FORWARD BIAS
     CURVE 1-1 EQUILIBRIUM POTENTIAL
     CURVE 2-2 TOTAL VOLTAGE WITH SMALL FORWARD BIAS
     CURVE 3-3 TOTAL VOLTAGE WITH LARGE FORWARD BIAS

Fig. 2.6 Forward bias of a PN diode.

N'_n = concentration of electrons at edge of depletion width in the N material.

Recalling the content of Eqs. (2.1) and (2.2) and substituting for the exponential factor which includes ϕ we obtain

$$\frac{P'_n}{P'_p} = \frac{P_n}{P_p} e^{qV_{PN}/kT} \tag{2.12}$$

$$\frac{N'_p}{N'_n} = \frac{N_p}{N_n} e^{qV_{PN}/kT} \tag{2.13}$$

Normally the presence of bias does not disturb the values of majority carrier concentrations from the values which exist at equilibrium. Thus

$$P'_p = P_p = P_a \tag{2.14}$$

$$N'_n = N_n = N_d \tag{2.15}$$

$$P'_n = P_n e^{qV_{PN}/kT} \tag{2.16}$$

and

$$N'_p = N_p e^{qV_{PN}/kT} \tag{2.17}$$

The magnitudes of injected carriers as given by Eqs. (2.16) and (2.17) are values of these injected minority carriers at the edge of the depletion layer.

We have mentioned that the injected minority carriers *diffuse* into the bulk material. The behavior of injected minority carriers in their new domain needs mention. The phenomenon of interest is *recombination*, the creation of a covalent bond between a conduction electron and a valence-state hole with the result that both are eliminated as carriers. It is an accepted postulation that numerous randomly-located crystal defects occur in both N- and P-type materials. These can be associated either with atomic discontinuities at the surface of the material or with lattice imperfections such as impurity atoms within the bulk of the material. These defects are called *traps*. Injected particles are considered to become held by a trap *before* they are susceptible to recombination with either electrons or holes. As a wave of injected particles diffuses into a material, successive entrapments and recombinations will ultimately reduce the number of unrecombined injected carriers to zero.

Electrons injected from an N material into P material will encounter traps and recombinations until the electron density in the P material is the basic level of N_p. Holes which are injected from a P material into an N material fare the same until the basic level becomes P_n. The shape of the injected-carrier concentration curves for a forward-biased junction is shown in Fig. 2.7. In order to explain the shapes of these curves, we must realize that the actual behavior of, for example, injected holes in the N material is given by a *minority carrier diffusion equation*. This is a second order differential equation. The qualitative aspects of the equation imply that the current is a function of the magnitude of injected carriers, the rate at which they recombine, and the diffusion constant for the particular carriers. We would find it permissable to deal with the magnitude of injected carrier as an indication of excess minority carrier and it would be found that the shape of the density concentration of injected carriers is a negative exponential function of distance from the junction. In addition, the initial slope of the density distribution of injected carriers is an indication of the *magnitude* of the diffusion current due to injected minority carriers. The appearance of the injected minority carrier distributions for a forward-biased PN junction are shown in Fig. 2.7. The slope of the density distribution for injected electrons as it initially starts to decay intercepts the N_p density level at a point B. The distance D_2B is called the *recombination distance* of electrons in P material. This distance symbolizes the finite distance through which injected electrons must diffuse in a P material before 63 per cent of them recombine with holes in the P material. The recombination distance for electrons in P material is typically symbolized as L_n. In like manner, the holes injected into the N material will encounter traps and recombinations until

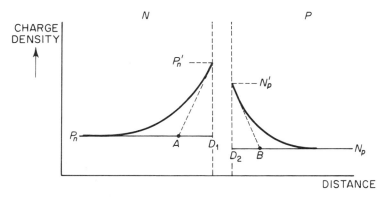

Fig. 2.7 Injected minority carrier distributions for a forward-biased PN junction. AD_1 = recombination distance of holes in N material, and D_2B = recombination distance of electrons in P material.

the hole density in the N material is the basic level P_n. The slope of the exponential density distribution as it initially starts to decay intercepts the P_n density level at a point A. The distance AD_1 is called the *recombination distance* of holes in N material. This distance symbolizes the finite distance through which injected holes must diffuse before 63 per cent of them recombine with electrons in the N material. The recombination distance for holes in an N material is typically symbolized as L_p.

It is of interest at this time to note pictorially the effects of the magnitude of forward bias on the distribution of injected minority carriers. Consider Fig. 2.8. At a reference value of forward bias V_{PN_1}, a certain amount of holes $(P'_n)_1$ are injected from the P into the N material. The density distribution of these carriers is shown. At a higher value of forward bias V_{PN_2}, a higher number of holes $(P'_n)_2$ are injected. The density distribution for this high injection level is noted. The steeper slope of the $(P'_n)_2$ distribution implies that the current associated with $(P'_n)_2$ injection is higher than the current associated with $(P'_n)_1$ injection.

The appearance of the current-voltage plot for a forward-biased PN junction can now be readily constructed. The basic governing equation is Eq. (2.8), that is

$$I = I_{\text{REC}} - I_{\text{TH}}$$

The expression for holes injected into the N material is obtained from Eq. (2.16) using the expected considerations that current is proportional to the number of carriers. We obtain

$$I_{\text{injected holes}} = I_{P_n} e^{qV_{PN}/kT} \qquad (2.18)$$

Likewise, the current expression for electrons injected into the P material

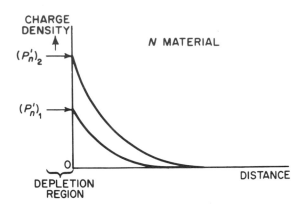

$(P_n')_2$ CARRIERS INJECTED AT V_{PN_2}
$(P_n')_1$ CARRIERS INJECTED AT V_{PN_1}
$V_{PN_2} > V_{PN_1}$

Fig. 2.8 Density distributions for various forward-biased injection levels.

is obtained from Eq. (2.17) and is

$$I_{\text{injected electrons}} = I_{N_p} e^{qV_{PN}/kT} \tag{2.19}$$

Since

$$I_{\text{REC}} = I_{\text{injected holes}} + I_{\text{injected electrons}} \tag{2.20}$$

$$\therefore \quad I_{\text{REC}} = (I_{N_p} + I_{P_n}) e^{qV_{PN}/kT} \tag{2.21}$$

Also, from Eq. (2.7)

$$I_{\text{TH}} = I_{N_p} + I_{P_n} \tag{2.22}$$

Thus

$$I = I_{\text{TH}}[e^{qV_{PN}/kT} - 1] \tag{2.23}$$

Equation (2.23) is commonly called the *diode equation*. It illustrates the most dramatic and meaningful attribute of forward-biased conduction in an NP diode: the forward-biased current-voltage relation is *exponential* and *voltage controlled*. The current is voltage-controlled because the exponential term increases rapidly even though the increases in V_{PN} are incrementally small. A plot of diode current vs forward-bias voltage for a PN junction is shown in Fig. 2.9(a).

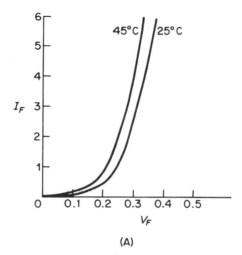

(A)

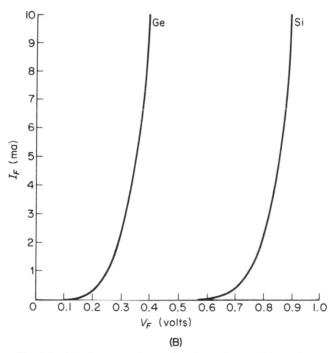

(B)

Fig. 2.9 (A) Current-voltage plot for a forward-biased junction. (B) Comparison of forward characteristics for a germanium NP junction and a silicon NP junction.

As before, it is of interest to note the effects of an increase in temperature. The dominant effect in the increase is the number of thermally-generated carriers which cause an increase in the magnitude of I_{TH}. Thus in Fig. 2.9(a) we observe that at an increased temperature, the total forward current is greater for each value of forward voltage. Figure 2.9(b) compares the forward characteristics of germanium and silicon PN junctions.

2.4. The reverse-biased junction.   Let us now consider the application of *reverse* or *back bias*. By definition, this is a voltage applied to make the

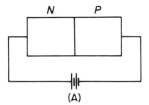

(A)

POLARITY OF APPLIED VOLTAGE TO REVERSE-BIAS OR BACK-BIAS A JUNCTION

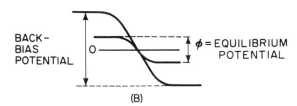

(B)

HEIGHT OF JUNCTION BARRIER VOLTAGE INCREASES AS REVERSE BIAS IS APPLIED

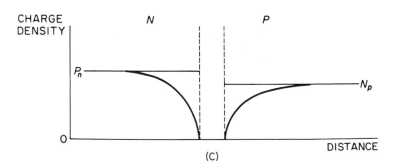

(C)

MINORITY CARRIER DISTRIBUTIONS FOR A REVERSE-BIASED *PN* JUNCTION

Fig. 2.10 Points of interest for a reverse-biased junction.

P material negative in relation to the N material. Figure 2.10(a) shows how such a voltage is applied. Its direction is such that the height of the potential hill across the junction becomes greater. This is seen in Figure 2.10(b). As the potential hill increases in height over the equilibrium value, the recombination current becomes less and less, and the majority carriers are, restricted more and more from climbing the barrier—that is, the amount of energy necessary to cross the hill is increased. If the potential hill becomes high enough, the recombination current is reduced to zero. In the meantime, the thermal current continues flowing unchanged in magnitude. The graphical representation of the minority-carrier distributions at a reverse-biased junction is shown in Fig. 2.10(c). We see that in our particular nonequilibrium condition of reverse bias all minority carriers which are thermally generated are responding to the presence of the bias voltage. The density of these charges is zero at the space-charge layer. Our charge density of minority carriers is zero at the depletion-region edge because there is no charge replenishment flow of majority carriers N_d and P_a from the opposite sides of the depletion region. This, of course, was the case in the equilibrium junction. As long as the external voltage is present to sustain an unbalanced charge flow across the junction, the intrinsic carriers will continue to flow across the junction. Actually a charge balance is still being maintained in each material in spite of the absence of recombination current. At equilibrium, charge balance was maintained by charge exchange across the junction. Now when an intrinsic electron crosses the junction from the P to the N side, the battery gives an electron by an external path to the P material. This, as was mentioned, is a current flow. When we now consider the nature of the net current, we realize that under back-bias conditions, the predominant current is the thermal current. When sufficient voltage is applied, the total current actually equals the thermal current in magnitude.

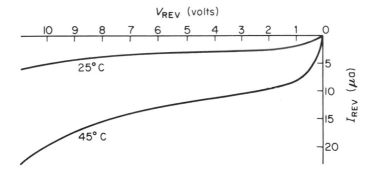

Fig. 2.11 Current-voltage characteristic for a junction under reverse bias.

This behavior is shown graphically in Fig. 2.11. The behavior of the reverse-biased junction can be shown mathematically from Eq. 2.23. The reverse bias is a condition whereby the quantity V_{PN} is a negative number. Thus, when the V_{PN} value in Eq. (2.23) is great enough, the exponential term becomes zero. Our total junction current becomes equal in direction and magnitude to the thermal current. Since all the thermally-generated carriers are participating in current flow under such a situation the thermal current which is equivalent to the asymptote value of reverse current is often called a *saturation current*.

Consider now the effect of increasing the temperature of our P and N materials. The energy of the N_d and P_a carriers increases, the number of intrinsic carriers p_1 and n_2 increases, and the height of the equilibrium potential barrier decreases. As our back bias is now applied, the effect of reducing the recombination current is again observed. Because of the reduced magnitude of equilibrium potential, however, a bigger back bias must be applied to achieve the total voltage level which makes the recombination current equal to zero. Since there is an increased number of intrinsic particles present, the thermal current is higher. Thus, at the increased value of voltage that causes the recombination current to be zero, the total current is seen to have as its value the new higher value of thermal current. This is shown in Fig. 2.11.

2.5. The PN junction as a rectifier. If, now, the forward- and reverse-bias phenomena were depicted on a single graph, we would obtain the

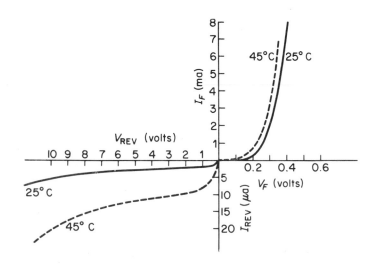

Fig. 2.12 Complete characteristic of a diode.

characteristic of Fig. 2.12. A PN junction is properly classified as a rectifying junction in that, as Fig. 2.12 shows, the junction conducts current easily in one direction (forward biasing), but conducts only very small currents in the other direction (reverse biasing). The rectifying junction is also called a *semiconductor diode.* If a small voltage, say 0.3 v is applied in the forward direction, we observe from Fig. 2.12 a forward current of 2.0 ma. The forward d-c resistance at this point is 150 ohms. When 0.3 v is applied in the reverse direction about 1.5 μa of reverse current flows, indicating a d-c resistance of 200,000 ohms. The forward-bias diode is a low-impedance device, whereas the reverse-bias diode is a high-impedance device. The symbol for a semiconductor rectifier is shown in Fig. 2.13.

Fig. 2.13 Symbol for a diode.

A typical application of a diode is to rectify or change an a-c voltage to a pulsating d-c voltage. Consider the circuit shown in Fig. 2.14. A sinusoidal signal is applied across the diode and resistor in series. From our discussions we know that the diode will conduct only when the P region is biased positive

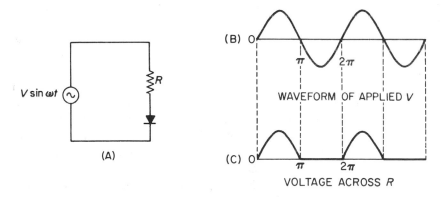

Fig. 2.14 Rectifier application of a diode.

in relation to the N region. This happens during the time interval 0 to π when the applied voltage is positive in relation to ground. Thus, since the diode conducts, a voltage drop is developed across the resistor R. During the time interval π to 2π, the applied voltage causes the P region to be negative in relation to the N region. This back-biases the diode, and no voltage drop will be developed across the resistor R. The nature of the voltage-waveform across the resistor is that of pulsating d-c and is shown in Fig. 2.14(c).

2.6. Voltage breakdown. A very practical limitation of a diode may be observed if a continuous increase in magnitude of reverse bias is applied across the junction. This phenomenon is called *voltage breakdown.* Figure 2.15 depicts the extension of back biasing to the point where voltage breakdown occurs. If a junction is broken down, the current flow is limited only

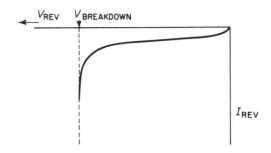

Fig. 2.15 Reverse characteristic extended to show breakdown effect.

by the external circuit impedance. Although all PN junctions exhibit a voltage breakdown, it is important to know that there are two distinct voltage breakdown mechanisms. One is called *Zener breakdown*—where the value of breakdown voltage decreases as temperature increases; the second mechanism is called *avalanche breakdown.* Here the breakdown voltage increases as temperature increases. Typical diode breakdown characteristics of each category are shown in Fig. 2.16. The factor determining which of the two breakdown mechanisms occurs is the relative concentrations of the impurities in the materials which comprise the junction. The concept of impurity concentrations and resultant depletion width effects has already been introduced. Let us reconstruct a practical example at this point. Two different resistivity P materials will be placed against two separate but equal and very low-resistivity pieces of N materials. As might be expected, the depletion width involving the less resistive P_{a_2} material will be smaller than the depletion width involving the more resistive P_{a_1} material. The charge picture and resultant voltage distributions are shown in Fig. 2.17. In both situations very little of the resultant potential lies in the N material. Because so little of the depletion width actually lies in the N material, it is permissible to consider that all of the depletion width lies in the P material. Generally speaking, the depletion width and the junction potential hill exist in the more resistive of the two materials comprising the junction. In proceeding further,

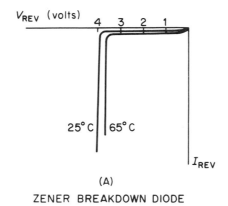

(A)

ZENER BREAKDOWN DIODE

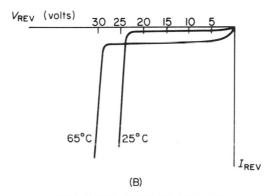

(B)

AVALANCHE BREAKDOWN DIODE

Fig. 2.16 Typical breakdown diode character-istics. Note effects of temperature for each mechanism.

we observe that the electric field in the P_2 material is greater than the electric field in the P_1 material. (By electric field, we mean the actual voltage per unit length of depletion width.) A junction that results in a *narrow* depletion width and, therefore, a *high* field intensity is one that will break down by the Zener mechanism. A junction that results in a *broader* depletion width and, thus, a *lower* field intensity is one that will break down by the avalanche mechanism.

The Zener mechanism can be described qualitatively as follows: because the total depletion width is very small [e.g., Fig. 2.17(b)] the application of

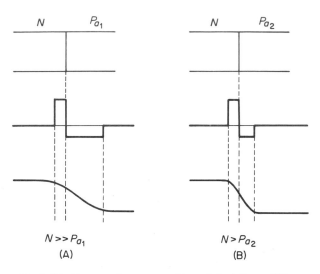

Fig. 2.17 Nature of narrow and broad depletion width junctions. N is constant for both junctions. $P_{a_1} < P_{a_2}$. (A) Broad depletion width junction will break down by avalanche mechanism. (B) Narrow depletion width junction will break down by Zener mechanism.

as little as 5 volts of reverse bias might cause a field across the depletion width in the order of 10^6 v/cm. A field of such high magnitude exerts a large force tending to separate the valence electrons from their respective nuclei. Actual rupture of the valence electrons from their shells does occur eventually. Thus, electrons and holes are generated in large numbers and a sudden increase of current is observed. Although we speak of a rupture of the atomic structure, it should be understood that this generation of electrons and holes may be repeated as long as limiting resistance in the external circuit prevents current from increasing to an unsafe value. The actual critical value of field causing Zener breakdown is believed to be 10^6 v/cm. On most commercially available silicon diodes, the maximum value of voltage breakdown by the Zener mechanism is 5 volts.

The decrease of Zener breakdown voltage as temperature increases can be explained in terms of the energies of the valence electrons. We know that an increase of temperature increases the energies of the valence electrons. This would serve to reduce the magnitude of the bonds holding the electrons in place. Less applied voltage is necessary, therefore, to pull the valence electrons from their position in relation to the nuclei. Thus, the actual value of breakdown voltage decreases as the temperature has increased.

The avalanche mechanism that causes junction breakdown is quite different. Because the depletion width is considerably larger [Figure 2.17(a)], it would require very high values of applied voltage to cause field strengths high enough to cause Zener breakdown. Before such high values of voltage can be applied, the avalanche mechanism takes place. One other point of difference: in Zener breakdown, the particles causing the increase in current are normally bound. They are, as mentioned, broken right out of the lattice structure. In avalanche, on the other hand, the particles that cause the current increase are the intrinsic particles already contributing to the thermal current. As established earlier, the applied reverse bias carries intrinsic electrons from the P material to the potentially positive N material, and intrinsic holes from the N material to the potentially negative P material. As the applied voltage gets larger and larger, the electrons and holes begin to experience noticeable increases in acceleration.

As might be expected, there are also collisions between these intrinsic particles and other bound electrons as the intrinsic particles are accelerated through the depletion region. If the applied voltage is such that the intrinsic electrons do not have much acceleration, then the collisions serve to do nothing more than to take some energy from the intrinsic particles and divert them somewhat from their direction of travel. When the applied voltage is increased, the acceleration of the intrinsic particle will increase. Ultimately, its collision with a valence particle occurs with such momentum that a lot of energy is given to the valence electron. If enough energy is transferred, the valence electron will actually leave its covalently-bonded location. Thus, one electron in colliding has made available a second electron and a hole. Since these secondary particles are in the potential field, they will move accordingly and add to the total current flow. This phenomenon which results from high-energy collisions is called *carrier multiplication*. If the total applied voltage is increased even further, the secondary particles (both electrons and holes) will be accelerated fast enough so that they also participate in collisions which generate new carriers. Carriers are generated so quickly and in such large numbers that there is truly an apparent avalanche or self-sustained multiplication process. The current is limited only by resistance external to the junction, and the junction is said to be in breakdown. Diodes are available commercially, with the avalanche breakdown controlled in the range of 5-500 volts.

As temperature increases, the value of avalanche breakdown increases. This occurs primarily because of the vibration of atoms in their lattice or crystalline array. As temperature increases, the thermal energy increase causes increase in the vibrational displacement of atoms in their crystalline array. This increase in the motion of atoms suggests an increase in the probability that intrinsic particles crossing the depletion width will experience more collisions with the lattice atoms. Since an intrinsic particle is apt to have more collisions it has less opportunity to gain momentum between

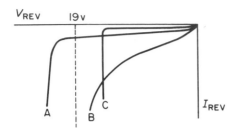

Fig. 2.18 Reverse characteristics of randomly selected diodes. (A) might be a high breakdown germanium diode. (B) might be a low breakdown silicon device. (C) might be a high leakage germanium device.

collisions. Thus in a collision with a covalent particle pair there is reduced chance of the covalent electron being energized away. Thus, to instigate the carrier-multiplication process we must apply more voltage. This will give the intrinsics more acceleration which, in turn, will cause the avalanche condition. Thus, for an increased temperature the value of avalanche voltage increases. It is interesting to note, as Fig. 2.16 suggests, that the Zener voltage changes a lot less than the avalanche voltage for a given change in temperature. This should be readily apparent, since we now know the nature of both breakdown phenomena. For both types of devices the value of thermal current does increase as expected with temperature.

It is interesting to consider further the application of a semiconductor diode used in rectifying an a-c voltage, taking into account the property of junction breakdown just discussed. The value of avalanche breakdown varies as a function of device fabrication. Even a given specified diode type reveals some variation in the value of avalanche breakdown voltage. The proper choice of diode for the given application requires that the diode selected actually handle the peak reverse voltage swing expected. If a diode with too low a breakdown is selected, the resultant waveform will *not* be pulsating d-c. Further, the diode may be permanently damaged so as to require replacement. Figure 2.18 shows the reverse characteristics of three diodes. If these diodes were to be used in the circuit of Fig. 2.14 and the amplitude of the applied voltage were 19 volts, the resultant waveforms would be those shown in Fig. 2.19. The desired result is obtained only with diode A. This is but one example of the need to evaluate and understand

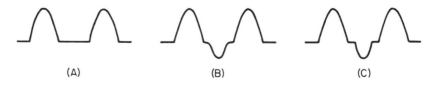

(A)   (B)   (C)

Fig. 2.19 Waveforms which are obtained at the output of rectifier circuit when the diodes of Fig. 2.18 are used with a peak a-c value signal of 19 v. (A) Diode A of Fig. 2.18. (B) Diode B. (C) Diode C.

thoroughly the properties of the device and the requirements of the application. Matters such as these will be developed more fully in later chapters.

2.7. Equivalent circuit of a diode. Thus far we have spoken of the diode only as a low-resistance device when forward-biased, and as a high-resistance device when reverse-biased. We are obliged to develop further the electrical nature of the diode at each specific operating point. Specifically, the a-c or dynamic nature of the diode is of interest to us. As far as the resistive nature of the device is concerned, this may be understood with the assistance of Fig. 2.20. There are two ways of determining the value of current

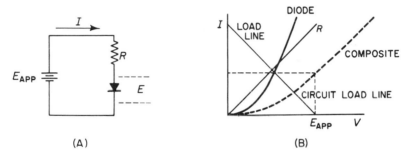

(A)   (B)

Fig. 2.20 Graphical approach to rectifier operation. (A) Rectifier circuit. (B) Graphical approaches.

    The *composite characteristic* is the sum of the diode and resistor voltage drops for any circuit current. The *circuit load line* is the pictorial representation of the equation $E = E_{app} - IR$. Note that the diode current indicated by the circuit load line is the same as the current indicated by the current value on the composite at the E_{app} voltage point.

in the circuit. One way involves the drawing of the composite current-voltage characteristic of the two components. This is accomplished by summing the voltage drops across each component for various currents, as shown in Fig. 2.20(b). The second method involves plotting a *circuit load line*. We know that at all times

$$E_{app} = IR + E$$

or

$$E = E_{app} - IR$$

where E is the diode voltage and E_{app} is the applied circuit-voltage source. By substituting various values of current, and determining the resultant voltage, we can draw the circuit load line. This is also shown in Fig. 2.20(b). Clearly the intersection of the circuit load line and the diode characteristic is the singular unique solution determining the current magnitude for the circuit in question. The intersection of the two characteristics is called the *operating point*. The slope of the diode characteristic at the operating point is the reciprocal of resistance. This particular resistance is called the *dynamic* or *a-c resistance* of the diode and would be used to depict the diode in an a-c circuit analysis. At any d-c operating point, the approximate magnitude of the a-c resistance is derived in works such as that by Lo and others [1], and is given by

$$r_p \cong \frac{26}{I} \qquad (2.24)$$

where r_p = dynamic resistance in ohms
        I = d-c operating point in ma

It should be understood that the calculations from Eq. (2.24) are applicable to an ideal-case diode. A real-case silicon diode for example more closely follows the expression

$$r_p \cong \frac{52}{I} \qquad (2.25)$$

The methods shown in Fig. 2.20(b) would be necessary to determine the instantaneous values of current for the rectifier applications previously mentioned.

Certain reactive attributes of the diode must be considered. When developing the nature of the diode junction at equilibrium and at back bias, we discovered a charge difference to exist across the depletion width. The positive charge that exists in the N material is counterbalanced by an equal amount of negative charge in the P material. From this viewpoint the junction is similar to a parallel plate capacitor. The capacitance that exists across the junction at equilibrium or under back bias is called the *barrier capacitance*. Since the amount of charge and the depletion width vary with the magnitude of the back bias, the capacitance will also vary with back bias. Specifically, as the voltage increases, the capacitance decreases.

The reactive nature of a forward-bias diode is somewhat more complex. As the diode is forward biased, finite quantities of charge are injected across the junction. These charges have been made available by the presence of a specific increment of forward voltage. The inter-relation of charge and voltage is also described by a capacitance. In this case, the capacitance is called the *diffusion capacitance* since it involves the forward-biased diffusion of charges across a junction. Authors such as Firle and Hayes [2] have presented excellent summaries of the forward-biased diode including an inductive property exhibited at high-current densities. For the scope of this volume, it suffices to depict the diode as shown in Fig. 2.21. Note that with the exception of the bulk resistance, the resistive and capacitive quantities shown are different for each current and voltage operating point.

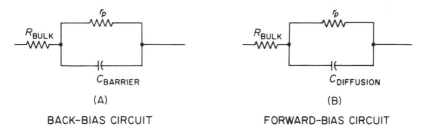

(A)　　　　　　　　　　　　　　　　　(B)

BACK–BIAS CIRCUIT　　　　　　FORWARD–BIAS CIRCUIT

Fig. 2.21　Diode equivalent circuits.

The a-c equivalent-circuit representation of a diode is an important tool in the analysis of circuits involving diodes. Some of the applications discussed in detail later on are voltage regulator circuits, voltage reference circuits, detectors, and logic and switching circuits. At that time, also, other circuit-oriented aspects of the diode will be introduced and discussed.

REFERENCES

1. A. W. Lo *et al.*, *Transistor Electronics*, Englewood Cliffs, N.J.: Prentice-Hall, Inc., 1955, pp. 272 ff.
2. T. E. Firle and O. E. Hayes, "Some Reactive Effects in Forward Biased Junctions," *IRE Transactions on Electron Devices*, vol. ED-6 (July 1959), pp. 330-334.

SUGGESTED READING

D. DeWitt and A. Rossoff, *Transistor Electronics*, New York: McGraw-Hill Book Co., Inc., 1957.

E. Spenke, *Electronic Semiconductors*, New York: McGraw-Hill Book Co., Inc., 1958.

R. Middlebrook, *An Introduction To Junction Transistor Theory*, New York: John Wiley and Sons, Inc., 1957.

PROBLEMS

1. Explain the manner in which the charge difference develops across a PN junction.
2. How is junction equilibrium established?
3. What is the meaning of recombination distance for, say, electrons in P material?
4. Explain the different recombination distances that result when different-resistivity N and P materials are placed together.

5. What is the situation that occurs when a PN junction is back-biased?

6. What are the reasons for the appearance of the back-bias characteristic when temperature is increased? [Refer to Fig. 2.11.]

7. What is avalanche breakdown?

8. What is Zener breakdown?

9. A 200-ohm resistor is connected in series with the diode of Fig. 2.12. Draw the composite characteristic applicable at 25°C.

10. Draw the circuit load line for the 200-ohm resistor and the diode of Fig. 2.12 when E_{app} is 1 volt, and determine the operating point.

11. For the conditions of Problem 10, give the voltage drop across the diode, and the voltage drop across the resistor.

12. Why does the barrier capacitance change with the magnitude of the back-bias voltage?

13. Three diodes are available. Their I-V plots in the back direction have the following values:

Diode 1		Diode 2		Diode 3	
V	I	V	I	V	I
volts	μa	volts	μa	volts	μa
.3	4	.3	4	8	8
.5	5	.5	5	10	90
1	6	1	5		
1.5	7	10	5		
2	8				
2.5	9				
3	11				
4	20				
5	30				
6	43				
7	59				
8	77				
9	100				

These three diodes are to be used in the circuit of Fig. 2.14, where $R = 22$ K.

(a) When peak a-c voltage is 9 volts, determine the peak current flowing in each diode in the reverse direction.

(b) Assuming the forward voltage drop to be zero for all diodes, plot the waveforms that result across R.

(c) Repeat (a) when peak voltage is 11 volts.

(d) Plot the resultant waveforms across R.

(e) Explain the difference in waveforms for diodes 1 and 3 as the peak voltage increased from 9 to 11 volts.

3

FUNDAMENTALS OF

TRANSISTOR

ACTION

The interesting characteristics of forward- and reverse-bias PN junctions were used to advantage to form semiconductor rectifiers. We will discover, in this chapter, that astutely arranged geometric configurations of P, N, and a second P material, or N, P, and a second N material, constitute devices with power-amplifying attributes. Such devices are called *transistors*. Whereas the diode operation involves a single applied voltage and resultant current, the transistor will be seen to have a greater number of interdependent voltage and current variables. The particular geometrical requirements that provide transistor action, the interrelations of current and voltage in the transistor regions, and an introduction to the action of a transistor circuit are discussed in this chapter.

3.1. Proximate, independent junctions. If we are to understand the many operational attributes of a transistor, we must fully appreciate the mechanism whereby two PN junctions interact to cause *transistor action*. The diode, as developed, presents a distinct electrical nature depending on the direction of the applied bias. The transistor has been depicted as two diodes back-to-back, illustrating the physical fact that transistors can be made either as two pieces of N material separated by a piece of P material, or as two pieces of P material separated by a piece of N material. Two diodes so oriented would not, however, display the dynamic attributes of a transistor, namely current gain, voltage gain, and power gain. We are obliged to distinguish between an array of materials that does not provide transistor action and one that does.

Consider Fig. 3.1 where we present a composite of two PN junctions that have been made on a single, rather wide piece of N material. Certain material requirements and operational observations should be mentioned. Both the P_1 and P_2 materials have a higher conductivity than the N material. Of

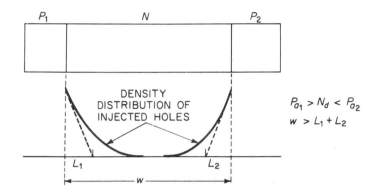

Fig. 3.1 Density distributions for injected carriers, and recombination distances for independent junctions which are forward-biased.

particular interest for the example cited are the density distributions of injected holes in the N material. The recombination distances are labeled L_1 and L_2 respectively. We can observe from Fig. 3.1 that the dimensions of

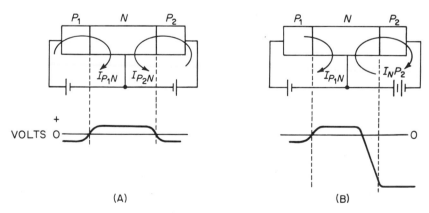

Fig. 3.2 Junction currents and junction potentials. (A) For independent junctions where both are forward-biased. (B) For independent junctions where one is forward-biased and the other is reverse-biased.

the N material are such that the width, W, of the N material is very much greater than L_1 plus L_2. In fact the density distributions of injected minority carriers in the N material do not even overlap. Herein is the key to the lack of interaction, electrically, between the P_1N and P_2N junctions. Since the density distributions for holes injected from P_1 and P_2 into the N material do not even approach an overlap, we postulate that there is no interaction between the carriers from P_1 and P_2 in N. Thus if both the P_1N and P_2N junctions were forward-biased, we would observe the situation of Fig. 3.2(a). A forward-bias current which we label I_{P_1N} circulates in the closed loop around P_1N. A second forward-bias current I_{P_2N} circulates in the closed loop around P_2N. If the bias for P_2N were now made a reverse bias a very small current I_{NP_2} would flow as shown. For both bias situations there would be no interaction of the junction currents. Since there is no coupling between the two regions, there is obviously no mechanism of current gain and power gain.

3.2. Phenomena of interacting junctions. How do we obtain coupling between two junctions and hence transistor action? The lack of coupling lay specifically with the fact that the density distributions of injected holes did not approach an overlap. Coupling then might be anticipated if the N material were narrower to a point where the density distribution of holes from P_1, for example, were made to interact with the P_2 region. In Fig. 3.3 we see a reduced width for the N material, and an analysis involving a forward-biased P_1N junction and a reverse-biased P_2N junction. The density distribution for holes injected from the P_1 region into a very wide N region is shown dotted in Fig. 3.3(a). Let us allude to this particular distribution as a reference or *unperturbed distribution*. The actual case distribution for injected holes must truly become zero, however, at a point in the N region coincident with the furthest penetration of the reverse-biased P_2N voltage curve. For convenience we present the density distribution lines of holes injected from P_1 drawn upside down from their earlier forms of presentation (as for example in Fig. 3.1). Although we now know that the unperturbed distribution does not remain fixed for a narrow width N region, let us consider it so for a moment and postulate the condition of charge interaction between P_1 and P_2. Point 0 in Fig. 3.3(a) is the intersection point of the P_2N back-bias potential and the unperturbed injected-charge density curve. At Point 0, some number of injected minority holes exist since they have not yet recombined with majority electrons in the N material. This is apparent because the distance from the P_1N junction to point 0 is less than the distance from the P_1N junction to point R. At point 0, the unrecombined holes feel the existence of the potential and see the P_2 material as a more negative and hence attractive domain. Any holes which exist at point 0,

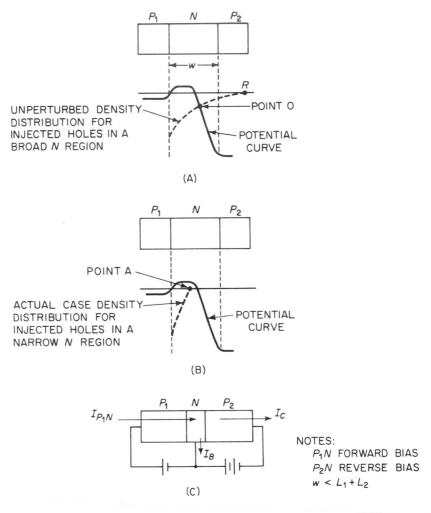

Fig. 3.3 Summary picture for interacting junctions. (A) Idealized interaction between close-spaced junctions. (B) Real-case density distribution for interacting junctions. (C) Current flow for interacting PNP junctions.

then, are diverted from diffusing further into the N material, and are carried through to the P_2 region. This is clearly a situation where there is coupling or interaction between the two junctions.

We have stated that a consideration of the unperturbed distribution is not truly a real-life possibility for an actual device. We adjust to the real-case situation by realizing that the true density of injected carriers is *zero* at the point where injected minority carriers encounter the reverse-bias potential curve. Thus in a real-case situation we consider an injected density distribution to reduce to zero at the extremity of the space-charge layer of the reverse-biased region. This situation is shown in Fig. 3.3(b). Point A is the zero value for injected minority carriers. Since the flow of minority carriers through the middle region is by *diffusion*, we should note by previous explanation (Sec. 2.3) that the initial slope of the injected minority-carrier distribution indicates the diffusion-current magnitude.

The forward-biasing of the P_1N junction injects many holes into the N region. It should be noted that the forward-bias behavior of the P_1N junction is a *voltage-controlled exponential* similar to an isolated junction diode. Some of the injected holes recombine in the N material. These carriers, which recombine in the N region return to the P_1 material through the forward-bias battery. A greater number of carriers, because of the proximity of the P_2N junction and its back-bias potential curve are carried to the P_2 material. Once in the P_2 material they travel through the external batteries to the P_1 material. The general case of the current components of I_{P_1N} are shown in Fig. 3.3(c). Here

$$I_{P_1N} = I_B + I_C \tag{3.1}$$

where I_{P_1N} = forward-biased P_1N current
      I_B — current in N due to recombination
      I_C = current gathered by P_2

The actual expression for I_{P_1N} is a modification of the diode equation and would be expressed for a PNP device as

$$I_{P_1N} \simeq \frac{qAD_pP_n}{W} e^{qV_{P_1N}/kT} \tag{3.2}$$

where   q = electronic charge = $1.6 \times (10^{-19})$ coulombs
      A = cross-sectional area of junction
      D_p = diffusion constant for holes in N material
      P_n = equilibrium minority-carrier density in N material
      W = width of middle region

The form of Eq. (3.2) shows specifically that the value of forward bias can be held *constant* and yet the magnitude of I_{P_1N} *increases* as the middle region width decreases.

We know now that as the N width changes, there is a change in the position of the P_2N back-bias potential curve and the resultant position of the forced termination of the density distribution for holes injected from P_1 into N. In particular as the width of the N material decreases, the back-bias potential moves successively closer to the P_1N junction, and the density-distribution curve for injected carriers is forced to a zero value at a point

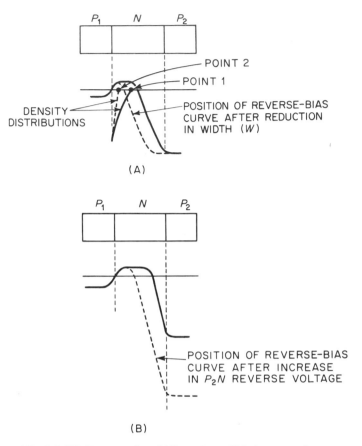

(A)

(B)

Fig. 3.4 (A) Decrease in middle region width increases I_{P_1N}.
(B) Increase in V_{P_2N} decreases effective width of middle region.

closer to the P_1N junction. We have stated that the flow of minority carriers in the middle region is by diffusion, so that the current is proportional to the slope of the minority-carrier distribution. Considering Fig. 3.4(a), the density distribution which terminates at point 2 has a steeper initial slope than the distribution terminating at point 1. This presents pictorially the content of Eq. (3.2); the I_{P_1N} level is seen to be higher as the width of the N region decreases, even though the magnitude of the forward bias on P_1N is held constant. The area under the distribution curve for our transistor is indicative of the charge which recombines in the middle region. Thus as the width W decreases the middle region current I_B decreases. Lastly, the slope of the distribution curve at the P_2N junction is indicative of the current level I_C. The net result for decreasing W is an increase in I_{P_1N} and I_C and a decrease in the recombination current I_B.

Note in passing that increases in the back-bias voltage V_{P_2N} cause effective decreases in the width W. Thus any time that the back-bias voltage on a transistor is changed we should anticipate current changes as we have just discussed. This is shown in Fig. 3.4(b).

It has been shown here, to develop the concept of transistor action, that the electrical requirements contributing to the interaction of the P_1 and P_2 materials are that one junction (P_1N) be forward-biased and that the second junction (P_2N) be reverse-biased. It is not shown here, but the truly basic electrical requirements for transistor action are that the second junction (P_2N) be less forward-biased than the forward-biased P_1N junction. The physical requirements are, generally, that the middle region be more resistive than the outer two regions, and that the middle region be narrow in width as compared to the recombination distance of carriers from either P_1 or P_2 in the middle region. These separate conditions if existing simultaneously permit current interaction between the outer regions and this constitutes what is called *transistor action*. The dynamic significance of transistor action is explained in a later section.

3.3. NPN and PNP comparisons. Thus far we have analyzed only the situation of PNP materials being placed together. NPN materials, if complying with the physical requirements mentioned, can also lend themselves to exhibiting transistor action. We need only be careful of the electrical requirements of forward and reverse biasing for the appropriate junction. Figure 3.5 summarizes the pertinent details. Both N_1 and N_2 have lower resistivity than the P region. The N_1P junction is forward-biased causing the injection of minority electrons into the P region. The N_2P junction is back-biased. The width of the P region is small enough to force a termination of the injected carrier distribution closer to the N_1P junction than the point

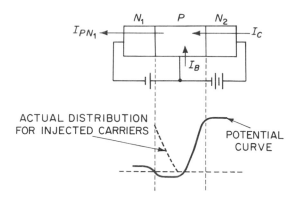

Fig. 3.5 Summary picture for an NPN transistor. Note applied biases, potential curve, and current flow.

normally associated with an unperturbed distribution. Thus the injected electrons which have not yet been trapped in the P material will be carried through to the more positive domain which exists in N_2. Just as in the PNP device, there is one component of current due to recombination in the middle region and a second component representing the current gathered by the N_2 region. The currents, as shown in Fig. 3.5, are *conventional* currents for the particular current components just described. For an NPN device, Eq. (3.1) might be rewritten as

$$I_{PN_1} = I_B + I_C \tag{3.3}$$

where I_{PN_1} = forward-biased N_1P current
        I_B = recombination current in P
        I_C = current gathered by N_2

The appropriate expression for I_{PN_1} is

$$I_{PN_1} = \frac{qA D_n N_p}{W} e^{qV_{PN_1}/kT} \tag{3.4}$$

where D_n = diffusion constant for electrons in P material
        N_p = equilibrium minority-carrier density in P material

Just as for a PNP device, successive reductions in the width of the middle region, a P material in this case, will cause I_B to decrease and I_{PN_1} and I_C to increase. At all times, however, the sum of these two components $I_B + I_C$ is equal to I_{PN_1}, as Eq. (3.4) stipulates.

Since we now have a basic knowledge of how a transistor operates, let us familiarize ourselves with the common names of the three specific regions in a transistor. Regions P_1 and N_1 were seen to be forward-biased with respect to the middle regions. Thus these P_1 and N_1 regions injected holes and electrons, respectively, into the middle regions. Since these quantities of holes and electrons represent the total amounts of charge or current everywhere else in the device, the P_1 and N_1 regions are truly the charge sources and hence are called *emitters*. The P_2 and N_2 regions, by virtue of their back bias in relation to the middle regions, gathered or received specific quantities of charge depending on the exact intersection of the back-bias curve and the density distribution of injected charges. Hence the P_2 and N_2 regions are called *collectors*. The middle regions can be considered references from whence the proper direction of bias voltages must be applied to the emitter and collector in order that transistor action take place. Thus the middle regions N and P are called *bases*. Figure 3.6 shows the conventional symbols used to depict NPN and PNP transistors.

Just as we have been able to reduce the functional regions of PNP and NPN to commonly applied definitions, we can reduce the current equations to a single general equation applicable to all three regions of ideal transistors.

In review of Eqs. (3.1) and (3.3) we might anticipate the following general equation:

$$I_E = I_B + I_C \tag{3.5}$$

where I_E = emitter current
I_B = base current
I_C = collector current

The current I_E is the forward-biased emitter-base current. The I_B component involves recombination in the base, and I_C involves the gathering of free injected minority carriers from the base. The specific directions of I_E, I_B, and I_C for NPN and PNP devices are shown in Fig. 3.6. An understanding

Fig. 3.6   Transistor circuit symbols.

of the mechanism in each device helps one remember the device symbol. For a PNP device, holes go from the emitter to the base. This constitutes a conventional current from the emitter to the base, and thus the emitter arrowhead is into the base for a PNP. For an NPN, electrons are injected from the emitter to the base. This constitutes a conventional current out of the emitter, and thus the emitter arrowhead is away from the base for an NPN.

It is important to remember that our discussions thus far deal with an *ideal* transistor—one in which the back-biased collector-base current is small enough to be ignored. Consideration of the back-biased collector-base current is reserved for the next chapter.

3.4. The transistor as an active device.   Thus far we have mentioned that the device known as a transistor possesses the attributes of power gain. We shall now verify that the interrelation of two junctions constitutes transistor action, and that transistor action provides power gain. This matter can be demonstrated for the moment on a d-c basis. We will use the concept of the transistor as it has been presented thus far. Thus the emitter-base terminals will be considered input terminals and the collector-base terminals will be considered output terminals.

The current gain of any active device can be expressed as the ratio of the output current divided by the input current. Mathematically for our transistor this could be expressed as

$$A_I = \frac{I_{\text{OUT}}}{I_{\text{IN}}}$$

$$= \frac{I_C}{I_E} \qquad (3.6)$$

where A_I = current gain
  I_C = collector or output current
  I_E = emitter or input current

Strangely enough, for the transistor as it is currently connected, A_I is a number less than unity. Recall that I_E is the sum of all currents in the device [Eq. (3.5)] and that I_C is less than I_E by the amount of current I_B lost in the base. At best I_C could be made very close in magnitude to I_E if the width of the base were very, very small, causing I_B to be very small. Thus, the resultant ratio A_I, even though less than unity, would be very close indeed to unity. As an example, it might be noted that a transistor connected with emitter and base regions as input, and collector and base regions as output, has an emitter current of 2 ma and a base current of 50 μa. A manipulation of Eq. (3.5) would reveal that the collector current is the difference between the emitter and base currents and is then 1.95 ma. For this example A_I is .975. Although this A_I attribute is less than unity, the transistor, so connected, does possess power-amplifying attributes. The compensation for an A_I less than unity is a voltage-gain attribute A_V that is very much greater than unity.

The emitter-base junction is essentially a forward-biased diode. Thus a very low value of resistance is presented as an input resistance at the emitter-base terminals. Such values might range from 30 to 200 ohms. The collector-base junction is a back-biased diode. Thus a high value of resistance is presented as an output resistance at the collector-base terminals. Such values might range from 500 K to 2 megohms. Mathematically an expression for voltage gain through our transistor might be stated as

$$A_V = \frac{I_{\text{OUT}} R_L}{I_{\text{IN}} R_{\text{IN}}}$$

$$= A_I \frac{R_L}{R_{\text{IN}}} \qquad (3.7)$$

where A_V = voltage gain
  R_L = load resistance
  R_{IN} = input resistance

Here the ratio A_I is a number less than unity, but the ratio of output to input resistances is very much greater than unity when the value of R_L is made of the same order of magnitude as the output resistance of the transistor. This, of course, would be the desired case in most amplifier circuits. Thus the voltage gain is a number considerably greater than unity. The one remaining step in our sequence is to realize that the product of A_I and A_V is the power gain A_P. Mathematically

$$A_P = A_I A_V \tag{3.8}$$

Suppose that for the transistor with the A_I equal to .975 that R_{IN} was 150 ohms and R_L was made equal to 1.5 megohms. The voltage gain would be 9750 and the power gain would be 9500 or 39.76 db. Transistors with A_I values as low as .9 will give typical power gains of 100 or 20 db.

One important matter must be acknowledged. When we speak of a transistor and its ability to amplify power, i.e., to display the attribute of power gain, we should not envision the device as a generator of power. Rather the power-gain concept is that the use or dissipation of small amounts of power at the input terminals will *control* large amounts of power at the output terminals. In all instances all power is being supplied by the bias batteries, with the power-amplifying transistor being used as a control device.

3.5. Transistor connections. Thus far we have considered the operation of the transistor with emitter and base as input terminals, and collector and base as output terminals. Some of the factors relating to transistor circuit connections are worthy of mention at this time. First of all, it should be recalled that most circuit theory considers "black box" situations to be four-terminal affairs—that is, two input terminals and two output terminals. The transistor, however, in having only three active terminals has one terminal common to both input and output circuit functions. Even though our current impression of the transistor involves the base as common to the input and output circuits, it is possible and usually more desirable to have the collector or especially the emitter lead as the common lead. If the base lead appears in both input and output, the transistor is said to be connected in the *common-base connection.* If the emitter or collector is the common terminal, the connections are said to be *common-emitter* and *common-collector*, respectively. Figure 3.7 shows the transistor in its various useful connections. Note especially which leads are the input and output terminals. As shown, the common-emitter connection has base and emitter as input terminals and collector and emitter as output terminals. The common-collector connection has base and collector as input terminals and emitter and collector as output terminals. Assuming that the necessary geometrical requirements are met, a transistor must be operated with its emitter-base junction forward-biased and its collector-base junction reverse-biased. This generality applies for all three transistor connections.

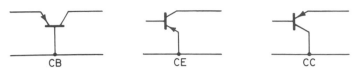

Fig. 3.7 Transistor circuit connections.

If we are to think very basically of two-battery biasing, it is easily seen how to obtain the emitter-base forward biasing and collector-base reverse biasing for the common-base connection. The base-emitter forward biasing in the common emitter is also straightforward in that the leads of interest are directly available. The reverse biasing of the collector-base junction requires only that we take proper heed of the potential of the base in relation to the emitter. Thus, if the base-emitter forward bias is .5 volt and we wish 6 volts reverse bias between collector and base, we apply a collector-to-emitter voltage of 6.5 volts. The net voltage collector to base is the required 6 volts. The collector-base reverse biasing of the common-collector connection is straightforward, as the leads of interest are directly available. Due consideration is required to obtain the necessary forward bias between the emitter and base terminals. If the collector-base reverse bias is 6 volts and an emitter-base forward bias of .5 volt is desired, we must make the emitter-collector voltage 6.5 volts. The desired electrode biasing can be obtained with a single battery and the proper biasing networks. We shall consider this more thoroughly in a later chapter.

The importance of the different configurations lies with the fact that the *performance nature* of the transistor changes as a function of its connection. We recall that the current gain of a transistor in the common-base connection is less than unity. For the common-emitter connection, the computation of current gain involves the collector current as the output current divided by the base current as the input current. This ratio is considerably greater than unity. For the example of Sec. 3.4, where I_C equals 2 ma and I_B equals 50 μa, the common-emitter current gain is 40. This is to be compared to the common-base current gain of .975. The transistor is not operating any differently; what is changing is our point of view in looking at the transistor. The difference in current gain in the common-base and common-emitter connections depends only on our considering the base as the common terminal for the common-base connection, or as the input terminal of the common-emitter connection.

As an aid in distinguishing the performance attributes of the various connections, different symbols or names have been established. For example, the common-base A_I is represented by symbol h_{FB}. The symbol for common emitter A_I is h_{FE}. Note that these symbols for d-c parameters involve lower-case h and capitalized subscripts.

Other transistor parameters such as voltage gain, power gain, and input and output impedances vary also. The reasons and explanations for these parameter variations will be presented as appropriate. For the present, it will suffice to note only which leads are the input and output terminals for the various connections, and to remember that the emitter-base junction is always forward-biased while the collector-base junction is always reverse-biased.

PROBLEMS

1. Sketch the potential curve for an NPN transistor.

2. Sketch the potential curve for a PNP transistor.

3. Explain the phenomenon of recombination.

4. How does decreasing base width serve to increase collector current?

5. Sketch the circuit for the common-base connection. Label all currents.

6. A transistor is operating common-base. $I_B = .15$ ma, $I_C = 1.35$ ma. What is the value of h_{FB}?

7. Sketch the circuit for a transistor in the common-emitter connection.

8. Consider a common-emitter connection. $I_E = 2$ ma, $I_C = 1.95$ ma. What is the value of h_{FE}?

9. A transistor is operating common-emitter. The forward voltage at the base-emitter junction is known to be .4 volt. The collector-to-emitter voltage measures 6.4 volts. What voltage must exist between the collector and base regions?

10. Discuss the physical and electrical requirements for NPN materials to display transistor action.

11. Why is the current gain of the common-base connection less than unity?

4

ATTRIBUTES OF

THE REAL

TRANSISTOR

In the preceding chapter we were introduced to the concept of transistor action. Among other things, we discovered that a transistor may be operated with reverse bias between collector and base. Our knowledge of the PN junction alerts us to the fact that a small thermal current flows across a junction in such a bias situation. This thermal or *leakage current* will now be discussed to show its effect on the magnitude of the collector current in the various transistor connections. We will also discuss another phenomenon of a PN junction under reverse bias, namely, the possibility of voltage breakdown. As in the case of leakage currents, the magnitude of junction breakdown voltage is a function of the transistor connection. The matters of leakage currents and voltage breakdown are mandatory considerations in explaining why a "real" transistor behaves as it does.

4.1. Common-base leakage current. The flow of currents I_E, I_B, and I_C in a PNP device connected in the common-base connection is shown in Fig. 4.1. An additional current of interest is I_{TH}, which flows because of the back-bias voltage between the collector and base regions. As is shown, this thermal current flows, conventionally, into the base and out of the collector for a PNP device. As we learned in Chapter 2, it is the exchange of intrinsic holes of an N material and intrinsic electrons of a P material when these materials are involved in a back-bias junction. To emphasize the significance of this collector-base thermal current, we find it advantageous to introduce a specific name for it. The name chosen is I_{CBO}. The I_{CBO} current is classified as a *leakage current*. It is always present, as it cannot be reduced to zero. In addition, it is usually considered an excess or undesirable component of current.

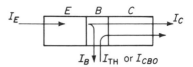

Fig. 4.1 Currents in a real PNP transistor connected common base with normal applied operating biases.

The name I_{CBO} relates in part to the circuit used to measure this leakage current. See Fig. 4.2. Typically, the current component I_C is much larger than I_{CBO}. Thus to measure I_{CBO} we must reduce the I_C component to zero. We do so by opening the emitter circuit, reducing the emitter current I_E to zero. If the emitter is not injecting minority carriers into the base, there will be no injected carriers available for interception by the collector-base potential. Thus, no transistor-action current I_C

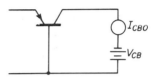

Fig. 4.2 Circuit for measuring I_{CBO} in a PNP device.

flows in the collector. Therefore, with the emitter open and the collector base back-biased, the only current flowing in the collector circuit is the I_{CBO} current.

A procedure has been established to properly label or name a leakage component by use of subscripts. The general leakage designation is I_{XYZ}. Here the subscripts X and Y stand for the regions between which the leakage current is flowing; the subscript Y, in addition, is the common terminal of the circuit connection; and the subscript Z indicates the condition of the third region in reference to the common or Y region. The third terminal reference applies only to the circuit condition that is necessary in the measurement of the leakage being defined. Thus, to denote the leakage current circulating between the collector and base regions in the common-base connection, we specify the leakage current as I_{CBO}. Following the established procedure, the first two subscripts denote the regions between which the leakage is flowing (collector and base), the second subscript denotes the common terminal of the connection (base), and the third subscript denotes the condition of the third lead in relation to the common terminal (emitter is open-circuited in relation to the base).

The significant aspect of the leakage I_{CBO} is that it is present and flowing across the collector-base junction at all times. This applies even when carriers are being injected from the emitter and being collected at the collector as I_C. Thus, for any operating transistor a current meter in the collector would measure I_C plus I_{CBO}. A current meter in the base would measure I_B minus I_{CBO}. For any transistor we have established

$$I_E = I_B + I_C \tag{4.1}$$

We also have, by definition, that

$$h_{FB} = \frac{I_C}{I_E} \tag{4.2}$$

where h_{FB} = common-base forward-current gain. Rewriting (4.2) to solve for I_C and then substituting into (4.1), we can state

$$I_C = h_{FB}I_E \tag{4.3}$$

$$\therefore I_E = I_B + h_{FB}I_E$$

$$\therefore I_B = I_E(1 - h_{FB}) \tag{4.4}$$

To acknowledge the presence of leakage current in the collector we define a new total or real collector current I_C as follows:

$$I_C = h_{FB}I_E + I_{CBO} \tag{4.5}$$

Likewise

$$I_B = I_E(1 - h_{FB}) - I_{CBO} \tag{4.6}$$

The interesting conclusion to be drawn from Eqs. (4.5) and (4.6) is that once the physical dimensions and material resistivities are set (to establish h_{FB} and I_{CBO}, respectively) all current magnitudes can be predicted in terms of I_E.

Equation (4.5) is very important in that it gives the true or total magnitude of common-base collector current. In many instances the magnitude of I_{CBO} will be very small in comparison to $h_{FB}I_E$ and can be overlooked. The real significance of Eq. (4.5) is obvious as temperature and hence I_{CBO} increase. The use of transistors in a good many applications requires that the circuit be operative over a wide temperature range. Germanium devices are expected to operate up to 50–60°C ambients, whereas silicon devices might be expected to operate in ambients greater than 125°C. The major contribution to the variation of transistor performance at high temperature is the magnitude of I_{CBO}. In Chapter 1 we pointed out that the number of intrinsic carriers increases as temperature increases. At high temperatures, all N and P materials become intrinsic in nature. The increased number of intrinsic particles will thus cause the thermal current to increase, as was demonstrated. This then means that in a transistor I_{CBO} increases as temperature is increased. In a germanium device I_{CBO} can be expected to double for every 11°C increase in temperature. In a silicon device I_{CBO} will double for approximately every 6°C increase in temperature. Such information is often expressed in graphical form as in Fig. 4.3. Thus a germanium device with an I_{CBO} leakage of 15 μa at room temperature has approximately 240 μa of leakage at a junction temperature of 65°C. If such a transistor is operated

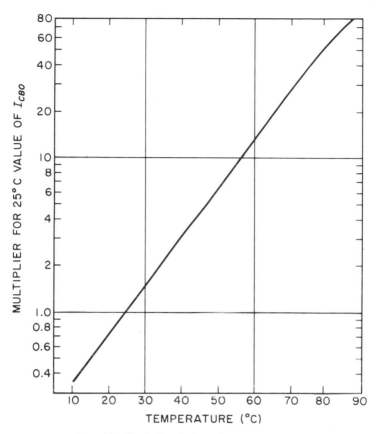

Fig. 4.3 Typical variation of I_{CBO} versus temperature for a Germanium device.

so that the $h_{FB}I_E$ current is .5 ma, the total collector current is seen to be .74 ma at 65°C. This indicates a particular situation where the leakage current can approach the magnitude of the $h_{FB}I_E$ component of current.

4.2. Common-base breakdown voltage. In any practical common-base circuit, there is interest as to how much voltage the transistor can withstand. Recalling the bias conditions at each junction, we see immediately that the back-bias collector-base junction will experience the higher voltage conditions. Further thought will reveal that the collector-base region is the same as a diode with back bias applied. Since it is desired that transistors withstand as high a voltage as possible, we might anticipate that the breakdown phenomenon in a collector-base junction is, by design, that of the avalanche

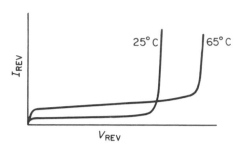

Fig. 4.4 Common-base breakdown curves.

mechanism. Thus, looking at the plot of leakage current versus collector voltage, we would observe the characteristic of Fig. 4.4. As might be expected, the value of breakdown voltage increases as temperature increases. This is also shown in Fig. 4.4.

More will be said on this matter of voltage breakdown when we develop more completely the static characteristics of devices connected in the common-base connection. We might mention now that the symbol for collector-base breakdown voltage in the common-base connection with the emitter open is BV_{CBO}.

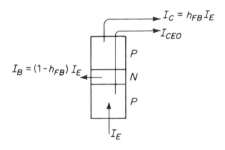

Fig. 4.5 Currents in a real PNP transistor connected and biased for common emitter operation.

4.3. Common-emitter leakage currents. The flow of carriers in a PNP device with the common-emitter connection is shown in Fig. 4.5. Here we see that the basic values of I_B and I_C are as defined in Eqs. (4.4) and (4.3), respectively. This is acceptable, since we have really only interchanged the base and emitter positions in changing a common-base connection to a common-emitter connection. We observe then in Fig. 4.5 that the basic currents I_E, I_B, and I_C are flowing. There is also a leakage current I_{CEO}, unique to the common-emitter connection, flowing in the collector circuit. Let us establish now the specific nature of this current I_{CEO}.

Consider first the information presented in Fig. 4.6(a). The application of a reverse bias between collector and emitter with the base open causes the junction potentials to appear as shown. A large reverse-bias collector-base voltage is created, and a small emitter-base forward bias. The difference in the magnitude of the two potentials is explained by the resistivities of the various regions. The presence of the reverse bias between the collector and base incites thermal-current flow or essentially a flow of I_{CBO} current across the collector-base barrier. Since, however, there is no external path from

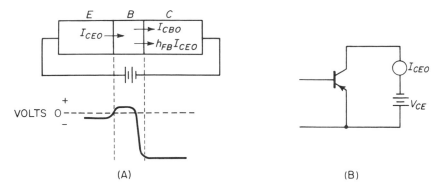

Fig. 4.6 Summary picture for I_{CEO} current. (A) Application of reverse bias between collector and emitter causes the potential shown. Current flow across each junction is shown for the floating-base condition. (B) Circuit for measuring I_{CEO}.

the base, the base becomes electron-plus in nature because of the electron component of thermal current coming from the P-type collector. These electrons in turn will cause a current to be injected from the emitter to the base. As Fig. 4.6(a) shows, some portion of this injected current or $h_{FB}I_{CEO}$ is transported through the base and collected by the collector. Analyzing the total equilibrium situation of current flow, we would see that

$$I_{CEO} = h_{FB}I_{CEO} + I_{CBO}$$

$$= \frac{1}{1 - h_{FB}} I_{CBO} \qquad (4.7)$$

The parameter, h_{FE}, as defined in Chapter 3 designates the forward-current gain of a common-emitter connection. Generally,

$$A_I = \frac{I_{OUT}}{I_{IN}}$$

Specifically,

$$h_{FE} = \frac{I_C}{I_B} \qquad (4.8)$$

$$= \frac{h_{FB}I_E}{(1 - h_{FB})I_E}$$

$$= \frac{h_{FB}}{1 - h_{FB}} \qquad (4.9)$$

where h_{FE} = common-emitter current gain
        h_{FB} = common-base current gain

Frequently in the literature, as well as in present and later material in this text, a variation of Eq. (4.9) is encountered. This variation is obtained by adding unity to both sides of Eq. (4.9). Hence,

$$1 + h_{FE} = 1 + \frac{h_{FB}}{1 - h_{FB}}$$

$$= \frac{1}{1 - h_{FB}} \qquad (4.10)$$

Substituting, now, Eq. (4.10) for the quantity $1/(1 - h_{FB})$ in Eq. (4.7), we get

$$I_{CEO} = (1 + h_{FE})I_{CBO} \qquad (4.11)$$

where I_{CEO} is the collector leakage current in the common-emitter circuit. In accordance with the established letter-subscript procedure, I_{CEO} is measured in the circuit shown in Fig. 4.6(b) as the current there is flowing between emitter and collector in a common-emitter circuit with the base open. The total collector current in a common-emitter circuit, as Fig. 4.5 implies, is

$$I_C = h_{FB}I_E + I_{CEO}$$

Rearranging Eq. (4.4) to substitute for I_E and substituting Eq. (4.11) for I_{CEO}, we get

$$I_C = h_{FE}I_B + (1 + h_{FE})I_{CBO} \qquad (4.12)$$

Equation (4.12) states the actual contributions to the real, measurable collector current that flows in any common-emitter connection. Since the I_{CBO} contribution is multiplied by h_{FE}, it can be expected to affect drastically the magnitude of common-emitter collector current as temperature is raised.

The leakage current I_{CEO} is the largest value of leakage that can flow in the collector of a common-emitter. configuration. As such it is almost always used as the worst-situation consideration of leakage contribution. There are, however, several possibilities that are technically of interest in common-emitter circuits. They are functions of the value of resistance that appears as an external termination between the base and emitter regions. The effect of external resistance can be shown with the aid of the measurement circuit of Fig. 4.7. If R is very, very big, we have essentially an open circuit and an analysis leading to the derivation of Eq. (4.11)—that is, that the collector leakage is I_{CEO} and has a value equal to the product of the quantity $(1 + h_{FE})$ and I_{CBO}. As R is reduced in value, however, some portion of the I_{CBO} current going into the base flows through R in returning to the collector. Hence the base is less electron-plus, less current is injected from the emitter, and the total collector leakage current becomes less than I_{CEO}. The proper notation of such a leakage current with an R between the base and the emitter

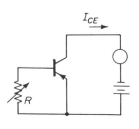

Fig. 4.7 Circuit for considering R_{BE} effects on magnitude of I_{CE}.

is I_{CER}. It is important to understand that the exact value of I_{CER} depends on the value of R; hence, when specifying values of I_{CER}, one must always indicate the value of R in mind. Continual reduction in R yields the limit condition of R equals zero. This is an external short circuit between base and emitter regions, representing a situation where a minimum of injection current is supplied by the

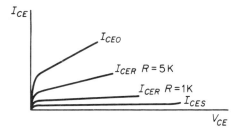

Fig. 4.8   Typical I_{CE} values versus V_{CE} for various base-to-emitter impedance levels. See circuit of Fig. 4.7.

emitter and hence the collector leakage current becomes minimum in value. The proper designation of the leakage current flowing when R equals zero is I_{CES}. Here the S stands for short circuit between the base and emitter regions. Figure 4.8 shows the typical values of common-emitter leakage currents at room temperature on a typical medium-power, low-frequency, germanium-alloy transistor.

4.4. Common-emitter breakdown voltages.   Just as the transistor displayed certain voltage limitations when connected in the common-base connection, so, also, certain voltage limitations will be observed in the device when it is connected in the common-emitter connection. The magnitude of resistance in the external base-emitter connection affects the effective value of common-emitter breakdown voltage just as it affected the magnitudes of common-emitter leakage current.

The simplest of the common-emitter breakdown voltages is called *punch-*

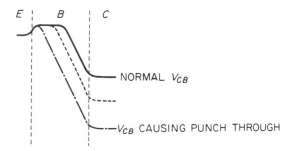

Fig. 4.9   Sufficiently high applied V_{CE} causes the collector-base voltage curve to reach through the base to the emitter. This is called *punch-through.*

Fig. 4.10 *I-V* characteristic at punch-through.

through or *reach-through*. This occurs typically in devices with relatively high base resistivity and hence relatively broad depletion-width distances existing in the base. As collector voltage is increased, the depletion width enlarges and will ultimately extend all the way to the emitter-base junction (Fig. 4.9). Once collector voltage reaches the emitter, transistor action ceases, and the current-voltage characteristic is resistive in its appearance (Fig. 4.10). The slope of the curve beyond punch-through would be determined strictly by the resistances of the emitter and collector regions. In most transistors of today, the design is such that punch-through is not a frequently occurring mode of voltage breakdown. Usually a breakdown by the avalanche mechanism is what is most frequently encountered. The symbol for punch-through voltage is V_{PT}.

The most straightforward of the common-emitter avalanche-breakdown voltages is the one that occurs when the base-emitter termination is an open circuit. This voltage is called BV_{CEO}. Consider Fig. 4.11. Here plots of

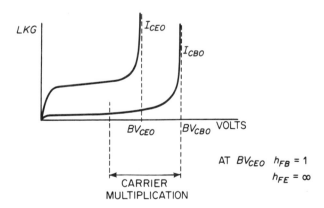

Fig. 4.11 Plots of I_{CBO} and I_{CEO} versus voltage.

both I_{CBO} and I_{CEO} are made against voltage. Insight has already been provided to account for the relative values of I_{CBO} and I_{CEO} in the low-voltage regions. The nature of the common-base breakdown contributes to the specific value of common-emitter breakdown. This is the real reason for the two curves being shown on the same graph. If you will recall, the breakdown of a common-base connection occurred by the avalanche mechanism. Thus, over some finite voltage range, the phenomenon of carrier multiplication occurs. For convenience, this voltage range is labeled as shown in Fig. 4.11. For any given transistor there is a value of voltage that, when it exists between the collector and base junctions, causes the apparent value of h_{FB} to be equal to unity. That is, at some value of voltage the value of I_{CBO} has become large enough to make the measured value of collector current equal to the value of emitter current. Hence, $h_{FB} = 1$. The importance of h_{FB} equals unity is apparent from a reconsideration of Eq. (4.10). As h_{FB} approaches unity, the value of h_{FE} approaches infinity. Consider Fig. 4.12.

In Fig. 4.12, the plot of h_{FB} versus voltage demonstrates the affects of carrier multiplication on the value of h_{FB}. The plot of h_{FE} versus voltage is made using Eq. (4.10) for the h_{FB} at a given voltage. As this plot shows, h_{FE} ap-

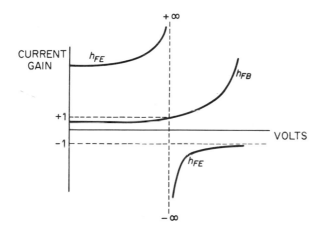

Fig. 4.12   Current gain versus voltage.

proaches infinity at the value of voltage where h_{FB} is unity, and approaches a value of -1 as h_{FB} approaches infinity. Since I_{CEO} at any time is equal to the product of $(1 + h_{FE})$ and I_{CBO}, the value of I_{CEO} approaches infinity as h_{FB} approaches unity. This, of course, is synonomous with a voltage-breakdown condition for the common-emitter connection. When this value of collector-to-emitter breakdown voltage is reached, the collector current is limited only by the impedance in the circuitry external to the transistor.

It is important to realize that in the condition of common-emitter breakdown, the emitter is dominant in the sustaining of collector current flow. Electron-hole pairs are still created in the collector-base depletion width by the ionizing and multiplying process. The first of such electrons thus created go to the base, making the base electron-plus. This in turn causes more holes to be injected from the emitter. Injected but unrecombined holes travel towards the collector and incite more ionization. This leads to a further enhancement of the emitter current. In the final analysis, the charge availability from the emitter is the controlling factor. The common-emitter breakdown voltage BV_{CEO} then is as shown in Fig. 4.11.

Just as the values of common-emitter leakage were discussed as a function of the base-emitter termination, so also will various conditions of common-emitter breakdown voltage be developed. Consider the presence of an arbitrary amount of resistance R between the base and emitter terminals. This has already been established as a shunt path through which some of the I_{CBO} current is diverted. Think for a moment in terms of that portion of the I_{CBO} current which causes carrier injection from the emitter. Anything less than the full I_{CBO} value (as would flow in the special case of the base open) means that more I_{CBO} carrier multiplication can be tolerated before the common-emitter circuit triggers to breakdown. This is shown in Fig. 4.13. As shown here, the lower the value of R between base and emitter,

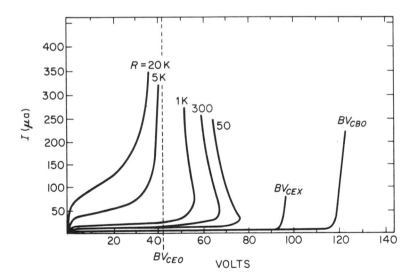

Fig. 4.13   Common-emitter breakdown curves.

the greater the value of voltage before triggering occurs to breakdown. The symbol for common-emitter breakdown when resistance is connected between emitter and base is BV_{CER}. Note that all common-emitter characteristics asymptote to the BV_{CEO} value. This is unavoidable, as once the breakdown is triggered, the emitter will ultimately gain control of the current. This is, in effect, the BV_{CEO} condition. As shown in Fig. 4.13, a negative-resistance characteristic occurs for some circuit conditions. Negative resistance can also appear in the knee region of the BV_{CEO} characteristic. Should the intended operating point inadvertently be placed in the negative-resistance region, uncontrolled oscillations might occur. The BV_{CER} rating applies to the peak voltage before the triggering to the BV_{CEO} condition. This is shown in the various curves of Fig. 4.13.

Another circuit condition that affects the value of common-emitter breakdown voltage is the presence of a back-bias voltage between base and emitter. The voltage rating that ensues is called BV_{CEX}. The back bias is very much more effective than resistance alone in delaying the triggering to a breakdown mode. Also, because of the back bias between the base and emitter, injection of carriers from the emitter is prevented until the moment of breakdown. Thus, until the breakdown occurs, the value of collector leakage is essentially I_{CBO} in value. The actual value of breakdown voltage that results lies between that of BV_{CES} and BV_{CBO}. This also is shown in Fig. 4.13.

4.5. Summary. The preceding discussions regarding leakage currents and voltage-breakdown phenomena are intended to expose the reader to transistor realities. It should be understood that each individual transistor type has its own specified controls on voltages and leakages. The values specified for leakages are maximum values. Such values can be used accordingly as worst-case viewpoints for amounts of leakage in the specified transistor. As presented, the voltage values are meant to imply minimum values of breakdown voltage. That is, all devices under said specification have voltage breakdowns greater than the specified value. As far as the user is concerned, the specified breakdown voltage is the value that must *not be exceeded* in the circuit application. The specific responsibility always lies with the user. Herein lies the importance of knowing the meaning of voltage breakdown, the relative values as a function of circuits, and the ways of measuring same. The circuit conditions for measuring I_{CBO} and I_{CER} leakages are shown in Fig. 4.2 and 4.7, respectively.

For the present we should consider this chapter an opportunity to learn of some of the real and practical aspects of a transistor. These are the matters that must be considered when we use transistors, and, therefore, are necessary considerations in bridging the gap between idealized concepts of transistor action, and the real problems of designing circuits successfully, acknowledging all the properties of a real transistor.

PROBLEMS

1. Show the directions of all of the currents in an NPN transistor when connected first in the common-base and then in the common-emitter connection.

2. A germanium transistor has an I_{CBO} of 10 μa at 25°C. What is the leakage at 75°C?

3. A transistor operating common-base has an $I_C = 2.98$ ma, $I_E = 3.00$ ma, and $I_{CBO} = .010$ ma. What current flows in the collector of this transistor when it is connected common-emitter with a base drive of 30 μa?

4. A transistor is measured and shows $I_{CBO} = 5$ μa, and $I_{CEO} = .8$ ma. What is the h_{FE} of this transistor?

5. Why is the I_{CEO} current greater than I_{CBO}?

6. Explain the effect of emitter-base shunt R in affecting the value of I_{CER}.

7. Explain voltage breakdown in the common-emitter connection as it relates to breakdown in the common-base connection.

8. Explain the effect of base-emitter shunt resistance as it affects the voltage at which a transistor connected common emitter will trigger to breakdown.

9. Explain why I_{CEX} is much less than I_{CEO}.

10. Can the presence of a back bias between emitter and base conceivably raise the collector-emitter breakdown to a value greater than collector-base breakdown?

5

TRANSISTOR

STATIC

CHARACTERISTICS

The material presented thus far has been mainly qualitative in nature. Its purpose has been to develop the physical concepts of the operation of both diodes and transistors. The material in this chapter is essentially the beginning of an analysis of transistors from an applications viewpoint. Specifically, we deal with the transistor and what are called *static characteristics*.

5.1. Static characteristics. Certain interrelations have been established for the currents in the emitter, base, and collector regions of a transistor. Also, certain basic requirements have been established for the polarities and relative magnitudes of the emitter-base and collector-base voltages. These matters have been discussed on a steady-state or static basis. In any typical circuit application, the transistor, with its dynamic mode of operation, passes through or experiences many different combination values of terminal currents and voltages. Questions typically arise: For a given collector voltage how much base voltage must be applied to cause a certain collector current to flow? What variations in input current result from variations in output voltage? These questions can be answered with the help of families of static characteristics. These measurable families give, for any specific transistor, complete information on the interdependence of input and output currents and voltages.

Whereas a large variety of plots are possible, four specific ones are of interest here. They are the *input characteristic*, the *output characteristic*, the *reverse-voltage characteristic*, and the *forward-current characteristic*. A format of general-case coordinate quantities exists for each given characteristic regardless of the connection for which it is drawn. Only the appearance of the plot changes. Thus, the input characteristic is always a plot of input voltage vs input current for various values of output voltage. The reverse-voltage characteristic is drawn from the input characteristic and is a plot of input voltage vs output voltage for various values of input current. The output characteristic is always a plot of output current vs output voltage for various values of input current. The forward-current characteristic is drawn from the output characteristic and is a plot of output current vs input current for various values of output voltage. These general formats are depicted and labeled in Fig. 5.1. The appearance of each characteristic will be discussed as a function of the specific transistor connection.

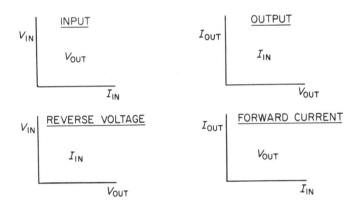

Fig. 5.1   Transistor current-voltage inter-relations.

5.2. Common-base input characteristic.   To properly create any specific picture, we must maintain firmly in our minds all significant information about each transistor connection. For example, for the common-base connection, as redrawn in Fig. 5.2, we observe that the emitter current is the input current, the emitter-base voltage is the input voltage, the collector current is the output current, and the collector-base voltage is the output voltage. From the general definition of the input characteristic we can anticipate that the common-base input characteristic is a plot of emitter-base voltage vs emitter current for various values of collector voltage.

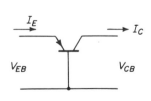

Fig. 5.2   Common-base designations.

How does such a characteristic look? Working on the knowledge we have gathered thus far, we know specifically that an emitter-base junction is forward-biased. Discounting for a moment the presence of the collector, the plot V_{EB} vs I_E will be nothing more than the plot of a diode biased in the forward direction. With this established and drawn in Fig. 5.3 as our beginning fact, we can proceed to consider the effects of collector-voltage variation. Any increase in collector voltage from zero will cause the collector-base potential curve to move closer to the emitter-base junction. As we saw in Sec. 3.2 such a decrease in base width causes the emitter current to increase even though the emitter-base bias voltage is held constant. The total input characteristic as developed, then, would appear as in Fig. 5.3.

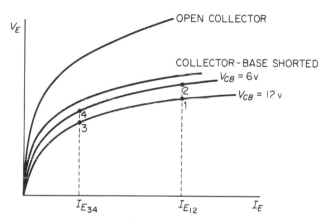

Fig. 5.3 Common-base input characteristic.

It is interesting to note, in passing, that the manner of attaining the zero-collector-voltage condition affects the shape of the input characteristic. With the collector open, the resultant curve can be assumed to be that shown in Fig. 5.3. If, however, the zero collector voltage was obtained with a short circuit between the collector and base, a different curve is obtained. Here, by its proximity only, the equilibrium back-bias potential of the collector succeeds now and again in taking an injected minority carrier from the base. When this happens, the majority carriers of the base are able to attract more carriers from the emitter. Hence, for the given emitter-base bias more emitter current flows. Thus the zero-collector-voltage curve shifts downward to the right. This is also shown in Fig. 5.3.

5.3. Common-base reverse-voltage characteristic. Since it is drawn from the input characteristic, the reverse-voltage characteristic is logically considered next. This characteristic, when drawn for the common-base connection, is a plot of emitter-base voltage vs collector-base voltage for various values of emitter current. The construction of this characteristic from the input plot can be accomplished by a point-by-point progression. Point 1 of Fig. 5.3 is one of high collector voltage, high emitter current, and moderate emitter voltage. It might fall as point 1' as shown in Fig. 5.4(a), a plot which we shall develop into the reverse-voltage characteristic.

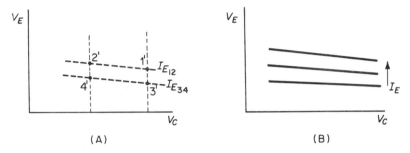

Fig. 5.4 Common-base reverse-voltage characteristic. (A) Construction curve. (B) Final characteristic.

Movement from point 1 to point 3 on the input characteristic is along a constant collector-voltage curve. At point 3, however, both the emitter-base voltage and emitter current have values lower than the point 1 values. This provides insight as to the placement of point 3' as shown in Fig. 5.4(a). Motion from point 1 to point 2 on the input characteristic involves a constant emitter-current value. At point 2, however, the collector voltage is lower and the emitter voltage higher than their respective values at point 1—thus the placement of point 2'. Point 4' can be developed similarly to point 2'. The result is obtained by connecting points 1' and 2', and points 3' and 4'. Such a composite is shown in Fig. 5.4(b). The interpretation of these curves is the same as for the input characteristic. After all, it is the same information in two modes of presentation.

5.4. Common-base output characteristic. The common-base output characteristic is a plot of collector current vs collector-base voltage for various values of emitter current. Here, as before, the electrical requirements for transistor action provide the insight as to the characteristic's general appearance. First of all, we know that the collector-base diode is reverse-biased. We should anticipate that if the presence of the emitter were for the moment neglected, the plot of collector current vs collector voltage would be essentially a plot of I_{CBO} vs collector voltage. The family attributes are to be developed in terms of I_E. Equation (4.5) is the key to this relationship and is restated at this time as follows:

$$I_C = h_{FB}I_E + I_{CBO} \qquad (4.5)$$

The characteristic as it would be developed is shown in Fig. 5.5. Here we

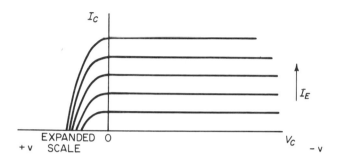

Fig. 5.5 Common-base output characteristic.

see relatively straight lines, uniformly spaced. The spacing between the lines is indicative of the common-base current amplification factor h_{FB}. For most transistors, at room temperature, the usual scale division of the ordinate prevents observation of the curve for I_E equals zero or I_{CBO}. As mentioned earlier, however, it cannot be ignored at higher ambient temperatures.

The region to the left of the origin is not as peculiar as it may at first seem to be. In developing any plot of current vs voltage, the voltage equals zero condition is typically obtained by a short-circuit condition. As was discussed in reference to the input characteristic, collector current will flow as long as there is emitter current and a return path from collector to the emitter. As indicated in the plot of Fig. 5.5, the collector-current value at the vertical intercept is essentially the same as the value of current at higher values of collector voltage. In order to reduce the collector current to zero, we must actually forward-bias the collector-base junction. Such a forward-bias current flows in a direction opposite to the carriers coming into the collector from the emitter. Depending then on the vertical intercept value of collector current, sufficient canceling current can be applied. The shape of the collector current-forward collector bias curve is similar to the current-voltage plot of a forward-biased diode.

5.5. Common-base forward-current characteristic. The last of the common-base characteristics to be considered is the forward-current char-

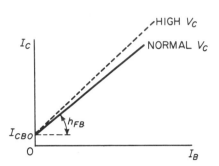

Fig. 5.6 Common-base forward-current characteristic.

acteristic. As has been stated, it is a different presentation of the information contained in the output characteristic. It is, specifically, a plot of collector current vs emitter current for various values of collector-base voltage. As the output characteristic itself implies, the value of collector-base voltage does not have any really dramatic effect on the shape of the characteristics. The appearance of the forward-current characteristic over the normal working values of collector-base voltage would be as shown in Fig. 5.6. Here we see a straight-line characteristic. The vertical intercept is I_{CBO}. The slope of the line is h_{FB}. The only significant effect of collector-base voltage would be at those very high values which cause carrier multiplication and an increase in the value of h_{FB}. This would cause a change in the characteristic such that its slope would be greater.

5.6. Common-emitter input characteristic. Having completed the basic characteristics for the common base, we pass on to a discussion of common-emitter characteristics. For the common-emitter connection, as shown in Fig. 5.7, we observe that the base current is the input current, the base-emitter voltage is the input voltage, the collector current is the output current,

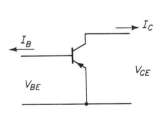

Fig. 5.7 Common-emitter designations.

and the collector-emitter voltage is the output voltage. From the general definition, the common-emitter input charactersitic is obtained by plotting base-emitter voltage vs base current, for various values of collector voltage. If we discount the presence of the collector by leaving the collector open, this characteristic appears the same as the common-base input characteristic, when drawn for the connection that has an open collector. If we now return the collector back to the emitter, the common-emitter input characteristic is seen to shift only slightly. The reason is that the collector is being forwardbiased simultaneously with the emitter. No significant transistor-action multiplication is occurring. This explains the close proximity of the curves representing the open- and short-circuit conditions of obtaining zero collector voltage noted in Fig. 5.8.

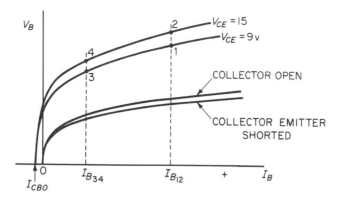

Fig. 5.8   Common-emitter input characteristic.

The application of collector-emitter voltage has interesting results as shown also in Fig. 5.8. We note first that I_{CBO} current is flowing across the collector-base junction. Even with no input voltage applied, I_{CBO} current will flow in the base circuit. This, of course, is opposite in direction to the normal base current in a transistor and is therefore shown as a minus current in Fig. 5.8. That is, the input characteristics drawn for various collector-emitter voltages asymptote a reference which is displaced from the origin by I_{CBO}. The second matter of interest is that increasing collector voltages cause a decrease in base current for constant emitter voltage. An effective reduction in base volume and hence reduced recombination in the base has been observed as a result of the shift in the collector potential curve towards the emitter. This, of course, is manifest as a reduction in base current. These several matters, when considered simultaneously, account for the complete characteristic as drawn in Fig. 5.8.

5.7. Common-emitter reverse-voltage characteristic. Here, we consider a plot of base-emitter voltage vs collector-emitter voltage for various values of base current. This plot, as the corresponding common-base plot, is drawn from the input characteristic. As before, a point-by-point transfer of information develops the complete picture. The characteristic to be developed will be established in Fig. 5.9(a). Point 1 in Fig. 5.8 corresponds to low collector-emitter voltage, high base current, and medium base-emitter voltage. This point could fall as shown by point 1′ in Figure 5.9(a). Movement from point 1 to point 3 on the common-emitter input characteristic is along a constant collector-emitter voltage line. At point 3 both the base-emitter voltage and base current have values lower than the point 1 values, respectively. Thus point 3′ might be placed as shown. Motion from point 1 to point 2 is along a constant I_B line. At point 2 both the base-emitter voltage

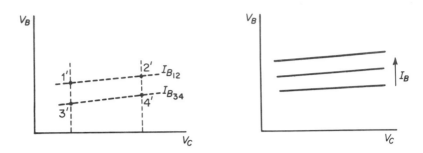

Fig. 5.9 Common-emitter reverse-voltage characteristics. (A) Construction curve. (B) Final characteristic.

and the collector-emitter voltage increase from their point 1 values. After the placement of point 2′, we could easily develop point 4′. Connection of points 1′ and 2′ and points 3′ and 4′ on Fig. 5.9(a) give the insight as to the fully developed characteristic shown in Fig. 5.9(b).

5.8. Common-emitter output characteristic. Unlike some of the other developed characteristics, which do not always lend themselves to exploitation in circuit analysis and design, the common-emitter output characteristic is very significant and often used. It is the most informative presentation of transistor attributes.

Since the transistor is most frequently used in the common-emitter mode, this particular characteristic is almost always found on transistor specification sheets. As might be anticipated, it is a plot of collector current vs collector-emitter voltage for various values of base current. Since there are more than the usual number of points to be explained, we will start first with the complete characteristic and explain successively the factors con-

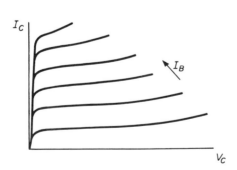

Fig. 5.10 Common-emitter output characteristic.

tributing to its overall appearance. The complete output characteristic is shown in Fig. 5.10. The points requiring explanation are as follows: the collector current is not zero when the base drive is zero, the individual curves show a general curvature upwards at increasing values of collector voltage and in addition possess positive slope, the distance between curves decreases at increasing collector currents, and finally there is a minimum value of collector voltage that can exist in the device for any given collector-current level.

The matter of minimum collector current is the unavoidable result of common-emitter leakage current. The exact value of this minimum current is determined by the nature of the base-emitter circuit. Common-emitter leakage is a maximum when the base is open and a minimum when emitter-base back bias is applied. From a worst-case viewpoint, the value of I_{CEO} is assumed, and used on the characteristic. The value of I_{CEO} is determined by Eq. (4.11).

The presence of positive slope and curvature upwards is a confirmation of the carrier-multiplication phenomenon explained in conjunction with both common-base and common-emitter voltage breakdowns. A transistor in a common-emitter circuit should never be operated to experience voltage values bordering the breakdown value. It is inevitable, however, that in the normal working range some curvature effects might be observed. This will certainly vary from transistor to transistor but, if for none other than academic reasons, attention is directed to the possibility at this time. The feature of positive slope always exists and is nothing more than an increase in h_{FE} as a function of voltage. (Refer to Fig. 4.12.)

The decrease in spacing or bunching of the curves at higher collector-current levels is effectively a decrease in current gain h_{FE} at these high collector-current levels. The precise formulation of change in h_{FE} with emitter current involves the impurity concentrations in the emitter and base regions, and the physical width of the base. In the interests of avoiding the higher mathematics involved in a complete description of these factors, a qualitative description will be provided. Recall that the three regions of a transistor are generally, for any static condition, in a state of charge equilibrium. As the emitter-current level increases, the minority-carrier density of the base approaches and then exceeds the equilibrium majority-carrier distribution. The actual majority-carrier density required for charge equilibrium rises in the base appreciably beyond its low-level equilibrium value. This increases the injection of electrons (for a PNP device) from the base into the emitter. Such a component of emitter current does not participate in transistor action, but does appear as part of the base current. Thus for high values of collector current the effective value of current gain is decreasing each time collector current increases.

Another effect of the greater than equilibrium majority-carrier population in the base is to introduce an electric field which aids minority carrier flow to the collector. At lower levels of current this effect causes current gain to increase, but its effect is overpowered at higher currents by the increased injection from base to emitter. This matter of h_{FE} variation with emitter current is completely within the control of the device designer. Possible results are shown in Fig. 5.11. Changes in concentration levels of the emitter or base (usually the emitter) or changes in base width are the control variables. In any event, the decrease in h_{FE} at higher emitter-current and hence collector-current levels causes the bunching together of the output characteristic curves as current is increased. Note that this condition does not prevent increasing collector voltage from causing the h_{FE} value to increase at the high values of collector voltage.

Fig. 5.11 Possible variations of h_{FE} with I_C.

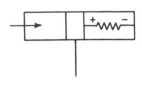

Fig. 5.12 Voltage drop in collector bulk resistance.

The last output-characteristic peculiarity to be accounted for is the minimum collector-to-emitter voltage-value condition. Here our attention must be directed to the collector and emitter regions of the transistor itself. These are regions of finite resistance per unit of volume. Thus, as a function of the materials, their resistivities, and their geometries, some amount of resistance can be thought of as existing between the collector contact and the collector-base junction, and the emitter contact and the emitter-base junction. The emitter, because of its typically high impurity concentration, is usually ignored. We have for our consideration, then, the resistance in the collector region of our device. This might be depicted as in Fig. 5.12.

In the PNP device of our example, collector current flowing in a conventional direction causes a voltage drop such that the external collector contact is minus in relation to the collector-base junction. The direction of this voltage is the same as the normally applied collector voltage. Hence, for any given collector current, there is a voltage due to the bulk resistance in the transistor, and as long as that value of collector current is flowing, the collector voltage cannot be less than the internal IR drop. The minimum value of collector voltage is called *saturation voltage*. The symbol for the common-emitter saturation voltage is $V_{CE(SAT)}$. The resistance that is responsible for $V_{CE(SAT)}$ is called *saturation resistance*. Its symbol for the common-emitter connection is $R_{CE(SAT)}$. In silicon grown diffused transistors, saturation resistance is of the order of 200 ohms. In alloy devices or planar epitaxials, saturation resistance can be as low as 20 ohms. The given transistor type under consideration will have on its specification sheet the value of $R_{CE(SAT)}$ to be expected.

These four matters, when lumped together, comprise the common-emitter output characteristic as it appears in Fig. 5.10. Please note that two additional attributes have been introduced for what we have called the real transistor. These are (1) h_{FE} variation with current, and (2) saturation resistance $R_{CE(SAT)}$. With the mention of these, all those factors which complicate the operation of a transistor at low frequency are now revealed.

5.9. Common-emitter forward-current characteristic. The common-emitter forward-current characteristic is a plot of collector current vs base current for various values of collector-emitter voltage. A transfer of information from the output characteristic to the new plot requirements would provide a family of characteristics as shown in Fig. 5.13. Here h_{FE}

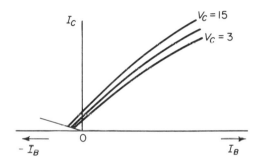

Fig. 5.13 Common-emitter forward-current characteristic.

falloff at high collector current manifests itself in the curves having slight curvature downward at higher currents. The individual curves move upward to the left as collector voltage increases. This, of course, is the effect of carrier multiplication causing an increase in h_{FE}. Note especially that when the base current I_B is zero, the collector current I_C is not zero. Rather, the collector current has I_{CEO} as its value. The value of collector current would be minimized if carriers were fed to the base with a value equal to I_{CBO}. At such time the emitter current would be zero. Since the emitter would not then contribute carriers to the collector circuit, the collector current would be a minimum at the I_{CBO} value. Note that, as voltage increases, the I_{CBO} value of current can be expected to increase. Therefore, in the origin region the various curves do not approach a single point; instead, each curve approaches the value of I_{CBO} that would flow at the voltage for which the specific curve in question was drawn.

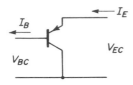

Fig. 5.14 Common-collector designations.

5.10. Common-collector comments. We take the liberty of discussing only the common-collector input characteristic in detail. The common-collector connection, as shown in Fig. 5.14, has base current as input current, base-to-collector voltage as input voltage, emitter current as output current, and emitter-to-collector voltage as output voltage. Since the collector-base junction of any transistor must be reverse-biased, we see a large voltage as our static input voltage. The emitter-base junction must be forward-biased. To accomplish a forward voltage between emitter and base we must, for a PNP device, make the emitter more positive to ground than the base is. Expressing this another way: the base-collector voltage must be less than the emitter-collector voltage if conduction is to occur from the emitter region.

The input characteristic is a plot of base-collector voltage vs base current for various values of emitter voltage. The developed characteristic is shown in Fig. 5.15. We see from the plot that for a given emitter voltage the mag-

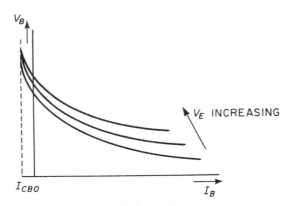

Fig. 5.15 Common-collector input characteristic

nitude of base current increases with decreasing base-collector voltage. Also, for a given base-collector voltage, the magnitude of base current increases with increasing emitter-collector voltage. The general shape of each curve is that of a forward-biased diode. We can note further that if the base voltage were equal to the emitter voltage, a current equal to I_{CBO} would flow in the base. Since this is opposite to the normal base current in the transistor, the base-voltage-equals-emitter-voltage coordinate lies slightly to the left of the ordinate axis.

For the base current to be equal to zero, some small forward bias must exist between the emitter and the base. This situation occurs when the line for a constant emitter voltage crosses the ordinate just above an equal base-value voltage. This provides the necessary increment of forward voltage to satisfy the requirements of zero base current. For the arbitrary condition of base voltage being greater than the emitter voltage, the base current is the leakage current for the specified value of base voltage.

5.11. Temperature effects.   All of the characteristics mentioned exhibit a tendency to shift as temperature is changed. The actual amount of shift depends on the extent to which leakage currents I_{CBO} or I_{CEO} contribute to the shape of the characteristic in question. Temperature effects are most noticeable in the common-emitter output characteristic. Here, by Eq. (4.11), I_{CEO} equals $(1 + h_{FE})$ times leakage current I_{CBO}. Thus, although changes in leakage I_{CBO} may not in themselves seem too significant, the resultant change in I_{CEO} may be a very significant increment of current. Figure 5.16 shows the

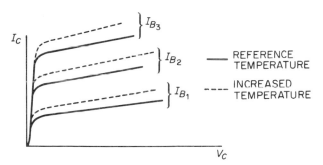

Fig. 5.16   Temperature effects on the common-emitter output characteristic.

typical results in a common-emitter output characteristic when temperature is increased. In addition to a vertical displacement, please note that there is an increase in the slope of each characteristic. This occurs because the increases in leakage cause an apparent increase in the current gain h_{FE}. This effect would also be seen as increased slope on the common-emitter forward-current characteristic.

The final point to be made about the common-emitter output characteristic is that the saturation-voltage region changes as temperature is changed. Figure 5.17 shows how saturation voltage in a transistor might be expected to change as temperature is changed.

One other temperature effect also deserves mention. This is the change

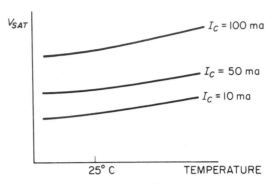

Fig. 5.17 Variation of $V_{CE(SAT)}$ with temperature.

in the common-emitter input characteristic as temperature is changed. We have already been exposed qualitatively to temperature effects in our diode plots. The facts here are essentially the same. For both germanium and silicon transistors, the decrease in base emitter voltage for a given current is about 2 millivolts per degree centigrade of temperature increase. The appearance of the input characteristic as temperature is changed is shown in Fig. 5.18.

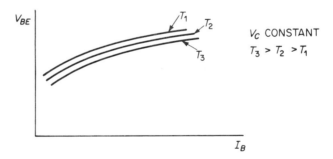

Fig. 5.18 Temperature effects on a common-emitter input characteristic.

For the common-base connection, the contribution in leakage is in terms of I_{CBO} itself. Thus, although we can theoretically expect the characteristics to shift, the actual shift may be difficult to discern.

5.12. Special characteristics. One other characteristic that appears now and again in certain design situations is the so-called transconductance characteristic. Here, output current is plotted against input voltage for various values of output voltage. The general shape of this characteristic for the common-emitter connection can be generated by recalling information on the emitter-base voltage dependency of injected minority carriers in the base, and on the diffusion phenomenon which describes the behavior of minority carriers injected into the base. Consider first the information presented in Fig. 2.8 and in, for example, Eq. 2.16. The number of injected carriers is an exponential function of the emitter-base forward-bias voltage. The slopes of the injected minority-carrier distribution at the edge of the base-emitter depletion width and at the edge of the collector-base depletion width are indicative of emitter current and collector current magnitudes, respectively. As base voltage increases, the slopes at each end of the injected carrier distribution increase. Thus collector current increases as base voltage increases, and for a constant value of collector voltage, a single plot of collector current vs base voltage would be as shown on one of the curves of Fig. 5.19. Consider now the effect of increasing collector voltage while we hold

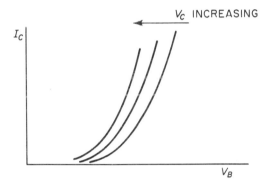

Fig. 5.19 Common-emitter transconductance characteristic.

the base-emitter voltage constant. The collector depletion region moves closer to the emitter reducing the effective width of the base. The injected minority-carrier distribution changes its appearance as was shown in Fig. 3.4. As the slope of this distribution increases, the diffusion current to the collector increases. Thus we see the curves moving in the direction shown. Increased values of V_C cause increases in I_c even though V_B is constant.

PROBLEMS

1. Explain the difference between an open- and short-circuited collector as indicated in the common-base input characteristic.

2. How do increases in collector voltage cause increases in emitter current when emitter-base voltage is held constant in the common-base connection?

3. Explain how the presence of collector voltage causes reversal of base-current flow when the base-emitter voltage is low for a common-emitter connection.

4. Explain completely the factors contributing to the shape of the common-emitter output characteristic.

5. A transistor has a V_{BE} of .7 v when the I_C is 6 ma at 25°C. If the I_C is held constant, what is the approximate V_{BE} at 65°C?

6

D-C BIAS

TECHNIQUES

It is prudent to continue our discussion of the d-c problems in a transistor before concerning ourselves with dynamically operating transistor circuits. The various attributes of leakage currents, breakdown voltages, and d-c families of characteristics have been discussed. We now turn our attention to the considerations and techniques involved in establishing the d-c operating point in a transistor.

6.1. General considerations. As observed in the development of the static characteristics, a vast number of possibilities exist in the way of current and voltage combination values. The specific combination value of current and voltage that is to be considered the design or reference value for a specific circuit is called the *operating point*. In practice, the actual choice of operating point depends on the circuit function. In that general class of circuits known as *small-signal amplifiers*, the operating point is adjusted to that current value at which the transistor power gain maximizes. In *large-signal amplifiers*, the operating point is adjusted so that the transistor can deliver maximum undistorted power output. The full meaning of these statements will be more apparent when the respective application areas are analyzed later. For the moment it suffices that there are basic justifications for having the operating point at a particular value.

The particular circuit that, in conjunction with the transistor's attributes, establishes the operating point is called the *bias circuit*. Since our immediate interests are the bias techniques themselves, we will analyze bias circuits in conjunction with the simplest of transistor circuits: one in which the load is ohmic resistance and connected directly in series with the collector. Such a circuit exclusive of the bias components, is shown in Fig. 6.1(a). An equation that describes the condition in the collector loop at any time is as follows:

$$V_{CC} = I_C R_L + V_{CE}$$

or

$$V_{CE} = V_{CC} - I_C R_L \qquad (6.1)$$

where V_{CC} = supply voltage in volts
             I_C = collector current in amperes
            R_L = load resistance in ohms
           V_{CE} = collector-to-emitter voltage

Equation (6.1) describes the *d-c circuit load line* or, more commonly, the

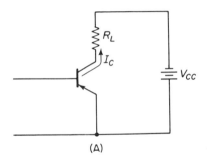

(A)

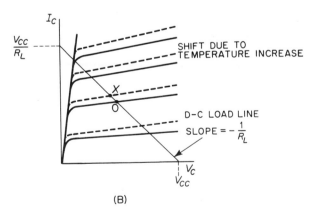

(B)

Fig. 6.1 (A) Simple-case load connection to collector. (B) d-c load line superimposed on collector characteristic. Shift in characteristic due to temperature increase is shown dotted.

d-c load line. A superposition of such a load line on the common-emitter output characteristic appears in Fig. 6.1(b). The slope of this d-c load line is $-1/R_L$, with the horizontal intercept having a value V_{CC}, and with the vertical intercept having a value V_{CC}/R_L.

The particular V_cI_c combination or operating point as we have defined it might be the point 0 as noted in Fig. 6.1(b). Establishing the operating point at this given desired value is a relatively simple matter. The problems of maintaining the operating point at the desired value complicate the bias picture. Such factors as ambient temperature and the distribution of pertinent transistor characteristics tend to make the operating point shift from the desired value. I_{CBO} and I_{CEO} depend on temperature. Equation (4.12), repeated here, states that

$$I_c = h_{FE}I_B + (1 + h_{FE})I_{CBO}$$

This equation shows that any variation of I_{CBO} due to temperature will manifest itself in a shift upwards in the collector characteristics of our transistor. At higher temperatures, then, our collector characteristics will appear as the dotted characteristics shown in Fig. 6.1(b). Our operating point may have shifted to point X. How detrimental this shift is depends on the circuit itself. We can anticipate that any such shift moves us off the optimum operating point, and causes reduced gain or reduced power output as the case may be. The distribution of values on such parameters as current gain, h_{FE}, saturation voltage, $V_{CE(SAT)}$, and common-emitter leakage, I_{CEO}, also affects the appearance of the output characteristics. High values of h_{FE} or I_{CBO} or I_{CEO} cause the characteristics to shift up, as was the case for elevated temperatures. Low values of h_{FE} or I_{CBO} or I_{CEO} cause the characteristics to shift down below the desired operating point. Lastly, variations in values of I_{CEO} and $V_{CE(SAT)}$ can shorten the effective useful length of the *a-c* load line of a circuit.

It is true that on a statistical basis there is a good deal of canceling out between the various factors. For the factors that do prevail—the actual value of I_{CBO}, the actual value of h_{FE}, and ambient temperature—the degree to which any bias circuit actually maintains the operating point is measured by what is called *stability factor*. There are several stability factors; one is a measure of the effects of I_{CBO} in moving the operating point, the second is a measure of the effects of h_{FE} in moving the operating point. Considering both factors sequentially, a third composite stability factor could be determined. Mathematically the stability factors can be stated as

$$S' = \frac{\Delta I_c}{\Delta I_{CBO}} \qquad (6.2)$$

$$S'' = \frac{\Delta I_c}{\Delta h_{FE}} \qquad (6.3)$$

where S' = leakage stability factor

ΔI_C = change in collector current

ΔI_{CBO} = change in leakage

S'' = current-gain stability factor

ΔI_C = change in collector current

Δh_{FE} = change in current gain

Each of the stability factors is a number. Such a number is obtained from calculations involving the equations that predict collector-current value as a function of bias-resistor magnitudes. In order to make use of the leakage stability-factor calculation, we first note the incremental change in leakage, in microamperes, as we proceed from a reference to a transistor with a high limit value of leakage current. If we now multiply this increment of leakage by the stability factor, we obtain the incremental shift in collector current that results in proceeding from the reference to the limit value of leakage. Suppose that for a given circuit we found the leakage stability factor to be 25. If we replace a transistor with an I_{CBO} of 2 μa with a transistor with an I_{CBO} of 10 μa, we would expect the 8-μa increment of leakage current to cause a .2-ma increment increase in collector current. If the reference unit were operating at 1 ma, the current would shift to 1.2 ma owing to leakage change alone.

The current-gain stability factor is used in a similar way. Determine the increment of h_{FE} change as we proceed from a reference transistor to a transistor with a high limit value of h_{FE}. This increment of current-gain change multiplied by the current-gain stability factor gives the increment of collector-current shift due to the current-gain shift. Suppose that for a given circuit the current-gain stability factor is .03 $\times$ 10^{-3} amp/unit of h_{FE}. If a transistor with a current gain of 20 is replaced by a unit with a current gain of 60, the incremental current-gain change of 40 causes a 1.2-ma increment increase in collector current. Thus, if the reference unit were operating at a collector current of 1 ma, we would expect the current to shift to 2.2 ma owing to current-gain change alone. For any transistor where both leakage and current gain are changing simultaneously, the total incremental change in current is approximately equal to the sum of the separate leakage and current-gain increments as predicted from the stability-factor calculations. We indicate an approximation because the stability factors are derivatives that are first-term parts of a series of terms. The calculations should, however, be within 10 per cent of actual observed results.

The various bias techniques that we will discuss exist mainly because they provide varying degrees of stability for the operating point.

6.2. Fixed-bias technique.   The simplest way of establishing collector-current flow in the circuit of Fig. 6.1 is to connect a resistor between the common connection of the collector load and the battery, and the base lead.

This is shown in Fig. 6.2. The equations that establish the performance of such a circuit are

$$I_C = h_{FE}I_B + (1 + h_{FE})I_{CBO}$$
$$V_C = V_{CC} - I_C R_L$$
$$I_B = \frac{V_{CC} - V_{BE}}{R_B} \qquad (6.4)$$

where I_B = base current
$\quad V_{BE}$ = base-to-emitter voltage
$\quad R_B$ = base resistor

Usually the value of V_{BE} is small in relation to V_{CC}, and often it is ignored. Equation (6.4) then reduces to

$$I_B = \frac{V_{CC}}{R_B} \qquad (6.5)$$

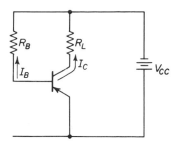

Fig. 6.2 Fixed-bias circuit.

Close scrutiny of Eq. (6.5) shows that once the value of R_B is fixed, the value of I_B depends only on supply voltage and is fixed at a constant value—hence the name *fixed-bias circuit.* Typically, a circuit design starts with a given transistor, a given supply voltage and load resistor, and a required operating point. The design equations do the rest.

In spite of its simplicity, the fixed-bias circuit has a major drawback. The operating point is very responsive to changes in I_{CBO} and h_{FE}. Since I_B is fixed in value, any changes in h_{FE} or I_{CBO} are factored directly into the collector-current expression. The shifts in collector current with changes in temperature and changes in transistors can be drastic. This can be predicted from the stability-factor calculations. First recall that Eq. (4.12) states that

$$I_C = h_{FE}I_B + (1 + h_{FE})I_{CBO}$$

The derivative of Eq. (4.12) with respect to I_{CBO} yields the leakage-stability factor for the fixed-bias technique.

$$S' = 1 + h_{FE} = \frac{\Delta I_C}{\Delta I_{CBO}} \qquad (6.6)$$

The derivative of Eq. (4.12) with respect to h_{FE} is

$$S'' = I_B + I_{CBO} = \frac{\Delta I_C}{\Delta h_{FE}} \qquad (6.7)$$

Both stability factors can be determined numerically by substituting the parameter values for the reference or design transistor. These numbers are used as explained in the paragraphs on the stability-factor concept. The aspects of the fixed-bias circuit are demonstrated by the following example.

6.3. Design example: fixed-bias circuit. Given a supply voltage of 6 v, and a load resistor of 1 K. (a) Design the bias circuit so that a germanium transistor with $h_{FE} = 20$ and $I_{CBO} = 2\,\mu a$ draws an I_C of 1 ma. Ignore the effect of V_{BE}. (b) What I_C is drawn if a second transistor with $h_{FE} = 50$ and $I_{CBO} = 8\,\mu a$ is placed into the circuit? (c) What is S', and (d) what is S''?

(a) By Eq. (4.12)

$$I_B = \frac{I_C - (1 + h_{FE})I_{CBO}}{h_{FE}}$$

$$= \frac{1 - (21)(.002)}{20} = .0478\text{ ma}$$

By Eq. (6.5)

$$R_B = \frac{V_{CC}}{I_B} = \frac{6}{.0478} = 125\text{ K}$$

(b) When the second transistor is used,

$$I_C = h_{FE}(I_B) + (1 + h_{FE})I_{CBO} = 50(.0478) + 51(.008) = 2.798\text{ ma}$$

(c) S' by Eq. (6.6) is 21.

(d) S'' by Eq. (6.7) is $.0498 \times 10^{-3}$.

Note that the current shift due to h_{FE} contributes the major part of the new current level of 2.798 ma.

The major observation is that there is no control over stability with the fixed-bias-current approach.

6.4. Current-feedback principles. In the fixed-bias approach, the variation of operating point is too excessive to be acceptable for most applications. It is necessary to improve the stability factors in order to minimize this variation. Looking into the situation of the fixed-bias circuit, we note that any increase in I_C causes a reduction in V_C. This can be seen also by noting the coordinates as an operating point moves along the load line of Fig. 6.1(b) or by the mathematical inferences of Eq. (6.1). Consider the situation if the bias resistor were returned to a point between the collector of the transistor and the transistor load as shown in Fig. 6.3(a). Again we use the approximation that the base-emitter voltage is small in relation to the supply voltage and collector voltage. We see now that the collector-emitter voltage V_{CE} determines the value of base current. In principle this is a situation of direct-current feedback, since the changes of collector voltage cause changes in base current that tend to compensate for the cause of initial voltage change.

Consider the graphical depiction of the current-feedback circuit shown in Fig. 6.3(b). Point 0 is the desired operating point for the circuit in question. As temperature increases, leakage increases, and the collector current

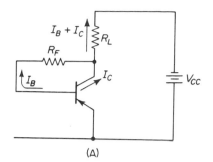

(A)

tends to increase towards point X. At this time, the effects of returning the bias resistor directly to the collector become obvious. The increase in collector current causes a decrease in the collector-to-emitter voltage. Since this voltage determines the base current, there is a decrease in the base current. The operating point does not move to point X but rather ends up at an interim point, Y.

The effectiveness of this circuit depends on the magnitude of collector-voltage change for a given collector-current change. That is to say, this type of biasing is most effective when the value of resistance in the collector circuit is high. This circuit compensates also for tendencies of the operating point to drift below the desired or reference value.

The mathematics of the current-feedback bias circuit are contained in the following equations:

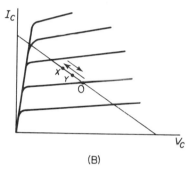

(B)

Fig. 6.3 (A) Current-feedback bias circuit. (B) Graphical depiction of operating point control due to V_{CE} variation.

$$I_C = h_{FE}I_B + (1 + h_{FE})I_{CBO}$$

$$V_c = V_{cc} - (I_c + I_B)R_L \qquad (6.8)$$

$$I_B = \frac{V_C - V_{BE}}{R_F} \qquad (6.9)$$

Here we should note the presence of I_B in adding to the total IR drop in the collector circuit. The approach in designing the bias circuit is really no different from that used in the fixed-bias situation. As given information, we have the transistor with known values of current gain and leakage, the value of supply voltage, the value of load resistance, and the required operating point. Using the block of design equations, we first determine the necessary value of base current, then the resultant value of collector voltage from Eq. (6.8), and finally the necessary value of bias resistance R_F from Eq. (6.9).

Further manipulation of the design equations is necessary, however, if we are to determine the effects of changing temperature or changes in transistors, or if we are to calculate the various stability factors. Equations for collector voltage V_C and then collector current I_C are necessary in terms of the circuit components and transistor parameter values. We can start by substituting the general equation for I_C into Eq. (6.8):

$$V_C = V_{CC} - [h_{FE}I_B + (1 + h_{FE})I_{CBO} + I_B]R_L$$

Since

$$I_B = \frac{(V_C - V_{BE})}{R_F}$$

$$\therefore \quad V_C = V_{CC} - \frac{(1 + h_{FE})(V_C - V_B)R_L}{R_F} - (1 + h_{FE})I_{CBO}R_L$$

Rearranging, we get

$$V_C = \frac{V_{CC} + \frac{(1 + h_{FE})V_B R_L}{R_F} - (1 + h_{FE})I_{CBO}R_L}{1 + (1 + h_{FE})\frac{R_L}{R_F}} \tag{6.10}$$

Substituting Eq. (6.9) into the general equation for I_C, we get

$$I_C = \frac{h_{FE}(V_C - V_B)}{R_F} + (1 + h_{FE})I_{CBO}$$

Substituting again with Eq. (6.10),

$$I_C = \frac{h_{FE}}{R_F}\left[\frac{V_{CC} - V_B - (1 + h_{FE})I_{CBO}R_L}{1 + (1 + h_{FE})\frac{R_L}{R_F}}\right] + (1 + h_{FE})I_{CBO}$$

$$= \frac{h_{FE}(V_{CC} - V_B) + (1 + h_{FE})(R_L + R_F)I_{CBO}}{R_F + (1 + h_{FE})R_L} \tag{6.11}$$

Working from Eq. (6.11) and taking the derivative of I_C with respect to I_{CBO}, we find

$$S' = \frac{(1 + h_{FE})(R_L + R_F)}{R_F + R_L + h_{FE}R_L} \tag{6.12}$$

Working from Eq. (6.11) and taking the derivative of I_C with respect to h_{FE}, we get

$$S'' = \frac{(R_L + R_F)(V_{CC} - V_B + R_F I_{CBO})}{(R_F + R_L + R_L h_{FE})^2} \tag{6.13}$$

Equation (6.11) is developed specifically so that we can calculate the stability factors S' and S'' for the current-feedback circuit. Actually, when determining a new operating point for a change in temperature or a change in transistor, the new V_C given by Eq. (6.10) is an adequate reference. Using the new V_C, the new I_B by Eq. (6.9) and then the new I_C can be calculated. A direct substitution in Eq. (6.11) also is possible; individual circumstances will dictate the approach to be used. The manipulations of the current-feedback design equations are illustrated in the following example.

6.5. Design example: current-feedback biasing.   Using a current-feedback bias circuit, satisfy the requirements of the example in Sec. 6.3. By Eq. (4.12), and as calculated in Sec. 6.3

$$I_B = .0478 \text{ ma}$$

By Eq. (6.8)

$$V_C = V_{CC} - (I_C + I_B)R_L$$
$$= 6 - (1.0478)10^{-3}(1 \text{ K}) = 4.95 \text{ v}$$

By Eq. (6.9)

$$I_B = \frac{V_C - V_{BE}}{R_F}$$

$$\therefore \quad R_F = \frac{4.95}{.0478} = 104 \text{ K}$$

Since the operating point for the second transistor is required, we substitute the appropriate values for the second transistor into Eq. (6.11) to get

$$I_C = \frac{h_{FE}(V_{CC} - V_B) + (1 + h_{FE})(R_L + R_F)I_{CBO}}{R_F + (1 + h_{FE})R_L}$$

$$= \frac{50(6) + 51(105 \text{ K})(.008)10^{-3}}{104 \text{ K} + 51(1 \text{ K})} = 2.22 \text{ ma}$$

The stability factor S' by Eq. (6.12) is

$$S' = \frac{(1 + h_{FE})(R_L + R_F)}{R_F + R_L + h_{FE}R_L} = \frac{21(105 \text{ K})}{104 \text{ K} + 1 \text{ K} + 20(1 \text{ K})} = 17.5$$

The stability factor S'' by Eq. (6.13) is

$$S'' = \frac{(R_L + R_F)(V_{CC} - V_B - I_{CBO}R_F)}{(R_F + R_L + h_{FE}R_L)^2} = \frac{105 \text{ K} [6 - 104 \text{ K}(.002)10^{-3}]}{(125 \text{ K})^2}$$
$$= .0416(10^{-3})$$

Note that the increment of current shift as predicted by the S'' calculation, in this case 1.25 ma, accounts for the total collector-current shift. The slight numerical error occurs because the derivative calculations are the first terms of series expansions.

A review of the typical numbers for the stability-factor magnitudes, as obtained in the examples, reveals that the current-feedback technique, as applied in Fig. 6.3(a), is not much improved over the fixed-bias approach. This condition exists because of the low value of R_L used in the examples. Higher values of R_L would enable the current-feedback technique to give superior operating point control. More complete bias circuits involving current feedback can, however, be very effective. This will be developed in a later section.

6.6. Basic voltage-feedback principles. Another type of feedback from the output is applied through a resistor in the emitter lead. This possibility is shown in Fig. 6.4, which is a simple extension of the circuit shown in Fig. 6.2. The value of R_B of Fig. 6.4 must obviously be modified to account for the IR drop in the emitter series resistor. In this circuit, any tendency for the

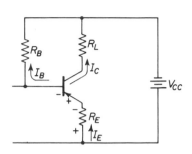

collector current and hence the emitter current to increase causes an increase in the IR drop in the emitter resistance. The polarity of this voltage is opposite to the normal forward-bias voltage between base and emitter. Such a change in voltage between base and ground causes a reduced forward-bias voltage. There is, then, some degree of compensation for operating-point excursion. The feedback mechanism depends on changes in collector current. The resultant voltage changes across the emitter resistor are the actual factors affecting the total forward-bias condition; thus, this feedback

Fig. 6.4 Basic form of providing voltage feedback to the input circuitry using emitter resistance R_E.

is called *voltage feedback*. The effectiveness of this approach depends on the constancy of the total voltage between the base and ground. Another factor is the magnitude of the load resistance as compared with the emitter resistance. Too large a load results in a load line with small slope; as a result, current variations and hence voltage-feedback effectiveness are minimized.

6.7. Voltage feedback—detalied analysis. The general-case circuit incorporating voltage feedback for bias stability is shown in Fig. 6.5. Here we note the presence of emitter resistance R_E and a base-to-ground resistance

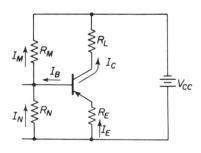

R_N. This circuit overcomes all the problems of simple fixed-biasing and the basic form of voltage feedback-biasing. We now have simultaneous control over the actual value of the operating point and the actual amount of overall operating-point stability. These matters will become apparent as the circuit analysis and design procedures are developed. The equations that establish the performance of this circuit (Fig. 6.5) are

Fig. 6.5 Complete voltage-feedback bias circuit.

$$V_C = V_{CC} - I_C R_L - I_E R_E \qquad (6.14)$$

$$V_{CC} = I_M R_M + I_N R_N \qquad (6.15)$$

$$I_N R_N = I_E R_E + V_B \qquad (6.16)$$

$$I_M = I_B + I_N \qquad (6.17)$$

Basic equations also applicable are

$$I_E = I_B + I_C$$

$$I_C = h_{FE} I_B + (1 + h_{FE}) I_{CBO}$$

The design equations are obtained by starting with Eq. (6.17) and substituting (6.15) and (6.16) for I_M and I_N. Manipulations involving the basic current relationships in a transistor yield

$$I_B = \frac{\dfrac{V_{CC} - V_B}{R_M} - \dfrac{V_B}{R_N} - I_{CBO}(1 + h_{FE})\left(\dfrac{R_E}{R_M} + \dfrac{R_E}{R_N}\right)}{1 + (1 + h_{FE})\left(\dfrac{R_E}{R_M} + \dfrac{R_E}{R_N}\right)} \qquad (6.18)$$

$$I_C = \frac{\dfrac{h_{FE}(V_{CC} - V_B)}{R_M} - \dfrac{h_{FE} V_B}{R_N} + (1 + h_{FE}) I_{CBO}\left(1 + \dfrac{R_E}{R_M} + \dfrac{R_E}{R_N}\right)}{1 + (1 + h_{FE})\left(\dfrac{R_E}{R_M} + \dfrac{R_E}{R_N}\right)} \qquad (6.19)$$

Reworking of Eq. (6.14) to include the basic relations gives

$$V_C = V_{CC} + \frac{R_E(1 + h_{FE}) I_{CBO}}{h_{FE}} - \left(R_E + R_L + \frac{R_E}{h_{FE}}\right) I_C \qquad (6.20)$$

where I_C is as given by Eq. (6.19).

Equations (6.18) (6.19) and (6.20) are truly general. The values of I_C and V_C that are obtained are unique for a given transistor with its particular h_{FE} and I_{CBO} when placed in the circuit with a given V_{CC}, R_L, R_M, R_N, and R_E. Determining the values for R_M, R_N, and R_E is what constitutes the true execution of circuit design.

The design approach used depends on the circuit requirements specified. A design always begins with the requirement that a certain operating point be obtained with a reference transistor. Such a reference transistor might have mean values of h_{FE} and I_{CBO} for the parameter distributions expected. The other circuit requirements will relate to the operating-point stability. This is expressed in terms of a required leakage-current stability factor, or a required current-gain stability factor. More practically, the operating-point stability is expressed in terms of limiting values to which the operating point might shift when limit combinations of leakage and current-gain values or temperature are used. This approach is most useful because the distributions on leakage and current gain are acknowledged straightforwardly in establishing the current or voltage excursions that can be tolerated and still provide acceptable circuit performance.

The several steps that constitute the bias circuit design are as follows.

(a) Assume a knowledge of V_{CC}, R_L, the desired operating point I_C, V_C, and the reference transistor's h_{FE} and I_{CBO}.

(b) A manipulation of this information in Eq. (6.14) or (6.20) yields

$$R_E = \left(\frac{h_{FE}}{1 + h_{FE}}\right)\left(\frac{V_{CC} - V_C - I_C R_L}{I_C - I_{CBO}}\right) \qquad (6.21)$$

(c) The values of R_M and R_N must now be calculated. The operating point for the reference transistor and the stability criteria provide the two bits of information for which a simultaneous solution yields the correct values of R_M and R_N. At the reference condition, Eq. (6.19) is solved for R_M.

$$R_M = \frac{R_N h_{FE}(V_{CC} - V_B) - B R_E}{C R_N + B R_E + h_{FE} V_B} \qquad (6.22)$$

where $\quad B = (I_C - I_{CBO})(1 + h_{FE})$
$\qquad\quad C = I_C - (1 + h_{FE})I_{CBO}$

At the value of operating point corresponding to limit values of leakage and h_{FE} we find

$$R_M = \frac{R_N[h'_{FE}(V_{CC} - V'_B) - B'R_E]}{C'R_N + B'R_E + h'_{FE}V'_B} \qquad (6.23)$$

where $\quad h'_{FE}$ = limit current-gain value
$\qquad\quad I'_{CBO}$ = limit leakage value
$\qquad\quad V'_B$ = base-emitter voltage at limit value
$\qquad\quad B' = (I'_C - I'_{CBO})(1 + h'_{FE})$
$\qquad\quad C' = I'_C - (1 + h'_{FE})I'_{CBO}$

Solving (6.22) and (6.23) simultaneously, we obtain

$$R_N = \frac{(V_{CC} - V'_B)h'_{FE}D - (V_{CC} - V_B)h_{FE}D' - R_E(B'h'_{FE}V_B - Bh'_{FE}V'_B)}{C'(h_{FE}V_{CC} - D) - C(h'_{FE}V_{CC} - D')} \qquad (6.24)$$

where $\quad D = h_{FE}V_B + B R_E$
$\qquad\quad D' = h'_{FE}V'_B + B'R_E$

If we now assume that $V_B = V'_B$, we find that

$$R_N = \frac{V_{CC}E R_E}{(V_{CC} - V_B)F - G R_E} \qquad (6.25)$$

where $\quad E = B'h_{FE} - Bh'_{FE}$
$\qquad\quad F = Ch'_{FE} - C'h_{FE}$
$\qquad\quad G = B'C - BC'$

Once the value of R_N is determined, we are able to go back and calculate the appropriate value of R_M. In practice, Eqs. (6.21), (6.25), and (6.22) are used in that order.

Alternate forms of design might relate to a desired S' or S'' calculation. The appropriate derivatives of Eq. (6.19) are

$$S' = \frac{(1 + h_{FE})\left(1 + \dfrac{R_E}{R_M} + \dfrac{R_E}{R_N}\right)}{1 + (1 + h_{FE})\left(\dfrac{R_E}{R_M} + \dfrac{R_E}{R_N}\right)} \qquad (6.26)$$

$$S'' = \frac{\left(\dfrac{V_{CC} - V_B}{R_M} - \dfrac{V_B}{R_N} + I_{CBO}\right)\left(1 + \dfrac{R_E}{R_M} + \dfrac{R_E}{R_N}\right)}{\left[1 + (1 + h_{FE})\left(\dfrac{R_E}{R_M} + \dfrac{R_E}{R_N}\right)\right]^2} \qquad (6.27)$$

Thus the second equation involving R_M and R_N is R_M as a function of h_{FE}, R_E, R_N, and S' or R_M as a function of V_{CC}, V_B, I_{CBO}, h_{FE}, R_E, R_N, and S'' as the requirement would have stipulated. Since the detailed sequence yielding Eq. (6.25) is the most practical, further development of (6.26) and (6.27) will not be provided.

As the design procedure permits, the combined requirements of desired operating point and desired stability can be satisfied simultaneoulsy. The amount of negative feedback that can be applied is established by the value of R_E. The degree to which the negative feedback is effective can be controlled by the ratio of the divider network R_M and R_N. The smaller the values of R_M and R_N, the greater the stability of the operating point. The bigger the values of R_M and R_N, the less the stability of the operating point is controlled.

6.8. Design example: voltage-feedback biasing.

In the examples of Secs. 6.3 and 6.5 rather poor operating-point stability resulted when first a fixed-bias circuit and then a self-bias circuit was used in conjunction with a reference transistor with $h_{FE} = 20$ and $I_{CBO} = 2\mu a$ and a limit transistor with $h'_{FE} = 50$ and $I'_{CBO} = 8\,\mu a$. When designing to obtain a 1-ma collector current, we observed that the fixed-bias circuit yielded a 2.798-ma and the self-bias circuit a 2.22-ma collector current for the limit transistor. To demonstrate how different the complete voltage feedback circuit is, let us design so that the reference transistor has an operating point of $I_C = 1$ ma and $V_C = 4.5$ v, and let us hold the total operating-point excursion to an $I'_C = 1.2$ ma for the limit transistor. Let us assume that $V_B = V'_B = .15$ v at the operating points of interest. $R_L = 1$ K and $V_{CC} = 6$ v as before.

In proceeding to satisfy the objectives just outlined, we calculate first the magnitude of the emitter resistance R_E. By (6.21)

$$R_E = \left(\frac{h_{FE}}{1+h_{FE}}\right)\left(\frac{V_{CC}-V_C-I_C R_L}{I_C-I_{CBO}}\right)$$

$$= \frac{20}{21}\left[\frac{6-4.5-1(1)}{10^{-3}-2(10^{-6})}\right]$$

$$= 477\ \Omega$$

The calculation constants are

$$B = (I_C - I_{CBO})(1 + h_{FE}) = [10^{-3} - 2(10^{-6})](21) = 20.9(10^{-3})$$

$$B' = (I'_C - I'_{CBO})(1 + h'_{FE}) = [1.2(10^{-3}) - 8(10^{-6})](51) = 60.8(10^{-3})$$

$$C = I_C - (1 + h_{FE})I_{CBO} = 10^{-3} - 21(2)10^{-6} = .958(10^{-3})$$

$$C' = I'_C - (1 + h'_{FE})I'_{CBO} = 1.2(10^{-3}) - 51(8)10^{-6} = .792(10^{-3})$$

$$E = B'h_{FE} - Bh'_{FE} = 60.8(10^{-3})20 - 20.9(10^{-3})50 = .168$$

$$F = Ch'_{FE} - C'h_{FE} = .958(10^{-3})50 - .792(10^{-3})20 = 32(10^{-3})$$

$$G = B'C - BC' = 60.8(.958)10^{-6} - 20.9(.792)10^{-6} = 41.6(10^{-6})$$

Now by (6.25)

$$R_N = \frac{V_{CC}ER_E}{(V_{CC} - V_B)F - GR_E}$$

$$= \frac{6(.168)(477)}{(6 - .15)32(10^{-3}) - 41.6(10^{-6})477} = 2.9\ \text{K}$$

Now by (6.22)

$$R_M = \frac{R_N[h_{FE}(V_{CC} - V_B) - BR_E]}{CR_N + BR_E + h_{FE}V_B}$$

$$= \frac{2.9\ \text{K}[20(5.85) - 20.9(10^{-3})477]}{.958(10^{-3})2.9(10^3) + 20.9(10^{-3})477 + 20(.15)} = 19.6\ \text{K}$$

6.9. Modified voltage-feedback biasing. If, for the circuit of Fig. 6.5, R_N is infinity and R_E is zero, we have a duplication of the circuit of Fig. 6.2. The same inability to stabilize the operating point applies. A similarly undesirable situation is obtained if the only change from Fig. 6.5 is the reduction of R_E to zero. In retaining the assumption that the base-emitter voltage is approximately zero, notice that negligible current flows through R_N. Hence the presence of R_N really does nothing to improve stability over the fixed-bias situation.

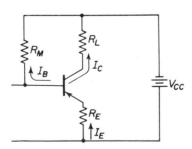

Fig. 6.6 Modification reverting to basic form of voltage feedback.

The modification of the general circuit to the one shown in Fig. 6.6 deserves some comment. The presence of the emitter resistance means that there will be some contribution towards operating-point stability. The fact the emitter resistance must do all the work of stabilizing tends to make the design values of emitter resistance very big. One limitation on the magnitude of emitter resistance is the total $I(R_E + R_L)$ drop in the collector loop and the actual ability to obtain the desired $I_C V_C$ operating point for the V_{CC} provided. Another factor deals with the a-c operation of the transistor. The effects of emitter resistance in changing the total input impedance of a transistor, and therefore the efficiency of power transfer to the transistor, will be dealt with later. For the present it is sufficient to realize that the emitter resistance must be less than certain limiting values as prescribed by other circuit requirements.

Since the cost of a resistor is saved, the design review of such a circuit is worthwhile, and proceeds as follows:

(a) Assume as before a knowledge of V_{CC}, R_L, the desired operating point I_C, V_C, and the h_{FE} and I_{CBO} of the reference transistor.

(b) Since a certain operating-point limit value is intended for a limit h'_{FE} and I'_{CBO}, the required combination of R_E and R_M must be calculated. For the reference operating point, a manipulation of Eq. (6.19) (with R_N equals infinity) gives

$$R_M = \frac{h_{FE}(V_{CC} - V_B) - R_E B}{C} \tag{6.28}$$

For the limit operating point

$$R_M = \frac{h'_{FE}(V_{CC} - V'_B) - R_E B'}{C'} \tag{6.29}$$

Solving (6.28) and (6.29) simultaneously gives the necessary value of emitter resistance:

$$R_E = \frac{(V_{CC} - V'_B)h'_{FE}C - (V_{CC} - V_B)h_{FE}C'}{G} \tag{6.30}$$

If we assume that $V'_B = V_B$,

$$R_E = \frac{(V_{CC} - V_B)F}{G} \tag{6.31}$$

The value of R_E as calculated from (6.31) must satisfy the operating-point requirements as dictated by Eq. (6.14); a-c requirements, if any, must also be considered, although for the moment such considerations are postponed. If the operating-point requirement is satisfied, the circuit design can be completed by going back to Eq. (6.28) or (6.29) and solving for R_M. If the operating-point requirements are not met, then a re-evaluation of the stability requirements is in order. If the stability requirements cannot be changed, consideration should be given to changing the magnitude of the supply voltage. This is not usually a likely possibility in ordinary circuit design. However, to obtain the magnitude of voltage necessary we should set Eq. (6.21) equal to Eq. (6.30) and solve for V_{CC}. We obtain

$$V_{cc} = \frac{h_{FE}G[V_c + I_cR_L] - B[V'_B h'_{FE}C - V_B h_{FE}C']}{Gh_{FE} - BF} \qquad (6.32)$$

If $V'_B = V_B$,

$$V_{cc} = \frac{h_{FE}G[V_c + I_cR_L] - BV_B F}{Gh_{FE} - BF} \qquad (6.33)$$

If the stability requirements cannot be reduced, and the supply voltage cannot be changed, then the complete voltage-feedback circuit must be used.

The leakage and current-gain stability factors for the modified voltage-feedback circuit are

$$S' = \frac{(1 + h_{FE})\left(1 + \dfrac{R_E}{R_M}\right)}{1 + (1 + h_{FE})\left(\dfrac{R_E}{R_M}\right)} \qquad (6.34)$$

$$S'' = \frac{\left(\dfrac{V_{cc} - V_B}{R_M} + I_{CBO}\right)\left(1 + \dfrac{R_E}{R_M}\right)}{\left[1 + (1 + h_{FE})\dfrac{R_E}{R_M}\right]^2} \qquad (6.35)$$

6.10. Design example: modified voltage-feedback biasing. To demonstrate the limitations in the applicability of the modified voltage-feedback circuit, let us attempt to duplicate the operating-point controls stated in Sec. (6.8). These are resummarized as follows:

$$V_{CC} = 6 \text{ v}$$
$$R_L = 1 \text{ K}$$
$$V_C = 4.5 \text{ v}$$
$$I_C = 1 \text{ ma} \qquad I'_C = 1.2 \text{ ma}$$
$$h_{FE} = 20 \qquad h'_{FE} = 50$$
$$I_{CBO} = 2 \ \mu a \qquad I'_{CBO} = 8 \ \mu a$$

We will first calculate the R_E necessary to obtain the required stability. By (6.31)

$$R_E = \frac{(V_{CC} - V_B)F}{G} = \frac{(5.85)32 \times 10^{-3}}{41.6 \times 10^{-6}} = 4.5 \text{ K}$$

Checking, we find that this value of emitter resistance will not satisfy the basic operating-point requirements. Since the desired operating-point stability cannot be obtained, let us check to find exactly what level of stability exists when a modified circuit design is completed using $R_E = 477$ ohms.

By (6.28)

$$R_M = \frac{h_{FE}(V_{CC} - V_B) - R_E B}{C}$$

$$= \frac{20(5.85) - 477(20.9)\,10^{-3}}{.958(10^{-3})} = 110 \text{ K}$$

The operating current for the limit transistor is obtained by substituting the limit parameters into Eq. (6.18) using R_N equals infinity. We obtain

$$I_c' = \frac{\dfrac{h_{FE}(V_{CC} - V_B)}{R_M} + (1 + h_{FE}')I_{CBO}'\left(1 + \dfrac{R_E}{R_M}\right)}{1 + (1 + h_{FE}')\dfrac{R_E}{R_M}}$$

$$= \frac{\dfrac{50(5.85)}{110 \text{ K}} + 51(.008)\,10^{-3}\left(1 + \dfrac{477}{110 \text{ K}}\right)}{1 + 51\left(\dfrac{477}{110 \text{ K}}\right)} = 2.52 \text{ ma}$$

This is not particularly good. In fact, it is in between the fixed-bias result of 2.798 ma and the self-bias result of 2.22 ma.

The final possibility is an increase in supply voltage V_{CC}. By (6.33)

$$V_{CC} = \frac{h_{FE}G(V_O + I_c R_L) - BV_B F}{Gh_{FE} - BF}$$

$$= \frac{20(41.6)\,10^{-6}[4.5 + (10^{-3})\,10^3] - .15(32)\,10^{-3}(20.9)\,10^{-3}}{41.6(10^{-6})20 - 32(10^{-3})20.9(10^{-3})}$$

$$= 27.6 \text{ v}$$

6.11. Combination current-voltage feedback—detailed analysis. The voltage-feedback circuit loses its effectiveness as R_L increases. At such a time, however, the introduction of current feedback is advantageous. Such a bias circuit is called *combination current-voltage feedback*, and is shown in Fig. 6.7. Operating-point stability is greatest at high values of R_L, but is almost always acceptable for any value of R_L. The use of combination current and voltage feedback allows simultaneous control over the actual value of the operating point and the actual amount of overall operating-point stability. The equations that establish the performance of this circuit are

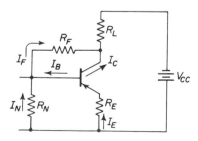

Fig. 6.7 Combination current-voltage feedback bias.

$$V_C = V_{CC} - (I_C + I_F)R_L - I_E R_E \tag{6.36}$$

$$V_C = I_F R_F + V_B \tag{6.37}$$

$$I_N R_N = I_E R_E + V_B \tag{6.38}$$

$$I_F = I_B + I_N \tag{6.39}$$

As before, basic applicable relations are

$$I_E = I_B + I_C$$

$$I_C = h_{FE}I_B + (1 + h_{FE})I_{CBO}$$

The equations for the operating-point variables are obtained by starting with Eq. (6.39), substituting (6.36) and (6.37) for I_N and I_F, and solving for I_B. Manipulations involving the basic current relations in the transistor give

$$I_B = \frac{\dfrac{V_{CC} - V_B}{R_L + R_F} - \dfrac{V_B}{R_N} - (1 + h_{FE})(I_{CBO})\left(\dfrac{R_L + R_E}{R_L + R_F} + \dfrac{R_E}{R_N}\right)}{1 + \dfrac{R_L h_{FE}}{R_L + R_F} + (1 + h_{FE})\left(\dfrac{R_E}{R_L + R_F} + \dfrac{R_E}{R_N}\right)} \tag{6.40}$$

$$I_C = \frac{\dfrac{h_{FE}(V_{CC} - V_B)}{R_L + R_F} - \dfrac{h_{FE}V_B}{R_N} + (1 + h_{FE})I_{CBO}\left(\dfrac{R_E + R_L + R_F}{R_F + R_L} + \dfrac{R_E}{R_N}\right)}{\dfrac{R_F}{R_L + R_F} + (1 + h_{FE})\left(\dfrac{R_E + R_L}{R_F + R_L} + \dfrac{R_E}{R_N}\right)} \tag{6.41}$$

$$V_C = \frac{R_F I_C}{h_{FE}}\left[1 + (1 + h_{FE})\frac{R_E}{R_N}\right]$$
$$- R_F\left(1 + \frac{R_E}{R_N}\right)\frac{(1 + h_{FE})I_{CBO}}{h_{FE}} + V_B\left(1 + \frac{R_E}{R_N}\right) \tag{6.42}$$

The I_C factor in Eq. (6.42) is given by Eq. (6.41). These equations give the operating point when a given transistor is placed in a circuit with a known V_{CC}, R_F, R_N, R_E, and R_L. As before, the significant knowledge is that of how to interpret circuit needs in terms of R_F, R_N, and R_E and how to actually calculate these bias-circuit components. The same design approaches exist as for the voltage-feedback circuit. The most practical way to execute the bias-network design is to express the operating-point stability in terms of a limiting value of operating point when limit combinations of leakage and current gain are used. The steps that yield the total circuit design are:

(a) Assume a knowledge of V_{CC}, R_L, the desired reference operating point I_C, V_C, and the h_{FE} and I_{CBO} of the reference transistor.

(b) Rearranging the terms of Eq. (6.36) to solve for R_E,

$$R_E = \frac{h_{FE}}{1 + h_{FE}}\left(\frac{V_{CC} - V_C - I_C R_L - I_F R_L}{I_C - I_{CBO}}\right) \tag{6.43}$$

(c) Establishing an operating point for the reference transistor and maintaining it in terms of a limit transistor are combination requirements which must be met simultaneously. The appropriate expressions involve R_F in terms of R_N. Solving these simultaneously gives the correct values for R_F and R_N for the successful fulfillment of the two basic circuit requirements. For the reference-condition variables, Eq. (6.41) yields

$$R_F = \frac{R_N[h_{FE}(V_{CC} - V_B) - B(R_E + R_L)] - R_L(BR_E + h_{FE}V_B)}{h_{FE}V_B + CR_N + BR_E} \qquad (6.44)$$

At the limiting value of the operating point we find

$$R_F = \frac{R_N[h'_{FE}(V_{CC} - V'_B) - B'(R_E + R_L)] - R_L(B'R_E + h'_{FE}V'_B)}{h'_{FE}V'_B + C'R_N + B'R_E} \qquad (6.45)$$

Solving (6.44) and (6.45) simultaneously for R_F, we obtain

$$R_N = \frac{Dh'_{FE}(V_{CC} - V'_B) - D'h_{FE}(V_{CC} - V_B) + H'h_{FE}V_B - Hh'_{FE}V'_B - GR_ER_L}{C'h_{FE}(V_{CC} - V_B) - Ch'_{FE}(V_{CC} - V'_B) + (R_E + R_L)G}$$

$$\qquad (6.46)$$

where $\quad H = CR_L - B(R_E + R_L)$
$$H' = C'R_L - B'(R_E + R_L)$$

If the approximation of $V_B = V'_B$ is valid, Eq. (6.46) reduces to

$$R_N = \frac{(V_{CC} - V_B)R_EE + V_B[FR_L - E(R_E + R_L)] + R_ER_LG}{(V_{CC} - V_B)F - (R_E + R_L)G} \qquad (6.47)$$

Once the value of R_N is determined, we can go back and calculate the appropriate value of R_F from either Eq. (6.44) or Eq. (6.45). Equations (6.43), (6.47), and (6.44) are usually used in the sequence mentioned.

Just as in the voltage-feedback circuit, an alternate form of circuit design might use a desired S' or S'' calculation. The appropriate derivatives of Eq. (6.41) are

$$S' = \frac{(1 + h_{FE})\left(1 + \dfrac{R_E}{R_L + R_F} + \dfrac{R_E}{R_N}\right)}{\dfrac{R_F}{R_L + R_F} + \left(\dfrac{R_E + R_L}{R_L + R_F} + \dfrac{R_E}{R_N}\right)(1 + h_{FE})} \qquad (6.48)$$

$$S'' = \frac{\left(\dfrac{V_{CC} - V_B}{R_L + R_F} - \dfrac{V_B}{R_N} + \dfrac{R_FI_{CBO}}{R_L + R_F}\right)\left(1 + \dfrac{R_E}{R_L + R_F} + \dfrac{R_E}{R_N}\right)}{\left[\dfrac{R_F}{R_L + R_F} + (1 + h_{FE})\left(\dfrac{R_E + R_L}{R_L + R_F} + \dfrac{R_E}{R_N}\right)\right]^2} \qquad (6.49)$$

Thus, instead of Eq. (6.45), the second expression for R_N and R_F is R_F as a function of h_{FE}, R_E, R_L, R_N, and S', or R_F as a function of V_{CC}, V_B, R_E, R_L, R_N, I_{CBO}, h_{FE}, and S'', as the design requirement would have indicated. The approach yielding Eq. (6.47) is, however, more practical and useful.

This circuit is generally capable of maintaining a very high degree of operating-point stability, owing to the combined current-feedback and voltage-feedback phenomena. If the required value of R_L is large, this combination current- and voltage-feedback circuit usually is used in preference to the voltage-feedback circuit. High values of R_L cause a small resultant change in collector current with current gain or leakage. Thus, the effectiveness of the voltage feedback is reduced. The changes of collector voltage, however, increase under such a circumstance; hence current feedback becomes very effective in helping to stabilize the operating point. The amount of voltage feedback that can exist depends on the value of R_E. Reduced values of R_F and R_N not only increase the effectiveness of the voltage feedback, but also increase the amount of current feedback. Thus we again have the very desirable situation of having separate control over the operating point and the operating-point stability.

6.12. Design example: combination current-voltage feedback biasing. We will now repeat a detailed design for the combination voltage- and current-feedback circuit using the information supplied in Sec. 6.8. Here we had

$$V_{CC} = 6 \text{ v}$$
$$R_L = 1 \text{ K}$$
$$V_C = 4.5 \text{ v}$$
$$I_C = 1 \text{ ma} \qquad I'_C = 1.2 \text{ ma}$$
$$h_{FE} = 20 \qquad h'_{FE} = 50$$
$$I_{CBO} = 2 \ \mu\text{a} \qquad I'_{CBO} = 8 \ \mu\text{a}$$

By (6.43)

$$R_E = \frac{h_{FE}}{1 + h_{FE}}\left[\frac{V_{CC} - V_C - (I_C + I_B)R_L}{I_C - I_{CBO}}\right]$$
$$= \frac{20}{21}\left[\frac{6 - 4.5 - (1 + .0478)10^{-3}(10^3)}{10^{-3} - 2(10^{-6})}\right] = 430$$

By (6.47)

$$R_N = \frac{(V_{CC} - V_B)R_E E + V_B[FR_L - E(R_E + R_L)] + R_E R_L G}{(V_{CC} - V_B)F - (R_E + R_L)G}$$
$$= \frac{(5.85)430(.168) + .15[32(10^{-3})(10^3) - .168(1430)] + 430(10^3)41.6(10^{-6})}{5.85(32)10^{-3} - 1430(41.6)10^{-6}}$$
$$= 3.2 \text{ K}$$

By (6.44)

$$R_F = \frac{R_N[h_{FE}(V_{CC} - V_B) - B(R_E + R_L)] - R_L(BR_E + h_{FE}V_B)}{h_{FE}V_B + CR_N + BR_E}$$

$$R_F = \frac{3.2\ \text{K}[20(5.85) - 20.9(10^{-3})1430] - 10^3[20.9(10^{-3})430 + 20(.15)]}{20(.15) + .958(10^{-3})3.2(10^3) + 20.9(10^{-3})430}$$

$$= 17.7\ \text{K}$$

6.13. Modified current-voltage feedback biasing. The only modification of the general-case circuit shown in Fig. 6.7 that is of interest is the one shown in Fig. 6.8. This circuit, with due consideration of the limitations mentioned with regard to Fig. 6.6, can sometimes be of use. The design review of such a circuit is as follows:

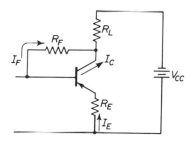

Fig. 6.8 Modified current-voltage feed-back bias.

(a) Assume a knowledge of V_{CC}, R_L, the desired operating point V_C, and I_C, and the h_{FE} and I_{CBO} of the reference transistor.

(b) A particular operating-point limit value is desired for the limit values h'_{FE} and I'_{CBO}. Thus, in terms of the reference and limit-value information, the appropriate combination of R_E and R_F must be calculated. For the reference operating point, a manipulation of Eq. (6.41) with R_N equals infinity gives

$$R_F = \frac{h_{FE}(V_{CC} - V_B) - B(R_E + R_L)}{C} \tag{6.50}$$

For the limit operating point

$$R_F = \frac{h'_{FE}(V_{CC} - V'_B) - B'(R_E + R_L)}{C'} \tag{6.51}$$

The simultaneous solution of Eqs. (6.50) and (6.51) gives

$$R_E = \frac{C[h'_{FE}(V_{CC} - V'_B) - B'R_L] - C'[h_{FE}(V_{CC} - V_B) - BR_L]}{G} \tag{6.52}$$

If we assume that $V'_B = V_B$, Eq. (6.52) reduces to

$$R_E = \frac{(V_{CC} - V_B)(F)}{G} - R_L \tag{6.53}$$

This value of R_E must satisfy the operating-point requirements as dictated by Eq. (6.36); a-c requirements, if a part of the problem, must also be considered and met. If all requirements are satisfied, the design of the bias circuit is completed by calculating R_F from either (6.50) or (6.51). If the stipulated requirements cannot be met, then a re-evaluation of the stability requirements is necessary. If the stability requirements cannot be changed, the possibility of changing the value of supply voltage V_{CC} should be considered. Setting Eq. (6.53) equal to Eq. (6.43) and solving for V_{CC}, we obtain

$$V_{CC} = \frac{h_{FE}G(V_c + I_C R_L + I_F R_L) - B[C(h'_{FE}V'_B + B'R_L) - C'(h_{FE}V_B + BR_L)]}{h_{FE}G - BF}$$

(6.54)

If $V'_B = V_B$,

$$V_{CC} = \frac{h_{FE}G[V_c + (I_C + I_F)R_L] - BFV_B - BGR_L}{h_{FE}G - BF}$$

(6.55)

When neither the stability requirements nor the supply voltage can be changed, the combination current- and voltage-feedback circuit must be used.

The stability factors as determined by taking the appropriate derivatives of Eq. (6.39) with R_N equals infinity can be shown to be

$$S' = \frac{(1 + h_{FE})\left(1 + \dfrac{R_E}{R_L + R_F}\right)}{\dfrac{R_F}{R_L + R_F} + (1 + h_{FE})\left(\dfrac{R_E + R_L}{R_L + R_F}\right)}$$

(6.56)

$$S'' = \frac{\left(\dfrac{V_{CC} - V_B + I_{CBO}R_F}{R_L + R_F}\right)\left(1 + \dfrac{R_E}{R_L + R_F}\right)}{\left[\dfrac{R_F}{R_L + R_F} + (1 + h_{FE})\left(\dfrac{R_E + R_L}{R_L + R_F}\right)\right]^2}$$

(6.57)

6.14. Design example: modified combination current-voltage feedback.
Let us check the factors involved in the use of the modified combination circuit shown in Fig. 6.8. We will repeat the design requirements of Secs. 6.8 and 6.12, using when possible the format of Sec. 6.10.

By (6.53)

$$R_E = \frac{(V_{CC} - V_B)F}{G} - R_L = 3.5 \text{ K}$$

This value of R_E is not acceptable for the basic or reference operating-point requirements. Let us check to find exactly what level of stability exists if the modified combination design is completed using $R_E = 430$ ohms.

By (6.50)

$$R_F = \frac{h_{FE}(V_{CC} - V_B) - B(R_E + R_L)}{C}$$

$$= \frac{20(5.85) - 20.9(10^{-3})(1.43)\,10^3}{.958(10^{-3})}$$

$$= \frac{87}{.958}(10^3) \cong 91 \text{ K}$$

The operating current for the limit transistor is obtained by substituting the limit parameters into Eq. (6.41) using R_N equals infinity. We obtain

$$I'_c = \frac{\dfrac{h'_{FE}(V_{CC} - V_B)}{R_L + R_F} + (1 + h'_{FE})I'_{CBO}\left(\dfrac{R_E + R_L + R_F}{R_L + R_F}\right)}{\dfrac{R_F}{R_L + R_F} + (1 + h'_{FE})\left(\dfrac{R_E + R_L}{R_L + R_F}\right)}$$

$$= \frac{\dfrac{50(5.85)}{1\,K + 91\,K} + 51(.008)\,10^{-3}\left(\dfrac{430 + 1\,K + 91\,K}{91\,K + 1\,K}\right)}{\dfrac{91\,K}{1\,K + 91\,K} + 51\left(\dfrac{430 + 1\,K}{1\,K + 91\,K}\right)} = 2.01\ \text{ma}$$

This is not too good and not too bad. It does represent improvement over the other "short-cut" techniques attempted thus far. Should there be interest in changing to a supply voltage that can provide the required stability, we would use Eq. (6.55) to get

$$V_{CC} = \frac{20(41.6)\,10^{-6}[4.5 + 1.05(10^{-3})\,10^3] - 20.9(32)\,10^{-6}(.15) - 20.9(10^{-3})41.6(10^{-6})\,10^3}{20(41.6)\,10^{-6} - 20.9(10^{-3})32(10^{-3})}$$

$$= 23.8\ \text{v}$$

One aspect of this modified combination circuit should be emphasized enthusiastically. When large values of R_L are encountered, this circuit is quite likely to be useful. The specific example for a modified combination of current-voltage feedback does not yield optimized results. Slightly more favorable conditions of a higher value of R_L yield an acceptable solution.

6.15. Nonlinear compensation techniques.

Thus far in our demonstrative examples for operating-point stability we have considered limit values of current gain and leakage. It is important not to forget that temperature, as well as unit-to-unit variation in current gain and leakage, contributes to shifts in operating point. In most situations, increases in temperature create more in the way of design problems than do the unit-to-unit variations in current gain and leakage. That is, more often than not temperature is the major contributor to the limit value of I'_{CBO} that must be handled in any design problem. This information does not in any way change either the design approach or the effectiveness of the bias circuits discussed thus far. It does, however, require mention of one final circuit technique to complete the story of bias circuits. This technique uses components whose attributes themselves change with temperature. Such components are diodes, and resistors with nonlinear temperature coefficients.

Consider, for example, the circuit of Fig. 6.9(a). Here we connect a diode in place of R_N. The direction of current through the diode and the voltage across it concur with the situation of Fig. 6.5. The significant thing here is that as temperature increases, the forward drop in the bias diode decreases,

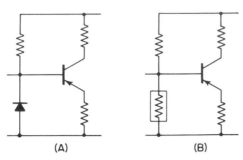

(A)   (B)

Fig. 6.9 Nonlinear components in bias circuits. (A) Semiconductor diode. (B) Thermistor.

cutting back on the forward bias of the transistor, compensating for what otherwise would have meant a shift in the operating point. By fabricating the diode with the same materials as the emitter-base portion of the transistor, we can attain very precise thermal compensation.

Negative-coefficient resistors or *thermistors* do not present the control latitude that diodes do. Their use might, however, be as shown in Fig. 6.9(b). Here we are taking advantage of a device that, as temperature increases, shows a decrease in its resistance value. Thus, as temperature increases for our circuit, there is a thermally induced cutback of the forward bias because of the decrease in the thermistor resistance. Since, however, the changes in resistance do not match the changes in transistor characteristic, the basic compromise is usually a single high-temperature and a single low-temperature match, with nonoptimum behavior in between. Such a situation is possible because thermistors are available with a wide variety of coefficients and room-temperature values. Whereas this approach might not be perfect for all temperatures between the two design temperatures, it may be adequate for certain circuits.

PROBLEMS

1. A circuit similar to Fig. 6.2 has an R_L equal to 3 K and V_{CC} equal to 9 v. What are the intercepts of the d-c load line?

2. What value of R_B will enable a transistor with an h_{FE} of 30 and an I_{CBO} of 3 μa to operate midway on the load line in Problem 1?

3. Calculate the stability factors S' and S'' for the situation of Problem 2.

4. Explain the principle of current feedback in bias circuits.

5. The circuit of Fig. 6.3(a) has $V_{CC} = 9$ v, $R_L = 2.2$ K, $R_F = 168$ K. Calculate I_B, I_C, and V_C when a transistor with $h_{FE} = 40$ and $I_{CBO} = 4$ μa is connected into the circuit.

6. Calculate the stability factors S' and S'' for Problem 5.

7. Using the stability factors calculated in Problem 6, calculate the magnitudes of collector-current increases when a second device with $h_{FE} = 60$ and $I_{CBO} = 6$ μa is substituted.

8. Explain the principles of voltage feedback in bias circuitry.

9. Using the component values obtained in Sec. 6.8, determine the collector current when a device with $h_{FE} = 60$ and $I_{CBO} = 4\ \mu$a is substituted.

10. Given the following information: $V_{CC} = 6$ v, $R_L = 1$ K. A reference transistor has $h_{FE} = 40$, $I_{CBO} = 3\ \mu$a. A desired operating point is $I_C = 1$ ma and $V_{CE} = 4.5$ v, at which time $V_{BE} = .15$ v. A limit transistor has $h'_{FE} = 100$ and $I'_{CBO} = 4\ \mu$a. The limit acceptable operating point is 1.3 ma. Design a complete voltage-feedback circuit. Assume $V'_{BE} = V_{BE}$.

11. Could the modified circuit of Fig. 6.6 handle the requirements of Problem 10? If so, complete the design. If not, design the modified circuit for the reference transistor and indicate the I_C level obtained when using the limit device.

12. What supply voltage is necessary for the modified voltage-feedback circuit to obtain the stability needed in Problem 10?

13. Given the following information: $V_{CC} = 12$ v, $R_L = 5$ K. A reference transistor has $h_{FE} = 50$, $I_{CBO} = 2\ \mu$a. The desired operating is $I_C = 1$ ma and $V_{CE} = 4.5$ v, at which time $V_{BE} = .15$ v. A limit transistor has $h'_{FE} = 100$ and $I'_{CBO} = 5\ \mu$a. The limit operating point is 1.3 ma. Assume $V'_{BE} = V_{BF}$.
   (a) Can this requirement be filled by the modified combination circuit of Fig. 6.8? If so, what is the emitter resistance as prescribed by the operating-point requirements?
   (b) What is the value of R_E as indicated by the stability requirements?
   (c) What is the minimum value of V_{CC} that yields the operating-point and stability requirements?
   (d) What is the value of R_E for part (c)?
   (e) What is the value of I_C obtained when the limit transistor is placed in the circuit of part (a)?

7

TRANSISTOR

A-C EQUIVALENT

CIRCUITS

We now begin the study of the dynamic or a-c attributes of a transistor. The transistor is widely used in a variety of power-amplifying and otherwise dynamic applications. It is most advantageous to learn the configurations of electrical components that are used to depict the transistor. Such a configuration, if it truly portrays the actual operation of a transistor, is called an *a-c equivalent circuit* of the transistor. Once this circuit is established, we can proceed to a consideration, analysis, and design of circuits that use transistors.

7.1. Equivalent-circuit possibilities.   There are a great number of circuit configurations that might be used to depict the transistor. Resistors, admittances, voltage generators, and current generators can be used in various combinations. What are the considerations encouraging the use of a particular array of elements? In developing our answer, we should appreciate that the transistor can be described mathematically just as any four-terminal network. There are, however, a multiplicity of solution forms possible, because the transistor as a bilateral device can be described by an extensive number of current and voltage relationships. This fact is corroborated by a recollection of the numerous static characteristics that describe the transistor. The derivation of any one of the possible equivalent circuits is highly mathematical and will not be treated here.

The most significant aspects in the choice of an equivalent circuit are (1) the ability to see in the circuit a relation to the operation of the transistor, and (2) the use of parameters that can be measured conveniently on available laboratory equipment. There are two equivalent circuits that we choose to deal with. One is the so-called *h-parameter equivalent circuit* (Fig. 7.1). The second is the so-called *r-parameter equivalent circuit* (Fig. 7.2). The *h*-para-

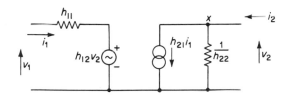

Fig. 7.1   *h*-parameter a-c equivalent circuit for a transistor.

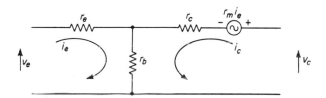

Fig. 7.2   *r*-parameter a-c equivalent circuit for transistor connected common base.

meter circuit is the most commonly used. One reason is that the *h*-parameters can be related to the slopes of various d-c static characteristics, so that one can predict quite easily the variation in *h*-parameter as the d-c operating point changes. A second reason for *h*-parameter preference is that the *h*-parameters are easily measured. The *h*-equivalent circuit conforms to the generalized *black-box* concept for replacing any network by an equivalent after performing four specific circuit measurements. These measurements are: (1) The open-circuit input voltage when a known voltage is applied to the output terminals. (2) The impedance looking into the input when the output is short-circuited. The series connection of a voltage source and an impedance, using the measurements just suggested, constitutes the Thévenin equivalent circuit for the input portion of the unknown circuit. (3) The short-circuit output current when a known current is flowing in the input. (4) The admittance at the output terminals when the input is open-circuited. The parallel connection of a current generator and an admittance, using the measurements just suggested, constitutes the Norton equivalent circuit for the output portion of our unknown circuit. We will observe in the next section that the *h*-parameters are measured using the black-box concept just mentioned, and they are therefore an equivalent array consistent with generalized circuit analysis theory.

The *r*-circuit is introduced because it serves as a tool in determining the expressions for the *h*-parameter interrelations for each transistor connection. This circuit is closely related to the physical regions and operation of the transistor.

One final comment: We will find that slopes of curves determine some of the a-c parameters. Since slopes are most accurately determined by small incremental changes of the graph variables, the resultant parameters are called *small-signal parameters*. The resultant equivalent circuit is often called a *small-signal equivalent circuit*.

7.2. Developing the *h*-parameters.   It is reasonable to wonder where the *h*-parameters have their origin, and what the units are for each of the four parameters of Fig. 7.1. For our answer we direct our attention to the static characteristics. Even though they were introduced as static or steady-state pictures of the current and voltage relations, we wish at this time to call attention to the slopes of these d-c characteristics. This is not anything really new. A similar approach was used on the static characteristics of diodes in order to develop the dynamic or a-c resistance parameter of a diode. (Refer back to Sec. 2.7 for a review of this material.) It might be stated that for any of the static characteristics of the transistor, the slopes at discrete and correspondent points have significance in describing the a-c performance of the transistor. Thus, for our purposes, we see that the d-c characteristics are the source or origin of the *h*-parameters. In particular, it will be shown that h_{11} is the slope of the input characteristic, h_{22} is the slope of the output characteristic, h_{12} is the slope of the reverse-voltage characteristic, and h_{21} is the slope of the forward-current characteristic. We need now to develop mathematical expressions and the units of each *h*-parameter.

First, let us consider the input characteristic. It is quite similar to the diode characteristic of Fig. 2.9 and will be an easy stepping stone to the other transistor characteristics. The input characteristic shown in Fig. 7.3 is for a general-case situation. That is, a plot of V_{IN} versus I_{IN} is made for various values of V_{OUT}. Let the point that is of interest to us be called V'_{IN}, I'_{IN}, V'_{OUT}. By definition, the slope of the curve at this point is determined by the slope of a straight line drawn tangent to the curve at the point in question. Thus the slope of the curve, as approximated by the slope of the straight line, is described as the ratio of $\Delta V_{IN}/\Delta I_{IN}$. To assure that the slope is referred to the point in question, the operating or reference point $V'_{IN} I'_{IN}$ is also specified. Intuitively, the smaller the values of ΔV_{IN} and ΔI_{IN}, the

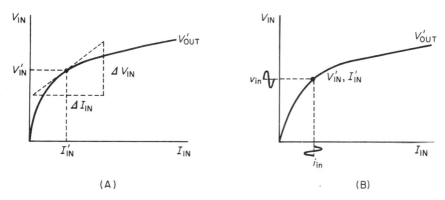

Fig. 7.3 Input characteristics. (A) Slope of tangent at $V'_{IN}I'_{IN}$ is $\Delta V_{IN}/\Delta I_{IN}$. (B) Slope of curve at $V'_{IN}I'_{IN}$ is v_{in}/i_{in}.

closer the straight line approaches the actual shape of the curve. Thus, for most accurate determination of slope, small increments of current and voltage should be used.

Instead of thinking in terms of increments of d-c current and voltage, we might also think in terms of a-c quantities. As shown in Fig. 7.3(b), the quantity i_{in} results when a variation v_{in} is made around the operating point. The ratio of the a-c voltage and current, v_{in}/i_{in}, is also a measure of the slope. Let us consider the transition from a d-c condition at the output, namely a specified V_{OUT}, to an equivalent a-c condition, v_{out}. We have noted that the value of d-c output voltage must be specified to indicate the specific input characteristic curve with which we are dealing. The value of output voltage must remain unchanging even as the input current and voltage are changing. If the output voltage is constant, there is no a-c component of output voltage present. If the a-c output voltage is zero, the output termination must be an a-c short circuit. The practical significance of the output short-circuited condition relates only to the measures that must be taken in order to measure the slope of the input characteristic. The slope calculation has units of voltage divided by units of current. Thus, the slope itself has units of ohms. The actual expression for the slope can be written as:

$$h_{11} = \left. \frac{v_{in}}{i_{in}} \right|_{\substack{V_{OUT} = \text{constant} \\ v_{out} = 0}} \tag{7.1}$$

where h_{11} = slope of the input characteristic

         = input impedance, output a-c shorted

     v_{in} = a-c input voltage

     i_{in} = a-c input current

    v_{out} = a-c output voltage

   V_{OUT} = d-c output voltage

The name for h_{11} is the *input impedance with the output a-c short-circuited*.

Consider now the output characteristic. For a general-case situation this is a plot of I_{OUT} versus V_{OUT} for various values of I_{IN}. Such a plot is shown in Fig. 7.4(a). As before, we must be concerned with a particular operating

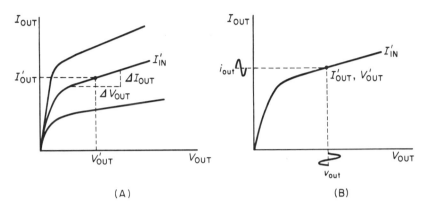

Fig. 7.4 Output characteristics. (A) Slope of tangent at $I'_{OUT}V'_{OUT}$ is $\Delta I_{OUT}/\Delta V_{OUT}$. (B) Slope of curve at $I'_{OUT}V'_{OUT}$ is i_{out}/v_{out}.

or reference point. This we will label I'_{OUT} V'_{OUT} and I'_{IN}. By definition, the slope of the output characteristic at such a point is h_{22}. Mathematically the slope can be expressed as the ratio of $\Delta I_{OUT}/\Delta V_{OUT}$. Reference to the particular V'_{OUT} and I'_{IN} must be made to assure that the slope is taken at the right point on the characteristic. As shown in Fig. 7.4(b), the slope of the curve can be described by a-c currents and voltages. In this case we are interested in the variation in output voltage v_{out} that results when a variation i_{out} is made around the operating point. The ratio of the a-c current and voltage i_{out}/v_{out} is the actual measure of the characteristic slope. The transfer of the specified d-c condition I_{IN} to an appropriate a-c condition is of interest. The value of input current must remain constant and unchanging even as the output current and voltage are changing. Since the input current is constant, there is no a-c component of current at the input terminals. The requirement that the a-c input current be zero implies an a-c open circuit at the input terminals at the time when this parameter is being measured. The slope calculation has units of current divided by units of voltage, which is mhos. This suggests that h_{22} is an admittance. The actual expression for the output admittance can be written as:

$$h_{22} = \frac{i_{out}}{v_{out}} \bigg|_{\substack{I_{IN} = \text{constant} \\ i_{in} = 0}} \tag{7.2}$$

where h_{22} = slope of the output characteristic
  = output admittance, input a-c open-circuited
  i_{out} = a-c output current
  v_{out} = a-c output voltage
  i_{in} = a-c input current
  I_{IN} = d-c input current

Before we proceed to the comments on h_{12} and h_{21}, one point needs to be emphasized. As part of the derivation of h_{11} and h_{22} we noticed conditions of output a-c short-circuited and input a-c open-circuited, respectively. These must *not* be interpreted as unique circuit terminations for which the h_{11} and h_{22} parameters can be used. Rather, these are the electrical conditions that must exist for the transistor when the respective parameters are being measured. Once the parameters are measured, they may be used in the equivalent circuit for any input and output termination that is of interest.

The last two parameters are h_{12} and h_{21}. These two parameters are derived from characteristics that are modifications of the already discussed input and output characteristics. An extensive discussion of these parameters is not necessary. The parameter h_{12} is derived from the reverse-voltage characteristic, which, as we learned, is a plot of V_{IN} versus V_{OUT} for various values of I_{IN}. It can be shown, then, that the expression for h_{12} is

$$h_{12} = \frac{v_{in}}{v_{out}} \bigg|_{\substack{I_{IN} = \text{constant} \\ i_{in} = 0}} \tag{7.3}$$

where h_{12} = slope of reverse-voltage characteristic
  = reverse-voltage feedback factor with the input a-c open-circuited
  v_{in} = a-c input voltage
  v_{out} = a-c output voltage
  i_{in} = a-c input current
  I_{IN} = d-c input current

As seen from Eq. (7.3), h_{12} is a dimensionless quantity.

The parameter h_{21} is derived from the forward-current characteristic. This characteristic is a plot of I_{OUT} versus I_{IN} for various values of V_{OUT}. It can be shown, then, that the slope of this characteristic or h_{21} can be written as:

$$h_{21} = \frac{i_{out}}{i_{in}} \bigg|_{\substack{V_{OUT} = \text{constant} \\ v_{out} = 0}} \tag{7.4}$$

where h_{21} = slope of forward-current characteristic
        = forward-current gain, output a-c short-circuited
i_{out} = a-c output current
i_{in} = a-c input current
v_{out} = a-c output voltage
V_{OUT} = d-c output voltage

This parameter, like h_{12}, is a dimensionless quantity.

Knowing now the source of the *h*-parameters, let us check the validity of the equivalent circuit shown in Fig. 7.1. The voltage-feedback factor appears as a voltage generator $h_{12}v_2$. The current gain appears as a current generator in the output. Summing voltage drops around the input loop, we obtain

$$v_1 = h_{11}i_1 + h_{12}v_2 \qquad (7.5)$$

Summing the currents into and out of point *X* in the output circuit we obtain

$$i_2 = h_{21}i_1 + h_{22}v_2 \qquad (7.6)$$

The legitimacy of the equivalent circuit is demonstrated first by setting $v_2 = 0$ and then $i_1 = 0$ in both Eqs. (7.5) and (7.6). We obtain for each substitution, equations that are the same as the definition equations of each of the four *h*-parameters.

Since the particular parameters include an impedance, an admittance, and pure numbers without dimension, we have what is considered a hybrid situation; hence the parameters are called *hybrid* or *h-parameters*. The values of the *h*-parameters change as a function of the transistor's being operated common-base, common-emitter, or common-collector. In order to properly designate which of the *h*-parameter values are appropriate, a triple-subscript notation is used. The letters *b* or *e* or *c* are added as subscripts with the numbers to designate either common base, common emitter, or common collector, respectively. The parameter h_{11} for the common-base connection is labeled h_{11b}. The forward-current gain for the common emitter is labeled h_{21e}. Another acceptable possibility is a double-letter subscript notation. In this system a single letter is used to replace the 11, 22, 12, and 21 subscripts of the other system. The letter *i* is used for the input-resistance parameter, the letter *o* for the output-admittance parameter, the letter *r* for the reverse-voltage factor, and the letter *f* for the forward-current-gain parameter. The input impedance for the common-base connection is designated h_{ib}. The forward-current gain for the common emitter is designated h_{fe}. Table 7.1 gives a complete listing of the *h*-parameter symbols.

One final, but extremely important, question: What is the relationship between the common-base, common-emitter, and common-collector *h*-parameters? As an answer we will demonstrate that the *r*-equivalent circuit is an aid in establishing the inter-relations of the *h*-parameters for each transistor connection. We digress then to introduce the *r*-equivalent circuit in the next section.

TABLE 7.1   *h*-parameter symbols.

	COMMON BASE	COMMON EMITTER	COMMON COLLECTOR
INPUT IMPEDANCE OUTPUT A-C SHORTED	h_{11b} h_{ib}	h_{11e} h_{ie}	h_{11c} h_{ic}
OUTPUT ADMITTANCE INPUT A-C OPEN	h_{22b} h_{ob}	h_{22e} h_{oe}	h_{22c} h_{oc}
FORWARD CURRENT GAIN OUTPUT A-C SHORTED	h_{21b} h_{fb}	h_{21e} h_{fe}	h_{21c} h_{fc}
REVERSE VOLTAGE FEEDBACK FACTOR INPUT A-C OPEN	h_{12b} h_{rb}	h_{12e} h_{re}	h_{12c} h_{rc}

7.3. The *r*-equivalent circuit.   The equivalent circuit of Fig. 7.2 is drawn specifically for the common-base connection. The usefulness of this circuit is its similarity to the actual physical transistor connected common-base. The resistor r_e simulates the dynamic impedance of the emitter region. The resistor r_c simulates the dynamic impedance of the collector region. The resistor r_b simulates the dynamic impedance of the base region. Since the transistor is an active device displaying power gain, voltage gain, and sometimes current gain, we indicate its amplifying ability by the presence of a voltage generator $r_m i_e$ in the output. The resistor r_m simulates the interaction that occurs between input and output terminals. The emitter current flowing at the input operates through the mutual resistance r_m to give us transistor action.

As mentioned, the *r*-parameters are a link in establishing the expressions for the relationships between the *h*-parameters for each transistor connection. We will proceed to review the *r*-circuit for each of the transistor connections. Using loop currents at input and output terminals of Fig. 7.2, we can proceed to sum voltage drops in both sides to obtain:

$$v_e = i_e(r_e + r_b) + i_c r_b \tag{7.7}$$

$$v_c = i_e(r_m + r_b) + i_c(r_c + r_b) \tag{7.8}$$

Letting $v_c = 0$ in Eq. (7.8), we obtain an expression for the common-base forward-current gain i_c/i_e and the *r*'s. That is,

$$\frac{i_c}{i_e} = \frac{-(r_m + r_b)}{r_c + r_b} \tag{7.9}$$

Substituting Eq. (7.9) into Eq. (7.7) for the quantity i_c, we obtain an expression for the common-base input impedance v_e/i_e and the *r*'s:

$$\frac{v_e}{i_e} = r_e + r_b\left(1 - \frac{r_m + r_b}{r_c + r_b}\right) \tag{7.10}$$

Now, if i_e were equal to zero in Eq. (7.8), we would find as a solution that

$$\frac{i_c}{v_c} = \frac{1}{r_c + r_b}$$ (7.11)

This is the mathematical statement for the common-base output admittance i_c/v_c. Using Eq. (7.11) and substituting back into Eq. (7.7) for the quantity i_c, we obtain

$$\frac{v_e}{v_c} = \frac{r_b}{r_c + r_{b'}}$$ (7.12)

This represents the expression for common-base voltage-feedback factor.

Suppose that the common emitter r-circuit is desired. Since the r's themselves simulate the respective regions, we need only interchange the position of the r_e and r_b quantities. The resultant common-emitter r-circuit is shown in Fig. 7.5(a). As it stands, however, this is less useful than it might be because the voltage generator is still in terms of i_e rather than the input current i_b. This is remedied by replacing the portion between x–x in Fig. 7.5(a) by an equivalent network consisting of a resistor r_d in series with a voltage generator $r_m i_b$. The resistor r_d is an equivalent resistance simulating the collector in the common-emitter connection. The equivalent network appears in the diagram of Fig. 7.5(b). If these two networks are truly equivalent, then the short-circuit current flowing from $r_m i_b$ through r_d must equal the

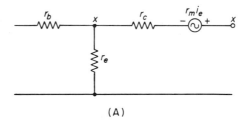

(A)

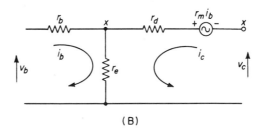

(B)

Fig. 7.5 Common emitter r-parameter equivalent circuit. (A) Basic form. (B) Useful form where $r_d = r_c (1 + h_{21b})$.

short-circuit current flowing from $r_m i_e$ through r_c. That is,

$$\frac{r_m i_b}{r_d} = \frac{r_m i_e}{r_c}$$

This is satisfied if

$$r_d = r_c(1 + h_{21b}) \qquad (7.13)$$

Equation (7.13) gives the relative values for the equivalent collector resistance in the common-emitter and common-base connections. Completing the analysis of the common-emitter connection, a summation of voltage drops at both input and output sides gives

$$v_b = i_b(r_b + r_e) + i_c r_e \qquad (7.14)$$

$$v_c = i_b(r_e - r_m) + i_c(r_d + r_e) \qquad (7.15)$$

Setting v_c equal to zero in Eq. (7.15), we obtain an expression for the common-emitter current gain i_c/i_b. That is,

$$\frac{i_c}{i_b} = \frac{r_m - r_e}{r_d + r_e} \qquad (7.16)$$

Substituting Eq. (7.16) into Eq. (7.14), we obtain an expression for the common-emitter input inpedance v_b/i_b:

$$\frac{v_b}{i_b} = r_b + r_e\left(1 + \frac{r_m - r_e}{r_d + r_e}\right) \qquad (7.17)$$

Now if i_b is made equal to zero, we find in Eq. (7.15) that

$$\frac{i_c}{v_c} = \frac{1}{r_d + r_e} \qquad (7.18)$$

This represents the common-emitter output admittance. Putting Eq. (7.18) into Eq. (7.14), one finds that

$$\frac{v_b}{v_c} = \frac{r_e}{r_d + r_e} \qquad (7.19)$$

This is the statement for the common-emitter voltage-feedback factor.

The final r-equivalent circuit is that of a transistor connected in the common-collector connection. When thinking of the common collector as compared with the common emitter, we note an interchange of the collector and emitter leads. Performing such an operation on the common-emitter circuit of Fig. 7.5(b), we obtain the

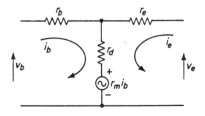

Fig. 7.6 r-parameter equivalent of common collector.

common-collector circuit shown in Fig. 7.6. The analysis of this circuit begins with the writing of the loop equations. A summation of the voltage drops in both loops gives

$$v_b = i_b(r_b + r_m + r_d) + i_e r_d \qquad (7.20)$$

$$v_e = i_b(r_m + r_d) + i_e(r_d + r_e) \qquad (7.21)$$

Setting v_e equal to zero in Eq. (7.43), we obtain an expression for the common-collector current gain:

$$\frac{i_e}{i_b} = -\frac{r_m + r_d}{r_d + r_e} \qquad (7.22)$$

Substituting (7.22) into (7.20), one finds:

$$\frac{v_b}{i_b} = r_b + \frac{r_e(r_m + r_d)}{r_d + r_e} \qquad (7.23)$$

This is a statement for the common-collector input inpedance. Now, if in Eq. (7.21) i_b is made equal to zero, the result is an expression for the common-collector output admittance. That is,

$$\frac{i_e}{v_e} = \frac{1}{r_d + r_e} \qquad (7.24)$$

Substituting Eq. (7.24) back into Eq. (7.20), we obtain the ratio v_b/v_e, which is the voltage-feedback factor for the common-collector connection:

$$\frac{v_b}{v_e} = \frac{r_d}{r_d + r_e} \qquad (7.25)$$

7.4. *h-r* parameter interrelations.   In the preceding section we obtained *r*-parameter expressions for each equivalent circuit entity: the input impedance with the output short-circuited, the forward-current gain with the output short-circuited, the voltage-feedback factor with the input open-circuited, and the output admittance with the input open-circuited. Since each *r*-parameter expression corresponds to the definition of a particular *h*-parameter, we can state *h* parameter-*r* parameter interrelations for each circuit connection. Since Eq. (7.9) was an expression for the common-base forward-current gain, we can say

$$h_{21b} = -\frac{r_m + r_b}{r_c + r_b}$$

$$\cong -\frac{r_m}{r_c} \qquad (7.26a)$$

From (7.10) for the common-base input impedance we say

$$h_{11b} = r_e + r_b\left(1 - \frac{r_m + r_b}{r_c + r_b}\right)$$

$$\cong r_e + r_b\left(1 - \frac{r_m}{r_c}\right) \tag{7.26b}$$

From (7.11) for the common-base output admittance

$$h_{22b} = \frac{1}{r_c + r_b}$$

$$\cong \frac{1}{r_c} \tag{7.26c}$$

From (7.12)

$$h_{12b} = \frac{r_b}{r_c + r_b}$$

$$\cong \frac{r_b}{r_c} \tag{7.26d}$$

These expressions can be reworked to become expressions of r-parameters in terms of h-parameters. Thus from Eq. (7.26c) we say

$$r_c = \frac{1}{h_{22b}} \tag{7.27}$$

From (7.26d) and (7.27)

$$r_b = \frac{h_{12b}}{h_{22b}} \tag{7.28}$$

From (7.28) and (7.26a) in (7.26b)

$$r_e = h_{11b} - \frac{h_{12b}}{h_{22b}}(1 + h_{21b}) \tag{7.29}$$

Equations (7.27), (7.28), and (7.29) will be of special interest, as we shall see in the next section.

Proceeding to the common-emitter circuitry, we can establish expressions to equate h-parameters and r-parameters. From (7.16)

$$h_{21e} = \frac{r_m - r_e}{r_d + r_e}$$

$$\cong \frac{r_m}{r_d} \tag{7.30}$$

From (7.17)

$$h_{11e} = r_b + r_e\left(1 + \frac{r_m - r_e}{r_d + r_e}\right)$$

$$\cong r_b + r_e\left(1 + \frac{r_m}{r_d}\right) \tag{7.31}$$

From (7.18)

$$h_{22e} = \frac{1}{r_d + r_e}$$

$$\cong \frac{1}{r_d} \tag{7.32}$$

From (7.19)

$$h_{12e} = \frac{r_e}{r_d + r_e}$$

$$\cong \frac{r_e}{r_d} \tag{7.33}$$

These expressions can now be reworked to become expressions of r-parameters in terms of h-parameters. From Eq. (7.32) we obtain

$$r_d = \frac{1}{h_{22e}} \tag{7.34}$$

From Eqs. (7.32) and (7.33)

$$r_e = \frac{h_{12e}}{h_{22e}} \tag{7.35}$$

Finally, putting (7.35) and (7.30) into (7.31) ,we get

$$r_b = h_{11e} - \frac{h_{12e}}{h_{22e}}(1 + h_{21e}) \tag{7.36}$$

For the common-collector connection we can make the following equivalencies. From (7.22)

$$h_{21c} = -\left(1 + \frac{r_m}{r_d}\right) \tag{7.37}$$

From (7.23)

$$h_{11c} = r_b + \frac{r_e(r_m + r_d)}{r_d + r_e} \tag{7.38}$$

Recall from (7.26) that

$$r_m = -h_{21b}r_c$$

and from (7.13) that

$$r_d = r_c + h_{21b}r_c$$

Equation (7.38) reduces then to

$$h_{11c} = r_b + \frac{r_e r_c}{r_d} \tag{7.39}$$

From (7.24)

$$h_{22c} = \frac{1}{r_d + r_e}$$

$$\cong \frac{1}{r_d} \tag{7.40}$$

From (7.25)

$$h_{12c} = \frac{r_d}{r_d + r_e}$$

$$\cong 1 \qquad (7.41)$$

7.5. *h*-parameter relations for each transistor connection. We stated in introducing the *r*-circuit that it served as a link in establishing the relationships between the *h*-parameters for each transistor connection. The relations that we have established in Sec. 7.4 can now be utilized to attain this result. Substituting Eqs. (7.34) and (7.27) into (7.13) for r_d and r_c, we obtain

$$h_{22e} = \frac{h_{22b}}{1 + h_{21b}} \qquad (7.42)$$

Likewise, substituting (7.13) into (7.30), we get

$$h_{21e} = \frac{r_m}{r_c(1 + h_{21b})} \qquad (7.43)$$

Substituting now the information of Eq. (7.26a), we find

$$h_{21e} = \frac{-h_{21b}}{1 + h_{21b}} \qquad (7.44)$$

If now we equate (7.29) to (7.35), include (7.42), and solve for h_{12e}, it can be shown that

$$h_{12e} = \frac{h_{11b}h_{22b} - h_{12b}(1 + h_{21b})}{1 + h_{21b}} \qquad (7.45)$$

Now, by equating (7.28) and (7.36), using (7.43), and solving for h_{11e}, we obtain

$$h_{11e} = \frac{h_{11b}}{1 + h_{21b}} \qquad (7.46)$$

The expressions for the common-base *h*-parameters in terms of the common-emitter *h*-parameters are of interest. The easiest way to convert to this form of presentation is to manipulate (7.44) to obtain

$$h_{21b} = \frac{-h_{21e}}{1 + h_{21e}} \qquad (7.47)$$

Therefore

$$1 + h_{21b} = \frac{1}{1 + h_{21e}} \qquad (7.48)$$

Equation (7.48) can be substituted into Eqs. (7.42) and (7.46) to obtain

$$h_{22b} = \frac{h_{22e}}{1 + h_{21e}} \qquad (7.49)$$

$$h_{11b} = \frac{h_{11e}}{1 + h_{21e}} \qquad (7.50)$$

The last expression, that for h_{12b}, can be obtained by equating (7.29) and (7.35), using (7.50), and solving for h_{12b}. The result is

$$h_{12b} = \frac{h_{11e}h_{22e} - h_{12e}(1 + h_{21e})}{1 + h_{21e}} \tag{7.51}$$

At this point we will proceed directly to the substitutions that yield the expressions for the common-collector h-parameters in terms of the common-emitter and common-base h-parameters. Substituting (7.13) and (7.26a) into (7.37), we get

$$h_{21c} = \frac{-1}{1 + h_{21b}} \tag{7.52}$$

Placing (7.28), (7.29), and (7.13) into (7.39),

$$h_{11c} = \frac{h_{11b}}{1 + h_{21b}} \tag{7.53}$$

TABLE 7.2 Common-emitter and common-collector h expressions in terms of common-base values.

$h_{11e} = \dfrac{h_{11b}}{1 + h_{21b}}$		$h_{11c} = \dfrac{h_{11b}}{1 + h_{21b}}$
$h_{22e} = \dfrac{h_{22b}}{1 + h_{21b}}$		$h_{22c} = \dfrac{h_{22b}}{1 + h_{21b}}$
$h_{21e} = \dfrac{-h_{21b}}{1 + h_{21b}}$		$h_{21c} = \dfrac{-1}{1 + h_{21b}}$
$h_{12e} = \dfrac{h_{11b}h_{22b} - h_{12b}(1 + h_{21b})}{1 + h_{21b}}$		$h_{12c} \cong 1$

TABLE 7.3 Common-base and common-collector h expressions in terms of common-emitter values.

$h_{11b} = \dfrac{h_{11e}}{1 + h_{21e}}$		$h_{11c} = h_{11e}$
$h_{22b} = \dfrac{h_{22e}}{1 + h_{21e}}$		$h_{22c} = h_{22e}$
$h_{21b} = \dfrac{-h_{21e}}{1 + h_{21e}}$		$h_{21c} = -(1 + h_{21e})$
$h_{12b} = \dfrac{h_{11e}h_{22e} - h_{12e}(1 + h_{21e})}{1 + h_{21e}}$		$h_{12c} \cong 1$

Placing (7.13) and (7.27) into (7.40),

$$h_{22c} = \frac{h_{22b}}{1 + h_{21b}} \tag{7.54}$$

We should now convert these expressions to a form involving the common-emitter h-parameters. Substituting (7.30) into (7.37), one finds

$$h_{21c} = -(1 + h_{21e}) \tag{7.55}$$

By inspection of Eqs. (7.53) and (7.54),

$$h_{11c} = h_{11e} \tag{7.56}$$

$$h_{22c} = h_{22e} \tag{7.57}$$

The reason for introducing the r-equivalent circuit is now explained. We have at our disposal an ability to determine the values of h-parameters for each of the possible transistor connections. The relations have been deliberately restricted to the use of common-base and common-emitter h-parameters as the independent variables, for these are the parameters that almost always appear on transistor specification sheets. A complete tabulation of the derived interrelations is given for convenience in Tables 7.2 and 7.3.

7.6. Sample of h-parameter calculations. A 2N1414 transistor has the following parameters specified at $V_{CB} = 5$ v and $I_{E} = 1$ ma:

$$h_{22b} = .62(10^{-6}) \text{ mhos}$$
$$h_{11b} = 29\ \Omega$$
$$h_{12b} = 5.2(10^{-4})$$
$$h_{21e} = 44$$

A calculation of the common-emitter and common-collector parameters requires first a calculation of h_{21b}. By (7.47)

$$h_{21b} = \frac{-h_{21e}}{1 + h_{21e}} = \frac{-44}{1 + 44} = -.978$$
$$\therefore 1 + h_{21b} = .022$$

By (7.42)

$$h_{22e} = \frac{h_{22b}}{1 + h_{21b}} = \frac{.62(10^{-6})}{.022} = 28.2(10^{-6}) \text{ mhos}$$

By (7.45)

$$h_{12e} = \frac{h_{11b}h_{22b} - h_{12b}(1 + h_{21b})}{1 + h_{21b}}$$
$$= \frac{29(.62)10^{-6} - 5.2(10^{-4})(.022)}{.022} = 2.45(10^{-4})$$

By (7.46)

$$h_{11e} = \frac{h_{11b}}{1 + h_{21b}} = \frac{29}{.022} = 1320\ \Omega$$

By (7.41)

$$h_{12c} = 1$$

By (7.56)

$$h_{11c} = h_{11e} = 1320 \ \Omega$$

By (7.57)

$$h_{22c} = h_{22e} = 28.2(10^{-6}) \text{ mhos}$$

By (7.55)

$$h_{21c} = -(1 + h_{21e}) = -(1 + 44) = -45$$

7.7. Effects of operating point. As noted in the preceding developments and example, the h-parameter values are specified by the manufacturer at a specific operating point. Obviously, a given transistor finds application at a considerable number of operating points other than the unique one for which data are supplied on a transistor specification sheet. Thus, we must know how the h-parameters vary with changes in the operating point. This information is usually provided graphically for the devices intended as small-signal amplifiers. A good example of such a graph from the General Electric type 2N1414 is shown in Fig. 7.7. In Fig. 7.7(a) the variation of the h-parameters is presented as a function of emitter-current variation, collector voltage being held at a constant value. Figure 7.7(b) presents the variation of h-parameters as a function of collector voltage, emitter current being held at a constant value. The data presentation is such that the new value of the h-parameter is normalized relative to the value of the h-parameter appearing on the specification sheet at the reference value of emitter current and collector voltage. Thus, the ordinate is a multiplier, which, when multiplied by the specified value of the h-parameter, gives the new value of the h-parameter at the new current or voltage level.

Suppose, for example, we were interested in h_{11b} at an emitter current of .3 ma. From Fig. 7.7(a) we find that at an abscissa value of .3 ma the h_{ib} or h_{11b} curve has an ordinate or multiplier value of 3.5. The reference value of h_{11b} was 29 ohms. The value of h_{11b} at the new emitter current is the product of the multiplier and the reference value of h_{11b}. The new h_{11b} is 3.5 times 29 or 102 ohms. Likewise, at an emitter current of 4 ma, the multiplier is .2; therefore the value of h_{11b} is .2 times 29 or 5.8 ohms. When a new operating point involves both emitter-current and collector-voltage changes, the graphs of Figs. 7.7(a) and 7.7(b) must both be used. Effectively a composite multiplier must be used to determine the new values of the h-parameters at the new values of emitter current and collector voltage.

EXAMPLE. To demonstrate the use of the curves in Fig. 7.7, let us consider the calculation of the common-emitter and common-collector h-parameters of the

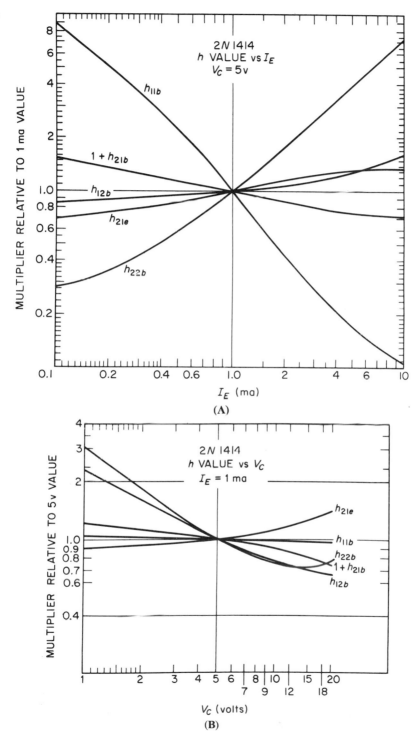

Fig. 7.7 Variation of h-parameters with I_E and V_C.

2N1414 used in Sec. 7.6 at an emitter current of .5 ma and a collector voltage of 9 v. We proceed as follows:

(a) From Fig. 7.7(a) at I_E equals .5 ma, multipliers for each parameter are

$$h_{ob} \text{ multiplier} = .59$$
$$h_{ib} \text{ multiplier} = 2.1$$
$$h_{rb} \text{ multiplier} = .94$$
$$h_{fe} \text{ multiplier} = .86$$
$$1 + h_{fb} \text{ multiplier} = 1.15$$

(b) From Fig. 7.7(b) at V_C equals 9 v, we find that the multipliers for each parameter are

$$h_{ob} \text{ multiplier} = .77$$
$$h_{ib} \text{ multiplier} = .99$$
$$h_{rb} \text{ multiplier} = .8$$
$$h_{fe} \text{ multiplier} = 1.1$$
$$1 + h_{fb} \text{ multiplier} = .92$$

(c) At the reference point of $I_E = 1$ ma and V_C equals 5 v, the values of the h-parameters were

$$h_{22b} = .62(10^{-6}) \text{ mhos}$$
$$h_{11b} = 29 \text{ ohms}$$
$$h_{12b} = 5.2(10^{-4})$$
$$h_{21e} = 44$$
$$1 + h_{21b} = .022$$

(d) At the new point, then, the values are

$$h_{22b} = .62(10^{-6})(.59)(.77) = .28(10^{-6}) \text{ mhos}$$
$$h_{11b} = 29(2.1)(.99) = 60 \text{ ohms}$$
$$h_{12b} = 5.2(10^{-4})(.94)(.8) = 3.9(10^{-4})$$
$$h_{21e} = 44(.86)(1.1) = 41.6$$
$$1 + h_{21b} = .022(1.15)(.92) = .0233$$

(e) The values of the common-emitter h-parameters can now be calculated. By (7.42)

$$h_{22e} = \frac{h_{22b}}{1 + h_{21b}} = \frac{.28(10^{-6})}{.0233} = 12(10^{-6}) \text{ mhos}$$

By (7.46)

$$h_{11e} = \frac{h_{11b}}{1 + h_{21b}} = \frac{60}{.0233} = 2580 \ \Omega$$

By (7.45)

$$h_{12e} = \frac{h_{11b}h_{22b} - h_{12b}(1 + h_{21b})}{1 + h_{21b}}$$
$$= \frac{60(.28)(10^{-6}) - 3.9(10^{-4})(.0233)}{.0233} = 3.3(10^{-4})$$

By calculation in step (d), $h_{21e} = 41.6$

(f) The common-collector h-parameters have the following values. By (7.57)

$$h_{22c} = h_{22e} = 12(10^{-6}) \text{ mhos}$$

By (7.56)

$$h_{11c} = h_{11e} = 2580 \ \Omega$$

By (7.41)

$$h_{12c} = 1$$

By (7.55)

$$h_{21c} = -(1 + h_{21e}) = -(1 + 41.6) = -42.6$$

7.8. Modified *h*-parameters. One other matter should be considered to complete our understanding of *h*-parameters and their use in equivalent circuits. In Figs. 7.1 and 7.2 we see equivalent circuits of transistors as entities unto themselves. In Chapter 6, however, we saw that resistive networks can appear in conjunction with the transistor in order for the transistor to operate at particular values of current and voltage. Resistors such as R_M, R_N, R_E, and R_F, whether they appear separately or in combination, can be considered a part of the transistor a-c equivalent circuit. If they are, parameters known as *modified h-parameters* come into existence and are said to be descriptive of the a-c nature of the modified equivalent circuit. Naturally, when several of the resistors appear simultaneously, as in the circuits giving good operating-point stability, the effects of all must be taken into account. The easiest way to do so, however, is by separate steps of modified *h*-parameter calculations. This is an ap-

proach similar to the determination of an *h*-parameter by determining separately a current multiplier and a voltage multiplier to account for an operating-point shift. The resistors that contribute to changes in the *h*-parameter values are shown in Fig. 7.8, as they would appear in relation to the transistor in a practical circuit. We should appreciate that all the resistors shown are part of the bias network. R_F is the current-feedback resistor, R_E is the voltage-feedback resistor, and R_S can be either R_N alone or R_M and R_N in parallel, as the case may be. In order to determine the composite effect of these bias resistors we must determine the effects of each one on an individual basis.

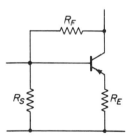

Fig. 7.8 Resistors which can affect a-c performance of a transistor.

Consider first the presence of R_S alone. An equivalent circuit showing the presence of R_S is shown in Fig. 7.9. We begin the analysis by writing the equations for the input and output circuits as follows:

$$v_1 = i_b h_{11} + h_{12} v_2 \tag{7.58}$$

$$i_2 = i_b h_{21} + h_{22} v_2 \tag{7.59}$$

$$v_1 = i_a R_S \tag{7.60}$$

$$i_1 = i_a + i_b \tag{7.61}$$

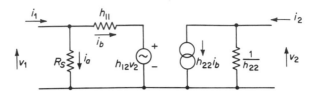

Fig. 7.9   Equivalent circuit for determining modification of h-parameters due to R_S.

Applying the general definitions of the h-parameters as given by Eqs. (7.1), (7.2), (7.3), and (7.4) to our specific circuit, the modified h-parameters are

$$h'_{11} = \frac{v_1}{i_1}\bigg|_{v_2} = 0 \tag{7.62}$$

$$h'_{21} = \frac{i_2}{i_1}\bigg|_{v_2} = 0 \tag{7.63}$$

$$h'_{22} = \frac{i_2}{v_2}\bigg|_{i_1} = 0 \tag{7.64}$$

$$h'_{12} = \frac{v_1}{v_2}\bigg|_{i_1} = 0 \tag{7.65}$$

Substituting Eq. (7.60) into (7.58) for v_1, and setting v_2 equal to zero, we find

$$i_a = i_b \frac{h_{11}}{R_S} \tag{7.66}$$

Substituting (7.61) into (7.63), we get

$$h'_{21} = \frac{i_2}{i_a + i_b} \tag{7.67}$$

Putting (7.66) into (7.67),

$$h'_{21} = \frac{i_2}{i_b \dfrac{h_{11}}{R_S} + i_b} \tag{7.68}$$

By the nomenclature of Fig. 7.9, the forward-current gain of the transistor itself can be determined by inspection or by Eq. (7.59):

$$h_{21} = \frac{i_2}{i_b} \tag{7.69}$$

Thus it can be shown that (7.68) will reduce to

$$h'_{21} = \frac{h_{21} R_S}{h_{11} + R_S} \tag{7.70}$$

Equation (7.70) indicates that the bias resistors that shunt the input tend to reduce the effective forward-current gain of the transistor. Let us proceed now to the modified input impedance h'_{11}. First, set v_2 equal to zero in Eq. (7.58), then substitute the relation of Eq. (7.61) for i_b and then again Eq. (7.60) for i_a. The result reduces to

$$h'_{11} = \frac{h_{11} R_S}{h_{11} + R_S} \tag{7.71}$$

In order to obtain h_{22}, we first substitute Eq. (7.60) in (7.58) for v_1 and then substitute again putting the relation as given by (7.61) for i_a. At the condition of i_1 equal to zero, this sequence of substitutions reduces to

$$i_b = -\frac{v_2 h_{12}}{h_{11} + R_S} \tag{7.72}$$

Putting (7.72) in (7.59) and recalling the definition of h'_{22} as given by (7.64), we obtain

$$h'_{22} = h_{22} - \frac{h_{21} h_{12}}{h_{11} + R_S} \tag{7.73}$$

In order to obtain h'_{12} we substitute (7.72) into (7.58) and manipulate to a direct solution of

$$h'_{12} = \frac{h_{12} R_S}{h_{11} + R_S} \tag{7.74}$$

In each instance, we observe that the input shunting impedance makes the value of the modified h-parameter less than the value of the h-parameter for the transistor alone. In obtaining each equation for a modified h-parameter, we have merely established the necessary terminal condition of input open, or output shorted, and then manipulated the known equations to obtain the parameter relations constituting the definition of the modified h-parameter.

The next bias component to be considered is the resistor R_E, which appears in series with the emitter. We cite the common-emitter circuit because of its frequent use. The equivalent circuit of a transistor when modified to include the presence of series emitter resistance is shown in Fig. 7.10. The equations of interest that may be written from this circuit are

$$v'_1 = i_1(h_{11} + R_E) + v_2 h_{12} + i_2 R_E \tag{7.75}$$

$$v'_2 = i_1 R_E + v_2 + i_2 R_E \tag{7.76}$$

$$i_2 = h_{21} i_1 + v_2 h_{22} \tag{7.77}$$

The modified h-parameters for this circuit will again involve the overall input and output currents and voltages. Bearing in mind the approach just completed for resistance-shunting the input, we find with discrete manipulation of Eqs. (7.75), (7.76), and (7.77) that

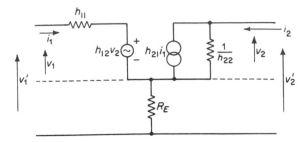

Fig. 7.10   Equivalent circuit for determining modification of h-parameters due to R_E.

$$h_{21}'' = \frac{h_{21} - h_{22}R_E}{1 + R_E h_{22}} \cong \frac{h_{21}}{1 + R_E h_{22}} \tag{7.78}$$

$$h_{11}'' = h_{11} + \frac{R_E(1 + h_{21})}{1 + R_E h_{22}} \tag{7.79}$$

$$h_{22}'' = \frac{h_{22}}{1 + R_E h_{22}} \tag{7.80}$$

$$h_{12}'' = \frac{h_{21} + h_{22}R_E}{1 + R_E h_{22}} \tag{7.81}$$

Series emitter resistance results in values of the modified input impedance and voltage-feedback factor that are greater than the values of the corresponding h-parameters for the transistor alone. The values of the modified current gain and output admittance are less than the values of the corresponding h-parameters for the transistor alone.

The final bias component to be considered is the resistor R_F, which appears between the output and input terminals. The equivalent circuit of a transistor, modified to include the presence of R_F, is shown in Fig. 7.11. The pertinent equations for this equivalent circuit are

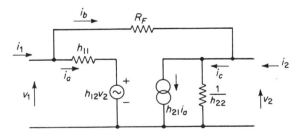

Fig. 7.11   Equivalent circuit for determining modification of h-parameters due to R_F.

$$v_1 = i_a h_{11} + h_{12} v_2 \tag{7.82}$$

$$i_c = i_a h_{21} + h_{22} v_2 \tag{7.83}$$

$$i_1 = i_a + i_b \tag{7.84}$$

$$i_c = i_2 + i_b \tag{7.85}$$

$$v_2 = v_1 - i_b R_F \tag{7.86}$$

A manipulation of these equations yields the following equations for the modified circuit of Fig. 7.11.

$$h_{21}''' = \frac{h_{21} R_F - h_{11}}{R_F + h_{11}} \simeq \frac{h_{21} R_F}{R_F + h_{11}} \tag{7.87}$$

$$h_{11}''' = \frac{h_{11} R_F}{R_F + h_{11}} \tag{7.88}$$

$$h_{22}''' = h_{22} + \frac{(1 + h_{21})(1 - h_{12})}{R_F + h_{11}} \tag{7.89}$$

$$h_{12}''' = h_{12} + \frac{h_{11}(1 - h_{12})}{R_F + h_{11}} \tag{7.90}$$

These equations show that when a current-feedback resistor is used, the values of modified forward-current gain and input impedance are less than the values of the corresponding h-parameters for the transistor alone. They

TABLE 7.4   Summary of modified h-parameter expressions.

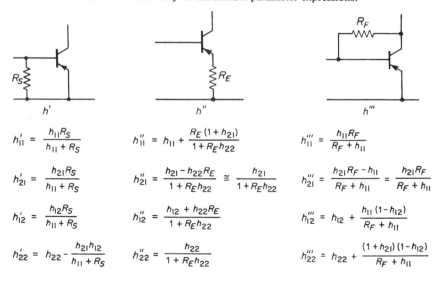

$$h_{11}' = \frac{h_{11} R_S}{h_{11} + R_S} \qquad h_{11}'' = h_{11} + \frac{R_E(1 + h_{21})}{1 + R_E h_{22}} \qquad h_{11}''' = \frac{h_{11} R_F}{R_F + h_{11}}$$

$$h_{21}' = \frac{h_{21} R_S}{h_{11} + R_S} \qquad h_{21}'' = \frac{h_{21} - h_{22} R_E}{1 + R_E h_{22}} \cong \frac{h_{21}}{1 + R_E h_{22}} \qquad h_{21}''' = \frac{h_{21} R_F - h_{11}}{R_F + h_{11}} = \frac{h_{21} R_F}{R_F + h_{11}}$$

$$h_{12}' = \frac{h_{12} R_S}{h_{11} + R_S} \qquad h_{12}'' = \frac{h_{12} + h_{22} R_E}{1 + R_E h_{22}} \qquad h_{12}''' = h_{12} + \frac{h_{11}(1 - h_{12})}{R_F + h_{11}}$$

$$h_{22}' = h_{22} - \frac{h_{21} h_{12}}{h_{11} + R_S} \qquad h_{22}'' = \frac{h_{22}}{1 + R_E h_{22}} \qquad h_{22}''' = h_{22} + \frac{(1 + h_{21})(1 - h_{12})}{R_F + h_{11}}$$

also show that the values of the modified voltage-feedback factor and output admittance are more than the values of the corresponding *h*-parameters for the transistor alone. For convenience all equations for the modified *h*-parameters are summarized in Table 7.4.

To demonstrate the use of the modified *h*-parameter equations, let us consider the execution of the following problem.

7.9. Example: *h*-parameter modification by single element. A 2N1414 transistor has the *h*-parameter values calculated in Sec. 7.6. It has a current gain $h_{FE} = 50$ and a leakage of 4 μa. Calculate the modified *h*-parameters when it is operated in the simplest of self-bias circuits (Fig. 6.3) at a $V_C = 5$ v and $I_C = 1$ ma. $V_{CC} = 6$ v. $R_L = 1$ K. The procedure is to determine the value of R_F yielding the proper operating point, and then use Eqs. (7.87), (7.88), (7.89), and (7.90) to calculate the modified *h*-parameters. By (4.12)

$$I_C = h_{FE}I_B + (1 + h_{FE})I_{CBO}$$

$$\therefore I_B = \frac{10^{-3} - 51(.004)10^{-3}}{50} = .0159 \text{ ma}$$

By (6.7)

$$V_C = V_{CC} - (I_C + I_B)R_L$$
$$= 6 - (1 + .0159)(10^{-3})10^3 = 4.98 \text{ v}$$

By (6.8)

$$R_F = \frac{V_C}{I_F} = \frac{4.98}{.0159(10^{-3})} = 315 \text{ K}$$

The pertinent *h*-parameters have been determined as follows:

$$h_{11e} = 1320 \ \Omega$$
$$h_{21e} = 44$$
$$h_{22e} = 28.2 \ (10^{-6}) \text{ mhos}$$
$$h_{12e} = 2.95 \ (10^{-4})$$

By (7.87)

$$h_{21}''' = \frac{h_{21} R_F}{R_F + h_{11}}$$
$$= \frac{44 \ (315\text{K})}{316.3 \text{ K}} = 43.8$$

By (7.88)

$$h_{11}''' = \frac{h_{11} R_F}{R_F + h_{11}}$$
$$= \frac{1320 \ (315 \text{ K})}{316.3 \text{ K}} = 1315 \ \Omega$$

By (7.89)

$$h_{22}''' \cong h_{22} + \frac{1 + h_{21}}{R_F + h_{11}}$$

$$= 28.2 \, (10^{-6}) + \frac{45}{316.3 \, \text{K}} = 170 \, (10^{-6}) \text{ mhos}$$

By (7.90)

$$h_{12}''' \cong h_{12} + \frac{h_{11}}{R_F + h_{11}}$$

$$= 2.95 \, (10^{-4}) + \frac{1320}{316.3 \, \text{K}} = 44.75 \, (10^{-4})$$

7.10. h-parameter modification due to several elements. The problem of Sec. 7.9 is one of the simplest that might be encountered, since only a single resistor R_F is used. This particular bias circuit is often adequate in *RC*-coupled amplifiers. More frequently we are apt to encounter the complete voltage-feedback or combination current-voltage feedback bias circuits. Thus, cither R_M, R_N, and R_E, or R_F, R_N, and R_E will appear simultane-ously in their respective circuits. A more realistic problem requires the calculation of modified *h*-parameters owing to the presence of R_M, R_N, and R_E, or R_F, R_N, and R_E simultaneously. The solution can be obtained only by successive calculation of the individual modifications taken one at a time. One word of caution at this point. The modification of the *h*-para-meters due to R_N, or R_M and R_N in parallel, must *always* be performed last. These impedances fall into the category of R_S, the resistance that shunts the input of the transistor. We must always start from the inside of our transistor circuit and work out to the actual input or output terminals. The shunt component R_S can change the modifications introduced by R_F and R_E but the converse is not true. As far as R_E and R_F are concerned, it makes no difference in which order the individual *h*-parameter modifications are calculated. To demonstrate the approach when more than one modifying element is present, let us consider the following example.

EXAMPLE 1: *h-parameter modification—voltage-feedback bias.*   Refer back to Sec. 6.8. Assume that the device has the a-c parameters of the 2N1414 of Sec. 7.6. It is required to calculate the modified *h*-parameters for the transistor that result from the bias resistors $R_M = 19.6$ K, $R_N = 2.9$ K, and $R_E = 477$ ohms. Figure 7.7(b) shows that the change in *h*-parameters in going from a collector voltage of 5 volts to 4.5 volts is negligible. We have as reference *h*-parameters

$$h_{11e} = 1320 \text{ ohms}$$
$$h_{21e} = 44$$
$$h_{22e} = 28.2 \, (10^{-6}) \text{ mhos}$$
$$h_{12e} = 2.95 \, (10^{-4})$$

Following the note of caution, we will first modify the parameters to take account of the 477-ohm emitter resistor. For convenience we calculate the product $R_E h_{22}$:

$$R_E h_{22} = 477\,(28.2)(10^{-6}) = .0135$$

By (7.78)

$$h_{21}'' = \frac{h_{21}}{1 + R_E h_{22}}$$

$$= \frac{44}{1.0135} = 43.4$$

By (7.79)

$$h_{11}'' = h_{11} + \frac{R_E(1 + h_{21})}{1 + R_E h_{22}}$$

$$= 1320 + \frac{477(45)}{1.0135} = 22.52 \text{ K}$$

By (7.80)

$$h_{22}'' = \frac{h_{22}}{1 + R_E h_{22}}$$

$$= \frac{28.2(10^{-6})}{1.0135} = 27.8\,(10^{-6}) \text{ mhos}$$

By (7.81)

$$h_{12}'' = \frac{h_{12} + R_E h_{22}}{1 + R_E h_{22}}$$

$$= \frac{2.95(10^{-4}) + .0135}{1.0135} = 136\,(10^{-4})$$

The parallel equivalent of R_M and R_N is the final modifying element. To use the terminology already established,

$$R_S = \frac{R_M R_N}{R_M + R_N}$$

$$= \frac{19.6 \text{ K}(2.9 \text{ K})}{19.6 \text{ K} + 2.9 \text{ K}} = 2.52 \text{ K}$$

Using as the new references the values as modified by R_E, we proceed to calculate the changes due to $R_S = 2.52$ K. To assist in the calculations we calculate

$$\frac{R_S}{h_{11}'' + R_S} = \frac{2.52 \text{ K}}{(22.52 + 2.52) \text{ K}} = .101$$

By (7.70)

$$h_{21}' = \frac{h_{21}'' R_S}{h_{11}'' + R_S}$$

$$= 43.4(.101) = 4.47$$

By (7.71)

$$h_{11}' = \frac{h_{11}'' R_S}{h_{11}'' + R_S}$$

$$= 22.52 \text{ K}(.101) = 2.25 \text{ K}$$

By (7.73)

$$h'_{22} = h''_{22} - \frac{h''_{21} h''_{12}}{h''_{11} + R_S}$$

$$= 27.8 \, (10^{-6}) - \frac{43.4 \, (136)(10^{-4})}{25 \, \text{K}} = 4.2 \, \mu\text{mhos}$$

By (7.74)

$$h'_{12} = \frac{h''_{12} R_S}{h''_{11} + R_S}$$

$$= 136(10^{-4})(.101) = 13.7 \, (10^{-4})$$

It is interesting to observe how the rather drastic increases of h_{11} and h_{12} due to R_E are compensated quite extensively by the presence of R_S. In addition R_S reduces h_{21} and h_{22} very significantly. The directions of these individual changes should have been anticipated from the form of the governing equation.

EXAMPLE 2: *h-parameter modification—current-feedback bias.*   Consider now the bias circuit developed in Sec. 6.12. We are interested in an $R_F = 17.7$ K, $R_N = 3.2$ K, and $R_E = 430$ ohms and the resultant modification of the h-parameters. As in the preceding example, we can use the 5-v, 1-ma h-parameters of the 2N1414 of Sec. 7.6 as our initial reference h-parameters. The values of these h-parameters are

$$h_{11e} = 1320 \, \Omega$$
$$h_{21e} = 44$$
$$h_{22e} = 28.2(10^{-6}) \, \text{mhos}$$
$$h_{12e} = 2.45(10^{-4})$$

Let us determine first the effects of $R_E = 430$ ohms. To assist in the calculations we first determine

$$R_E h_{22} = 430 \, (28.2)(10^{-6}) = .0121$$

By (7.78)

$$h''_{21} = \frac{h_{21}}{1 + R_E h_{22}}$$

$$= \frac{44}{1.0121} = 43.5$$

By (7.79)

$$h''_{11} = h_{11} + \frac{R_E(1 + h_{21})}{1 + R_E h_{22}}$$

$$= 1320 + \frac{430 \, (45)}{1.0121} = 20.42 \, \text{K}$$

By (7.80)

$$h''_{22} = \frac{h_{22}}{1 + R_E h_{22}}$$

$$= \frac{28.2 \, (10^{-6})}{1.0121} = 27.8(10^{-6}) \, \text{mhos}$$

By (7.81)

$$h_{12}'' = \frac{h_{12} + R_E h_{22}}{1 + R_E h_{22}}$$

$$= \frac{2.95(10^{-4}) + .0121}{1.0121} = 122.5(10^{-6})$$

We must now modify again, taking into account the presence of $R_F = 17.7$ K. We use the h's just obtained as our new references. To assist in the computations we calculate

$$\frac{R_F}{h_{11}'' + R_F} = \frac{17.7 \text{ K}}{(20.42 + 17.7) \text{ K}} = .465$$

By (7.87)

$$h_{21}''' = \frac{h_{21}'' R_F}{h_{11}'' + R_F}$$

$$= 43.5(.465) = 20.2$$

By (7.88)

$$h_{11}''' = \frac{h_{11}'' R_F}{h_{11}'' + R_F}$$

$$= 20.42 \text{ K}(.465) = 9.5 \text{ K}$$

By (7.89)

$$h_{22}''' = h_{22}'' + \frac{(1 + h_{21}'')(1 - h_{12}'')}{h_{11}'' + R_F}$$

$$= 27.8(10^{-6}) + \frac{44.5(1)}{38.12 \text{ K}}$$

$$= 1196(10^{-6}) \text{ mhos}$$

By (7.90)

$$h_{12}''' = h_{12}'' + \frac{h_{11}''(1 - h_{12}'')}{R_F + h_{11}''}$$

$$= 122.5(10^{-4}) + \frac{20.42 \text{ K}(1)}{38.12 \text{ K}} = 5472(10^{-4})$$

The final modification will take into account the presence of $R_N = 3.2$ K. Maintaining prior terminology we have, for this particular configuration, the condition that $R_S = R_N$ on a direct-substitution basis. We use the h's just obtained as new references. For ease of computation

$$\frac{R_S}{h_{11}''' + R_S} = \frac{3.2 \text{ K}}{9.5 \text{ K} + 3.2 \text{ K}} = .252$$

By (7.70)

$$h_{12}' = \frac{h_{21}''' R_S}{h_{11}''' + R_S}$$

$$= 20.2(.252) = 5.1$$

By (7.71)

$$h_{11}' = \frac{h_{11}''' R_S}{h_{11}''' + R_S}$$

$$9.5 \text{ K}(.252) = 2.4 \text{ K}$$

By (7.72)

$$h'_{22} = h'''_{22} - \frac{h'''_{21} h'''_{12}}{h'''_{11} + R_S}$$

$$= 1196(10^{-6}) - \frac{20.2(5472)10^{-4}}{12.7 \text{ K}} = 326 \ \mu\text{mhos}$$

By (7.73)

$$h'_{12} = \frac{h'''_{12} R_S}{h'''_{11} + R_S}$$

$$= 5472(10^{-4}).252 = 1380(10^{-4})$$

7.11. Normalizing *h*-parameter modifications. Studying the manipulations in the successive steps of the examples in Sec. 7.10 reveals that the *h*-parameters are modified least when R_E is small, R_F is large, and R_S is large. It is most important to realize that thus far we have been observing the resultant changes in *h*-parameters due to the presence of the d-c bias network. The operating-point requirements have been established first, and by our calculations we are determining the resultant effective values of the *h*-parameters. It is certainly reasonable to anticipate that the d-c requirements do not always predominate over desired a-c requirements. We may be interested, then, in shaping the frequency response of an amplifier. We might also be interested in emphasizing the change in a particular parameter such as h_{11} or h_{22} to optimize terminal impedance levels. We need to know more specifically how the various magnitudes of R_E, R_S, or R_F, either individually or in combination, will cause a desired level or value of modified *h*-parameter. In such situations it is useful to have a presentation of modified *h*-parameter value normalized to the transistor *h*-parameter value and the modifying resistor. Consider, for example, Eq. (7.71). A rearrangement of the quantities yields

$$\frac{h'_{11}}{h_{11}} = \frac{1}{1 + \dfrac{h_{11}}{R_S}} \tag{7.91}$$

This form of information is useful as the modified *h*-parameter is normalized to the *h*-parameter of the transistor alone, and the input shunting impedance is in effect normalized to the output-shorted input impedance of the transistor alone. We can see immediately from the form of Eq. (7.91) that if the quantity h_{11}/R_S equals unity, the modified *h*-parameter becomes equal to one-half the value of the parameter for the transistor alone. The graphical presentation of Eq. (7.91) is shown in Fig. 7.12. Equations (7.70) and (7.74) are of the same form as (7.71). Thus the equations for the normalized h'_{21} and h'_{12} will be of the same form as Eq. (7.91). It is permissible to use a common scale for normalized values of h'_{11}, h'_{21}, and h'_{12}. This is shown in Fig.

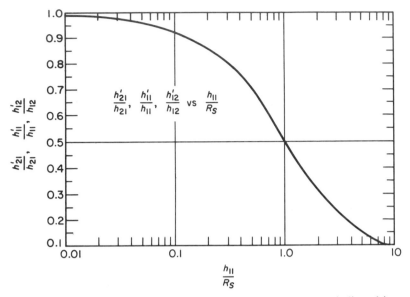

Fig. 7.12 Normalized h-parameter modifications due to R_S as indicated in Eq. (7.91).

7.12. To show graphically normalized values of h'_{22} we must manipulate the information as it stands in Eq. (7.73). Clearing fractions, we obtain

$$h'_{22} = \frac{h_{11} h_{22} + h_{22} R_S - h_{21} h_{12}}{h_{11} + R_S} \qquad (7.92)$$

Multiplying the third term of the numerator first by h_{22}/h_{22} to allow the h'_{22}/h_{22} normalizing ratio and then by h_{11}/h_{11} to allow a better grouping of the terms, we obtain

$$\frac{h'_{22}}{h_{22}} = \frac{1 + \dfrac{h_{11}}{R_S}\left(\dfrac{\Delta^h}{h_{11} h_{22}}\right)}{1 + \dfrac{h_{11}}{R_S}} \qquad (7.93)$$

where

$$\Delta^h = h_{11} h_{22} - h_{12} h_{21} \qquad (7.93a)$$

Since the quantity $\Delta^h/h_{11} h_{22}$ is a function of the particular transistor and operating point in question, this information is most appropriately shown by a family of curves as in Fig. 7.13. Each of the curves is for a particular value of $\Delta^h/h_{11} h_{22}$.

In considering the modified h-parameters due to series emitter resistance, it should be immediately apparent that Eqs. (7.78) and (7.80) have the

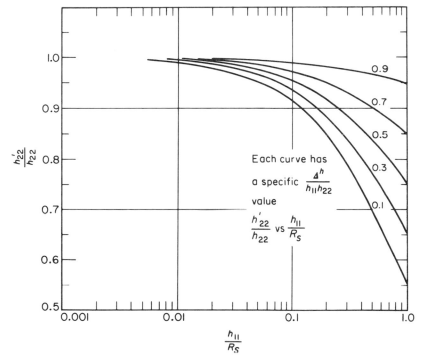

Fig. 7.13 Normalized h_{22} modification due to R_S as indicated by Eq. (7.93).

same general form as Eqs. (7.70), (7.71), and (7.74), except that the modifying parameter is $R_E h_{22}$ rather than h_{11}/R_S. Thus we might write

$$\frac{h_{21}''}{h_{21}} = \frac{h_{22}''}{h_{22}} = \frac{1}{1 + R_E h_{22}} \qquad (7.94)$$

This information could be plotted on the same graph shown in Fig. 7.12. For clarity, however, Eq. (7.94) is shown in Fig. 7.14. The procedure for normalizing h_{11}'' and h_{12}'' is quite similar to that used in obtaining h_{22}'. For h_{11}'' we start with Eq. (7.79) and clear fractions to obtain

$$h_{11}'' = \frac{h_{11} + h_{11} R_E h_{22} + R_E(1 + h_{21})}{1 + R_E h_{22}} \qquad (7.95)$$

Multiplying the third term by h_{11}/h_{11} to allow the h_{11}''/h_{11} normalizing ratio and then by h_{22}/h_{22} to allow better grouping of terms, we obtain

$$\frac{h_{11}''}{h_{11}} = \frac{1 + R_E h_{22}\left(1 + \dfrac{1 + h_{21}}{h_{11} h_{22}}\right)}{1 + R_E h_{22}} \qquad (7.96)$$

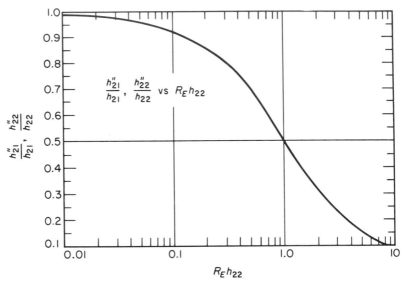

Fig. 7.14 Normalized h-parameter modification due to R_E as indicated by Eq. (7.94).

The relative magnitudes of the terms in the brackets permit a further reduction to

$$\frac{h_{11}''}{h_{11}} = \frac{1 + R_E h_{22}\left(\dfrac{1 + h_{21}}{h_{11} h_{22}}\right)}{1 + R_E h_{22}} \tag{7.97}$$

The quantity $(1 + h_{21})/h_{11}h_{22}$ depends on the particular transistor and its operating point. Hence the plot of Eq. (7.97) versus values of $R_E h_{22}$ will take the form of a family of curves. Such a family is plotted in Fig. 7.15. Each of the curves is for a typical value of $(1 + h_{21})/h_{11}h_{22}$. A similar treatment of Eq. (7.81) yields

$$\frac{h_{12}''}{h_{12}} = \frac{1 + R_E h_{22}\left(\dfrac{1}{h_{12}}\right)}{1 + R_E h_{22}} \tag{7.98}$$

Here we have the quantity $1/h_{12}$ dependent on the particular transistor. A plot, then, of h_{12}''/h_{12} versus $R_E h_{22}$ takes the form of a family of curves such as the generalized plot shown in Fig. 7.16. Each of the curves is for a particular value of $1/h_{12}$.

Proceeding now to the modified h-parameters occurring because of a

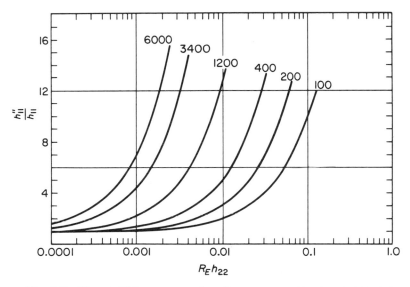

Fig. 7.15 Plot of h_{11}''/h_{11} versus $R_E h_{22}$. Curves are specific $(1 + h_{21})/(h_{11} h_{22})$ values. The value of h_{11}'' due to R_E is indicated by Eq. (7.97).

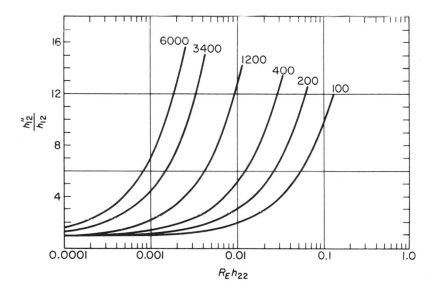

Fig. 7.16 Plot of h_{12}''/h_{12} versus $R_E h_{22}$. Curves are specific $1/h_{12}$ values. The value of h_{12}'' due to R_E is indicated by Eq. (7.98).

current-feedback resistor, we should note by inspection that Eqs. (7.87) and (7.88) are of a form whereby

$$\frac{h_{21}'''}{h_{21}} = \frac{h_{11}'''}{h_{11}} = \frac{1}{1 + \dfrac{h_{11}}{R_F}} \qquad (7.99)$$

A plot of Eq. (7.99) is shown in Fig. 7.17. Using the same approaches that we have used in the past, it can be shown that the normalized equivalent of Eq. (7.90) is

$$\frac{h_{12}'''}{h_{12}} = \frac{1 + \dfrac{h_{11}}{R_F}\left(\dfrac{1}{h_{12}}\right)}{1 + \dfrac{h_{11}}{R_F}} \qquad (7.100)$$

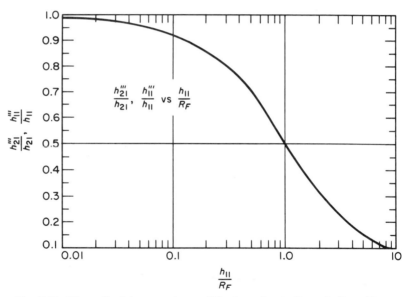

Fig. 7.17 Normalized h-parameter modifications due to R_F as indicated by Eq. (7.99).

A plot of normalized h_{12}'''/h_{12} versus h_{11}/R_F is shown in Fig. 7.18. Here we should note that each curve in the family is for a particular value of $1/h_{12}$.

The final equation to be processed is Eq. (7.89). Again using our established procedures, it can be shown that

$$\frac{h_{22}'''}{h_{22}} = \frac{1 + \dfrac{h_{11}}{R_F}\left(1 + \dfrac{1 + h_{21}}{h_{11}h_{22}}\right)}{1 + \dfrac{h_{11}}{R_F}} \qquad (7.101)$$

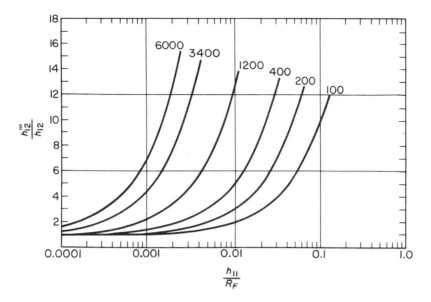

Fig. 7.18 Plot of h_{12}'''/h_{12} versus h_{11}/R_F. Curves are specific $1/h_{12}$ values. The value of h_{12}''' due to R_F is indicated by Eq. (7.100).

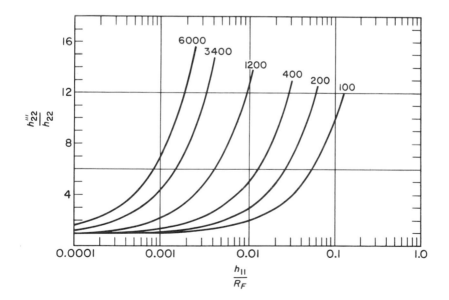

Fig. 7.19 Plot of h_{22}'''/h_{22} versus h_{11}/R_F. Curves are specific $(1 + h_{21})/h_{11}h_{22}$ values. The value of h_{22}''' due to R_F is indicated by Eq. (7.102).

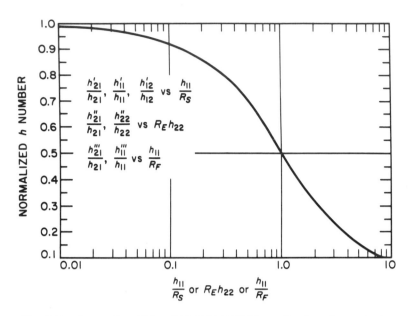

Fig. 7.20 Composite of Figs. 7.12, 7.14, 7.17. Normalizations for particular modified h's as a function of appropriate modifying resistor.

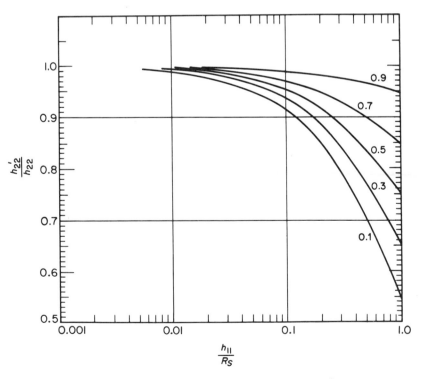

Fig. 7.21 Plot of h'_{22}/h_{22} versus h_{11}/R_S. Curves are specific $\Delta^h/h_{11}h_{22}$ values. Normalized h_{22} modification due to R_S is indicated by Eq. (7.93).

The relative magnitudes of the terms in the parentheses allow a further reduction to

$$\frac{h_{22}'''}{h_{22}} = \frac{1 + \dfrac{h_{11}}{R_F}\left(\dfrac{1 + h_{21}}{h_{11}h_{22}}\right)}{1 + \dfrac{h_{11}}{R_F}} \tag{7.102}$$

A plot of normalized h_{22}'''/h_{22} versus h_{11}/R_F is shown in Fig. 7.19. Each of the curves is for a particular value of the quantity $(1 + h_{21})/h_{11}h_{22}$.

Figures 7.12 to 7.19 have been presented as a generalized reference for the effects of the bias resistors taken individually. Curves 7.12, 7.14, and 7.17 were all of the same general form. Figure 7.20 combines each of these individual curves onto one curve more useful in design work. Figure 7.13 is redrawn as Fig. 7.21 and shows typical values for the $\Delta^h/h_{11}h_{22}$ quantity. Curves shown in Figs. 7.15, 7.16, 7.18, and 7.19 are redrawn in Fig. 7.22.

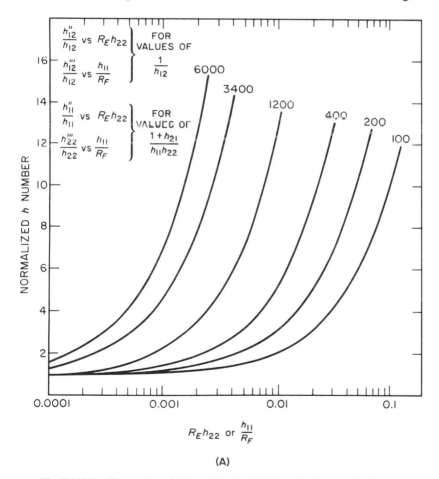

(A)

Fig. 7.22(A)   Composite of Figs. 7.15, 7.16, 7.18, 7.19. Low-multiplier range.

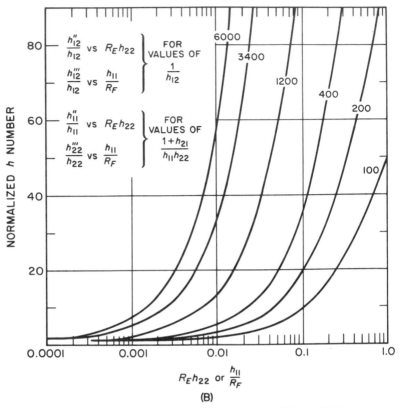

Fig. 7.22(B)   Composite of Figs. 7.15, 7.16, 7.18, 7.19. High-multiplier range.

Figure 7.22(a) shows the low multiplier range and Fig. 7.22(b) shows the high multiplier range.

EXAMPLE.   To illustrate by the simplest of exercises how the normalized curves are used, let us reconsider the example in Sec. 7.9. Here a 2N1414 was operating in a self-bias circuit with $R_F = 315$ K. The values of the reference h-parameters are

$$h_{11e} = 1320 \ \Omega$$
$$h_{21e} = 44$$
$$h_{22e} = 28.2(10^{-6}) \text{ mhos}$$
$$h_{12e} = 2.45(10^{-4})$$

The ratio h_{11}/R_F equals .0042. Using this abscissa value in Fig. 7.20, we observe that the ratio of h_{21}'''/h_{21} and h_{11}'''/h_{11} equals .995. To find h_{12}'''/h_{12}, we first calculate the quantity $1/h_{12}$ and find it equals 3390. Thus in Fig. 7.22(b) the intersection of the abscissa value of .0042 and the 3390 curve gives an ordinate value of 15 for h_{12}'''/h_{12}. The quantity $(1 + h_{21})/h_{11}h_{22}$ equals 1200 for our typical 2N1414. Thus in Fig. 7.22(a) we find that the ratio h_{22}'''/h_{22} is equal to 6. Using these graphically determined ratios we find

$$h_{21}''' = .955(44) = 43.8$$
$$h_{11}''' = .995(1320) = 1310 \ \Omega$$
$$h_{12}''' = 15(2.95)(10^{-4}) = 44.3(10^{-4})$$
$$h_{22}''' = 6(28.2)(10^{-6}) = 169(10^{-6}) \ \text{mhos}$$

As seen, these values correlate quite closely with the more exact calculations in the reference example.

The normalized h-parameter curves are of most use when we are interested in the enhancing or diminishing of the effective value of a given h-parameter. This could occur, for example, where we are trying to modify the terminal impedances of a transistor, or where we are trying to change h-parameters with frequency to make the gain vary a prescribed way with frequency. It should be understood that in such situations dynamic or a-c requirements are essentially taking priority over the d-c or operating-point requirements. It is likely, then, that the resultant operating-point stability will not be as good as if it were the highest-priority design requirement. In any design there are usually compromises between the d-c and a-c requirements.

One design problem that might be encountered is the control of the input impedance of a transistor stage. This can be accomplished by a manipulation of the h_{11} parameter. Increases in h_{11} are most effectively obtained by use of the emitter resistor R_E. The associated resistors R_M and R_N, or R_F, which appear to complete the bias picture, tend to *reduce* h_{11}. We see, then, modifying contributions that tend to compensate. Coping with these compensations, obtaining the desired level of h_{11}, and setting the operating point at a meaningful value are facets of the problem, all of which must be accounted for simultaneously.

7.12. Design example: obtaining specific modified h's. Let us attempt to adjust the h_{11e} parameter of the 2N1414 of Sec. 7.6 so that the modified h_{11e} is 3000 ohms. Let us use the circuit shown in Fig. 7.23. Several matters must be known: supply voltage, R_L, operating point (to establish the reference or unmodified values of the h-parameters), and the current gain and leakage of the reference transistor. We know that some amount of R_E is needed. How much or how little depends ultimately on the magnitude of R_S. Let us try to obtain an operating point of 1 ma from a 6-v supply with an R_L of 1 K, and still obtain the modified h_{11} of 3 K from our 2N1414 with

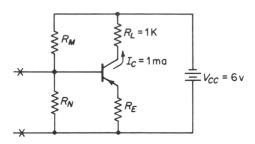

Fig. 7.23 Circuit for the design example of Sec 7.12.

its $h_{FE} = 20$ and $I_{CBO} = 2\ \mu a$. To note mentally the successive changes that will occur due to R_E, R_M, and R_N, let us itemize the following. Let

h_{11} = the reference parameter value

$(h_{11})_1$ = the modification due to R_E

$(h_{11})_2$ = the final modification caused by R_S

Figure 7.22(a) for the moment, then, becomes a plot of $(h_{11})_1/h_{11}$ versus $R_E h_{22}$. Figure 7.20 becomes a plot of $(h_{11})_2/(h_{11})_1$ versus $(h_{11})_1/R_S$. We can see that if R_E is made too large, $(h_{11})_1$ will get excessively large. This in turn will require that $(h_{11})_1/R_S$ be a large number to obtain the desired $(h_{11})_2$ value. A ratio of $(h_{11})_1/R_S$ that is a large number is not desirable from an a-c viewpoint. When R_S is less than $(h_{11})_1$, abnormal losses in gain occur. There is need to assume at the beginning some limit relation between R_S and $(h_{11})_1$, even though its exact value is unknown. The choices are as follows: as $(h_{11})_1/R_S$ goes greater than unity, we tend to lose a-c gain but achieve decent d-c operating-point stability; as $(h_{11})_1/R_S$ goes less than unity, we tend to lose on d-c operating-point stability but improve the a-c performance. Every problem requires its own specific compromise considerations. Let us choose for our problem that we do not want the final value of a-c current gain to be less than half of the reference value (R_E does not affect h_{21} typically). This imposes immediately the requirement that $(h_{11})_1/R_S$ equals unity. This information is available from Fig. 7.20 with the new coordinates superimposed. The following facts are now available:

(a) I_C equals 1 ma is the desired operating point. Therefore, the h-parameters calculated previously will apply. These h-parameters are

$$h_{11e} = 1320\ \Omega$$
$$h_{21e} = 44$$
$$h_{22e} = 28.2\ (10^{-6})\ \text{mhos}$$
$$h_{12e} = 2.45\ (10^{-4})$$

(b) A final h_{11} value of 3 K = $(h_{11})_2$ is desired.

(c) An $(h_{11})_1/R_S$ ratio of unity is chosen to prevent unreasonable losses in a-c gain.

(d) From Fig. 7.20 we note that when the ratio $(h_{11})_1/R_S$ equals unity, the ratio of $(h_{11})_2/(h_{11})_1$ equals .5. Since it is desired that $(h_{11})_2$ equal 3 K, the $(h_{11})_1$ value must equal 6 K.

(e) Using $(h_{11})_1$ equal to 6 K and h_{11} equal to 1320 ohms, the ratio of $(h_{11})_1/h_{11}$ equals 4.55.

(f) The calculation of $(1 + h_{21})/h_{11}h_{22}$ for our typical 2N1414 at $I_C = 1$ ma is 1200.

(g) From Fig. 7.22(a), we find that the ratio of $(h_{11})_1/h_{11}$ equals 4.55 for $(1 + h_{21})/h_{11}h_{22}$ equals 1200 at an $R_E h_{22}$ product value of .0029.

(h) Since $h_{22} = 28.2 (10^{-6})$, R_E calculates to be approximately 100 ohms (103 ohms, to be exact).

At this point we should make some confirming checks on our operating point. We know we can adjust R_M and R_N so that $I_C = 1$ ma. We ought to check to establish the level of V_C.

By (6.21)

$$R_E = \frac{h_{FE}}{1 + h_{FE}} \left(\frac{V_{CC} - V_C - I_C R_L}{I_C - I_{CBO}} \right)$$

Substituting for all quantities except our unknown V_C, we obtain

$$100 = \frac{20[6 - V_C - 10^{-3}(10^3)]}{21[10^{-3} - .002(10^{-3})]}$$

$$V_C = 4.93 \text{ v}$$

This is not a sufficient deviation to require recalculation of the reference h-parameters. At the moment we know numerically that $R_E = 100$ ohms, $(h_{11})_2 = 3$ K, $(h_{11})_1 = 6$ K, $(h_{11})_1/R_S = 1$ and therefore $R_S = 6$ K. The values for R_M and R_N need to be determined.

We know

$$R_S = \frac{R_M R_N}{R_M + R_N} \tag{7.103}$$

$$R_M = \frac{R_S R_N}{R_N - R_S} \tag{7.104}$$

From (6.22)

$$R_M = \frac{R_N [h_{FE}(V_{CC} - V_B) - BR_E]}{CR_N + BR_E + h_{FE} V_B}$$

Solving these two equations simultaneously will provide the unique value of R_N satisfying both the operating point and h_{11} modification requirements. We obtain

$$R_N = \frac{R_S h_{FE} V_{CC}}{h_{FE}(V_{CC} - V_B) - BR_E - R_S C} \tag{7.105}$$

Substituting the values for our problem, we obtain

$$R_N = \frac{6\,K(20)6}{20(5.85) - 20.9(10^{-3})100 - 6\,K(.958)10^{-3}}$$
$$= 6.6\,K$$

By (7.104)

$$R_M = \frac{6K(6.6\,K)}{6.6\,K - 6\,K} = 66\,K$$

A bias network of $R_M = 66\,K$, $R_N = 6.6\,K$, and $R_E = 100$ ohms provides simultaneously an operating point of 1 ma, a modified h_{11} of 3 K, and not too excessive losses in gain. To demonstrate the operating-point shift when a transistor with $h_{FE} = 50$ and $I_{CBO} = 8$ μa is used, we obtain By (6.18)

$$I_C = \frac{h_{FE}\left(\dfrac{V_{CC} - V_B}{R_M}\right) - \dfrac{h_{FE}V_B}{R_N} + (1 + h_{FE})I_{CBO}\left(1 + \dfrac{R_E}{R_M} + \dfrac{R_E}{R_N}\right)}{1 + (1 + h_{FE})\left(\dfrac{R_E}{R_M} + \dfrac{R_E}{R_N}\right)}$$

$$= \frac{\dfrac{50(5.85)}{66\,K} - \dfrac{50(.15)}{6.6\,K} + 51(.008)10^{-3}\left(1 + \dfrac{100}{66\,K} + \dfrac{100}{6.6\,K}\right)}{1 + 51\left(\dfrac{100}{66\,K} + \dfrac{100}{6.6\,K}\right)}$$

$$= 2\,ma$$

This stability is not as good as that which we demonstrated could be obtained. Refer back to Sec. 6.8. However, we have seen in this chapter that the final modified parameters are vastly different from those that we just designed into a circuit.

It is conceivable that some problems would not require the presence of R_N. The problem presented here is meant to stimulate the thinking required to consider all the aspects in the execution of a practical requirement in a real circuit. Shaping a gain characteristic, or modifying values of h_{22} and h_{12}, is accomplished using R_F singly or in combination with R_E. The execution of these matters is reserved for later chapters, which are more application-oriented.

7.13. Summary comments. The h-parameter equivalent shown in Fig. 7.24 is the most useful equivalent circuit for the transistor. As it stands, the circuit truly portrays the transistor in either the common-base, common-emitter, or common-collector connection. It does so because the appropriate values of the h-parameters make the circuit specifically applicable to the particular connection of interest. The h-parameters, as we found, were slopes of the static characteristics. Since the slopes are accurately determined only when the voltage and current determining increments are small, the use of the h-parameters is restricted to circuit applications where the voltage swing

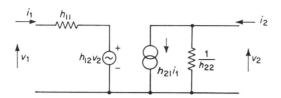

Fig. 7.24 h-parameter equivalent circuit.

to be handled is in the order of microvolts or millivolts. That is, the h-parameters apply only in what is categorically defined as a *small-signal circuit*. It should also be understood that the h-parameter circuit, as developed, is useful only for low-frequency applications of the transistor—up to 20,000–30,000 cycles as a general top-limit figure. The factors that void the applicability of the equivalent circuit at higher frequencies will be discussed in later chapters.

The expressions for the relative values of the h-parameters for the various connections, as tabulated in Tables 7.2 and 7.3, and the information about the variation of the h-parameters with operating point, as shown in Fig. 7.7, give us complete freedom in using and understanding the transistor's behavior.

The bias resistors can be considered a part of the transistor itself. If this is done, however, we are compelled to calculate what are known as modified h-parameters. Modified h-parameters are useful and necessary in practical applications to be discussed later.

The next matter to consider is an entire circuit involving not only the transistor but a power source as an input termination, and a load as an output termination. This material will be developed in the next chapter.

PROBLEMS

1. Give the generalized definitions of the h-parameters. Include the mathematical expression for each.

2. Write the mathematical expressions for the h-parameters for the common-emitter connection.

3. Use the h-parameters calculated in Sec. 7.4 for a typical 2N1414 at V_C equals 5 v and I_E equals 1 ma and determine r_b, r_e, r_c, and r_d.

4. A 2N1414 has $h_{11b} = 30$ ohms, $h_{22b} = .56(10^{-6})$ mhos, $h_{21e} = 35$, and $h_{12b} = 4(10^{-4})$, at $V_C = 5$ v and $I_E = 1$ ma. Calculate the common-emitter and common-collector h-parameters at $V_C = 12$ v and $I_C = 2$ ma.

5. Consider Sec. 7.10, Example 2. Perform the modification due to R_F before the modification due to R_E. Confirm that the resultant h's are the same as those obtained in the text.

6. Compare the execution of the example in Sec. 7.9 and Example 2 in Sec. 7.10. Why is it that R_F affects h_{11} and h_{21} in the latter but not in the former?

7. Except for the modification due to R_S, a transistor has the following modified h-parameters: $h_{11} = 8$ K, $h_{22} = 800(10^{-6})$, $h_{12} = 4000(10^{-4})$, $h_{21} = 30$. (a) If $R_S = 4$ K, what are the final values of the h-parameters? (b) If $R_S = 12$ K, what are the final values of the h-parameters?

8. A circuit has $V_{CC} = 9$ v, $R_L = 2.2$ K, $R_M = 47$ K, $R_N = 3.9$ K, and $R_E = 300$. Calculate the resultant modified h-parameters when a 2N1414 with $h_{11b} = 30$ ohms, $h_{21e} = 50$, $h_{12b} = 6.3(10^{-4})$, $h_{22b} = .62(10^{-6})$ mhos, $h_{FE} = 30$ and $I_{CBO} = 3$ μa is placed into the circuit. Assume $V_{BE} = .15$ v. V_C values within 10 per cent of the 5-v reference do not require h-parameter adjustment.

9. Use the transistor of Problem 8 and design a circuit with an operating point of 1.6 ma, a modified h_{11} of 5 K, and a minimum modified h_{21} of 33. V_C levels within 10 per cent of 5 v do not require adjustment of reference h-parameter levels.

8

PROPERTIES OF

LOW-FREQUENCY

AMPLIFIERS

The availability of an a-c equivalent circuit for the transistor allows us to proceed to a consideration of dynamic transistor circuits. Of particular interest for the present are those circuits generally classed as *small-signal amplifiers*. These circuits legitimately use the *h*-parameter equivalent circuit for the transistor, and the attribute of power amplification is usually of primary concern. Other circuit attributes exist and under certain circumstances may be of prime design importance. However, the usual purpose in the design of a small-signal amplifier is to provide a maximum of power gain. In this chapter we will deal with the mathematics of circuit analysis and will derive the equations that describe the performance of transistors in small-signal amplifiers.

8.1. General-case situation. If a transistor is to serve as an active amplifying device, it must receive power at its input terminals and must be terminated at its output terminals with a load, into which it can deliver amplified power. This suggests a circuit as shown in Fig. 8.1. The a-c power source that feeds the input terminals is depicted as a voltage generator, e_g, with its internal impedance, R_g. Incidentally, we could just as well present this as a current generator in parallel with a source impedance, although we need not do so at present. The load of the transistor is the resistor R_L. Since an a-c circuit analysis is of prime interest, the simplest of biasing tech-

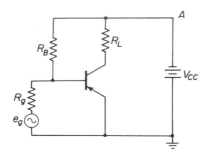

Fig. 8.1 Simple-case a-c amplifier connection.

niques is incorporated. The resistor R_B is present, then, to adjust the operating point to the desired value.

The a-c equivalent circuit of the circuit of Fig. 8.1 is shown in Fig. 8.2. Any circuit can be reduced to its a-c equivalent by shorting out all d-c supplies and replacing them by their internal impedances, if any exist. When point A of Fig. 8.1 is shorted to ground, and the transistor replaced by its equivalent circuit, the resultant a-c circuit is as shown in Fig. 8.2. Since R_B

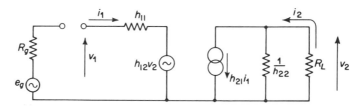

Fig. 8.2   A-C equivalent circuit for circuit of Fig. 8.1.

is usually so very large, its shunting effect on the input is negligible; thus it is not shown in the a-c equivalent circuit. Even though our actual sample circuit was shown common-emitter, the equivalent circuit will be left in the general form. The a-c power source is deliberately left unconnected for the time being.

The first steps in the analysis will be to write the input and output loop equations. Summing voltages around the input side, we find

$$v_1 = h_{11}i_1 + h_{12}v_2 \tag{8.1}$$

Summing currents at point Y, we get

$$i_2 = h_{21}i_1 + h_{22}v_2 \tag{8.2}$$

For the current directions as shown through $1/h_{22}$ and R_L, we note

$$i_2 = -\frac{v_2}{R_L} \tag{8.3}$$

Substituting (8.3) into (8.2), we get

$$0 = h_{21}i_1 + \left(h_{22} + \frac{1}{R_L}\right)v_2 \tag{8.4}$$

Equations (8.1) and (8.4) contain all the information of interest in determining the various performance attributes of the transistor circuit. The particular attributes that are of interest are defined as follows:

$$A_i = \frac{i_{\text{out}}}{i_{\text{in}}} = \frac{i_2}{i_1} \qquad (8.5a)$$

$$A_v = \frac{v_{\text{out}}}{v_{\text{in}}} = \frac{v_2}{v_1} \qquad (8.5b)$$

$$A_p = \frac{P_{\text{load}}}{P_{\text{in}}} \qquad (8.5c)$$

$$R_{\text{in}} = \frac{v_1}{i_1} \qquad (8.5d)$$

$$R_{\text{out}} = \frac{v_2}{i_2} \qquad (8.5e)$$

where A_i = circuit current gain
      A_v = circuit voltage gain
      A_p = circuit power gain
      R_{in} — input resistance
      R_{out} = output impedance

The input resistance, R_{in}, is a measure of the impedance looking in at the input terminals when the output is terminated with the load R_L. The output resistance, R_{out}, is a measure of the impedance looking in at the output terminals when the input is terminated with the power source and its impedance R_g. The current, voltage, and power gains are, as indicated, ratios of the pertinent a-c quantities in the load and at the input of the transistor.

Equations (8.1) and (8.4) must be solved simultaneously to obtain the expression for the circuit attributes. Equations (8.1) and (8.4) are of a general form, which can be written

$$x = ai_1 + bv_2 \qquad (8.6a)$$

$$y = ci_1 + dv_2 \qquad (8.6b)$$

The quantities i_1 and v_2 are the unknowns of interest. The use of determinants is appropriate for problems of this kind. Using determinants, the solution format is

$$i_1 = \frac{xd - by}{\Delta} \qquad (8.7)$$

$$v_2 = \frac{ay - xc}{\Delta} \qquad (8.8)$$

where

$$\Delta = ad - bc \qquad (8.9)$$

Equations (8.7), (8.8), and (8.9) apply generally to all simultaneous equations and can be referred to in any problem of a similar nature.

The quantities A_i, A_v, and A_p will be obtained first. For convenience Eqs. (8.1) and (8.4) are repeated.

$$v_1 = h_{11}i_1 + h_{12}v_2 \tag{8.1}$$

$$0 = h_{21}i_1 + \left(h_{22} + \frac{1}{R_L}\right)v_2 \tag{8.4}$$

By (8.7)

$$i_1 = \frac{v_1\left(h_{22} + \frac{1}{R_L}\right)}{\Delta} \tag{8.10}$$

By (8.8)

$$v_2 = \frac{-v_1 h_{21}}{\Delta} \tag{8.11}$$

By (8.9)

$$\Delta = h_{11}\left(h_{22} + \frac{1}{R_L}\right) - h_{12}h_{21} \tag{8.12}$$

First of all, let us inspect Eq. (8.12) more closely. It can be rewritten as

$$\Delta = (h_{11}h_{22} - h_{12}h_{21}) + \frac{h_{11}}{R_L} \tag{8.13}$$

If we were to apply our solution format to Eq. (7.5) and (7.6), the equations for the transistor alone, we would realize that the quantity $(h_{11}h_{22} - h_{12}h_{21})$ is the determinant of the transistor alone. This quantity appears frequently in our calculations. We have already encountered this quantity and introduced symbolism for it in Eq. (7.93a). For equation continuity in this chapter we rewrite Eq. (7.93a) as

$$\Delta^h = h_{11}h_{22} - h_{12}h_{21} \tag{8.14}$$

Substituting Eq. (8.14) into (8.13), we get

$$\Delta = \Delta^h + \frac{h_{11}}{R_L} \tag{8.15}$$

By inspection of Eq. (8.11), one observes that

$$A_v = \frac{-h_{21}}{\Delta} \tag{8.16}$$

$$A_v = \frac{-h_{21}R_L}{R_L\Delta^h + h_{11}} \tag{8.17}$$

In order to obtain the expression for the circuit current gain we begin by substituting Eq. (8.11) into (8.10) for the quantity v_1.

$$i_1 = \frac{-v_2\left(h_{22} + \frac{1}{R_L}\right)}{h_{21}} \tag{8.18}$$

Substituting (8.3) into (8.18) for the quantity v_2,

$$i_1 = \frac{i_2 R_L \left(h_{22} + \dfrac{1}{R_L}\right)}{h_{21}} \qquad (8.19)$$

$$A_i = \frac{h_{21}}{R_L h_{22} + 1} \qquad (8.20)$$

In order to calculate power gain we must determine the a-c power into the transistor and the a-c power in the load. Several expressions are possible.

$$P_{\text{load}} = i_2^2 R_L \qquad (8.21)$$

$$= i_2 v_2 \qquad (8.22)$$

$$P_{\text{in}} = i_1^2 R_{\text{in}} \qquad (8.23)$$

$$= i_1 v_1 \qquad (8.24)$$

Using a ratio of Eqs. (8.22) and (8.24), we note that the power-gain expression can be reduced to

$$A_p = A_i A_v \qquad (8.25)$$

Substituting (8.17) and (8.20) into (8.24), one obtains

$$A_p = \frac{-h_{21}^2 R_L}{(R_L h_{22} + 1)(R_L \Delta^h + h_{11})} \qquad (8.26)$$

The negative signs that appear in Eqs. (8.17) and (8.26) need not cause concern. All signs obtained are a function of the current and voltage directions assumed in the conventional depiction of the circuit of Fig. 8.2. For the common-base and common-collector circuits, the h_{21}-parameter is a negative quantity and therefore the voltage gain is a positive number. For the common-emitter connection the calculation of voltage gain does come out as a negative number. This means that in the actual common-emitter circuit the output voltage v_2 is really 180° out of phase with the direction shown conventionally in Fig. 8.2. In a similar manner, the calculation of current gain for the common-base and common-collector connections results in a solution of negative numbers. This means that in the actual common-base and common-collector circuits, the output current is really 180° out of phase with the direction shown conventionally in Fig. 8.2. The negative sign that appears in the power-gain expression is a quirk of mathematics which results when the current and voltage directions of Fig. 8.2 are used, and when the product of current gain and voltage gain is used. Power is truly being delivered to the load. The negative sign, then, should cause no concern.

The input resistance, R_{in}, can be calculated directly from Eq. (8.10):

$$\frac{v_1}{i_1} = \frac{\Delta}{h_{22} + \dfrac{1}{R_L}} \qquad (8.27)$$

$$R_{in} = \frac{R_L \Delta^h + h_{11}}{R_L h_{22} + 1} \tag{8.28}$$

In order to calculate the output resistance, R_{out}, we must redraw the equivalent circuit to the form consistent with the definition of R_{out}. Thus we must connect the source impedance R_g to the input terminals and look in at the opened output. This is shown in Fig. 8.3. Since this circuit is not the same as that for which circuit equations were previously written, we must write a new set of equations. Using known approaches,

$$0 = (h_{11} + R_g)i_1 + h_{12}v_2 \tag{8.29}$$

$$i_2 = h_{21}i_1 + h_{22}v_2 \tag{8.30}$$

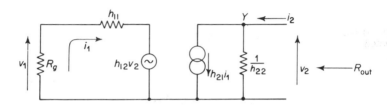

Fig. 8.3 A-C equivalent circuit for determining the behavior of R_{out}.

The solutions are

$$v_2 = \frac{(h_{11} + R_g)i_2}{\Delta} \tag{8.31}$$

$$\Delta = (h_{11} + R_g)h_{22} - h_{12}h_{21}$$

$$\Delta = \Delta^h + R_g h_{22} \tag{8.32}$$

The output resistance can now be written

$$R_{out} = \frac{R_g + h_{11}}{R_g h_{22} + \Delta^h} \tag{8.33}$$

The entire approach yielding the circuit-attribute expressions was general in nature. Accordingly, the equations themselves are in terms of the general-form h-parameters. To apply the attribute equations to a particular connection, we need only use the appropriate h-parameter values. Thus, if the common-emitter circuit is being studied, we will substitute the common-emitter h-parameters; and likewise for each of the other connections.

8.2. Comparison of the possible connections. The question naturally arises as to the merits of each of the connections. We have already been exposed to the phase shift between input and output currents for the common-base and common-collector connections. There is also a phase shift between input and output voltage for the common-emitter connection. The relative values of the circuit attributes for each of the connections are of interest at this time. Since the terminal impedances R_L or R_g are involved as independent variables in all of the expressions, graphs of the attributes versus the pertinent terminal impedance will be quite enlightening. For convenience the h-parameters and pertinent parameter ratios for a typical 2N1414 at an operating point of 5 volts and 1 ma are provided in Table 8.1.

Consider first the variation of current gain versus load resistance R_L. Equation (8.20) shows that for any connection,

$$\text{when } R_L = 0, \qquad A_i = h_{21} \qquad (8.34)$$

$$\text{when } R_L = \infty, \qquad A_i = 0 \qquad (8.35)$$

Using the h-parameter values of the 2N1414 from Table 8.1, a plot of the absolute value of A_i versus R_L would appear as in Fig. 8.4. As indicated, for

TABLE 8.1   Tabulation of h-parameter quantities for a 2N1414 at I_E = 1 ma, V_C = 5 v.

	COMMON BASE	COMMON EMITTER	COMMON COLLECTOR
h_{11}	29	1320	1320
h_{22}	0.62×10^{-6}	28.2×10^{-6}	28.2×10^{-6}
h_{21}	-0.978	44	-45
h_{12}	5.2×10^{-4}	2.95×10^{-4}	1
Δ^h	5.24×10^{-4}	242×10^{-4}	$\cong 45$
$\dfrac{h_{21}}{\Delta^h}$	-1865	1820	-1
$\dfrac{h_{21}}{h_{11}h_{22}}$	-5.43×10^4	1180	-1200
$\dfrac{\Delta^h}{h_{11}h_{22}}$	29.1	0.65	1200
$\dfrac{\Delta^h}{h_{22}}$	845	857	1.6×10^6
$\dfrac{h_{11}}{\Delta^h}$	5.55×10^4	5.45×10^4	29.4
$\dfrac{1}{h_{22}}$	1.61×10^6	35.4×10^3	35.4×10^3
$\dfrac{1}{h_{12}}$	1920	3390	1
$\dfrac{1+h_{21}}{h_{11}h_{22}}$	1220	1200	-1180

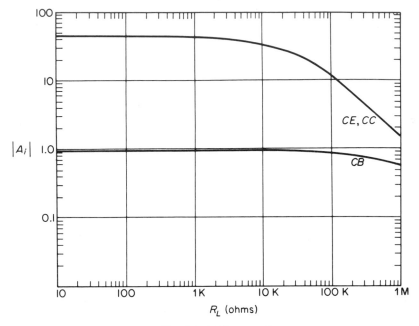

Fig. 8.4 $|A_i|$ versus R_L.

all values of terminations, the common-emitter and common-collector connections have greater current gains than does the common-base connection. As R_L approaches the high-limit value, all of the current gains are seen to approach the same low value.

An alternate method of graphical presentation is also possible. A close look at the mathematics of Eq. (8.20) reveals that the variation of A_i depends

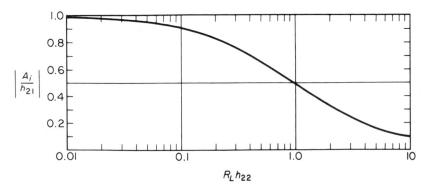

Fig. 8.5 A_i/h_{21} versus $R_L h_{22}$.

on the quantity $R_L h_{22}$. When $R_L h_{22}$ is smaller than unity, A_i is very close to the short-circuit value, h_{21}. As the quantity $R_L h_{22}$ increases to values greater than unity, the value of A_i decreases steadily. To help the user to comprehend the variation of A_i for a given level and span of R_L values, a plot of A_i normalized with respect to h_{21} versus the quantity $R_L h_{22}$ is often used. Using the h-parameter values of the 2N1414 at 5 v and 1 ma, a plot of absolute value of A_i / h_{21} versus the quantity $R_L h_{22}$ would appear as in Fig. 8.5. From this figure we observe that when the quantity $R_L h_{22}$ equals unity, the current gain of the circuit is equal to one-half the short-circuit current gain of the transistor alone. Even though the ordinate values in Fig. 8.5 are for the 2N1414 in particular, the per cent changes of the ordinate values for given magnitudes and changes in $R_L h_{22}$ are applicable to any transistor type.

Since the voltage gain is also a function of load resistance R_L, we are interested in the variation of voltage gain A_v as the load resistance R_L changes. Equation (8.17) shows that in the general case

$$\text{when } R_L = 0, \qquad A_v = 0 \tag{8.36}$$

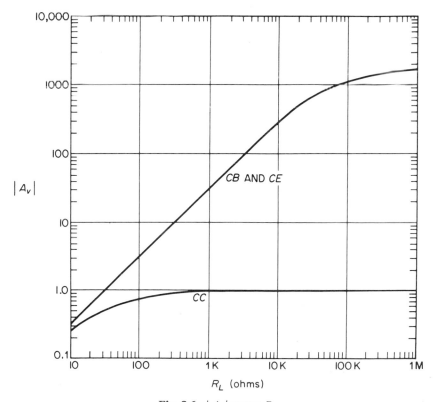

Fig. 8.6 $|A_v|$ versus R_L.

$$\text{when } R_L = \infty, \qquad A_v = \frac{h_{21}}{\Delta^h} \qquad (8.36a)$$

A plot of the absolute value of A_v versus R_L appears in Fig. 8.6. The common-collector connection has a voltage gain equal to unity for all expect very small values of R_L. The common-base and common-emitter connections have essentially the same voltage gains for the same value of R_L. Also, the values of voltage gains are extremely high for these connections as compared to the common-collector connection.

A plot of voltage gain can also be made versus the quantity $R_L h_{22}$. This tends to be the more useful presentation, as will be seen. Equation (8.17) must be modified to a form involving $R_L h_{22}$. Multiplying the first term of the denominator by h_{22}/h_{22}, dividing the denominator by h_{11}, and multiplying both numerator and denominator by h_{22}, we can change Eq. (8.17) to

$$A_v = \left(\frac{h_{21}}{h_{11}h_{22}}\right)\left[\frac{R_L h_{22}}{R_L h_{22}\left(\dfrac{\Delta^h}{h_{11}h_{22}}\right) + 1}\right] \qquad (8.37)$$

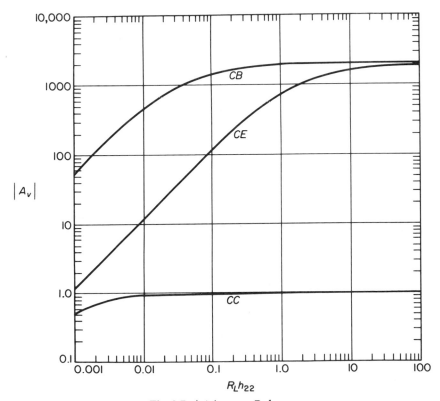

Fig. 8.7 $|A_v|$ versus $R_L h_{22}$.

Working from Eq. (8.37), a plot of voltage gain versus $R_L h_{22}$ can be developed. Such a plot for the 2N1414 is shown in Fig. 8.7. The values of the factors $h_{21}/h_{11}h_{22}$ and $\Delta^h/h_{11}h_{22}$ are provided in Table 8.1. The information here places the relative values of voltage gain in better perspective as regards the typical values of terminations used in real circuits.

The variation of input resistance R_{in} as a function of R_L can be determined through an analysis of Eq. (8.28). This equation shows that

$$\text{when } R_L = 0, \qquad R_{in} = h_{11} \tag{8.38}$$

$$\text{when } R_L = \infty, \qquad R_{in} = \frac{\Delta^h}{h_{22}} \tag{8.39}$$

The actual plot of R_{in} versus R_L is shown in Fig. 8.8. Here we see the input

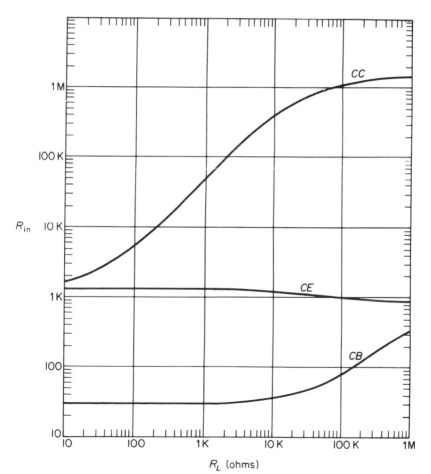

Fig. 8.8 R_{in} versus R_L.

impedances of the common base and common collector increasing as R_L increases, and the input impedance of the common emitter decreasing as R_L increases. This is explained by the fact that the h_{21} factor is negative for the common-base and common-collector connections. Therefore the quantity Δ^h/h_{22} is bigger than h_{11} in the common-base and common-collector connections. Also, because Δ^h is a number much greater than unity for the common collector, the input resistance of this connection is very much greater than the input resistances of the other two connections. We also can see from Fig. 8.8 that at very low values of R_L the common-emitter and common-collector input impedances approach the same value, and that at very high values of R_L the common-emitter and common-base input impedances approach the same value. The 2N1414 with its typical h-parameters does not display a really extensive variation of R_{in} as R_L is varied for the common-emitter connection. This is just a coincidental situation for the typical values of the 2N1414. It is possible for transistors to exhibit as much as four or five times change in common emitter R_{in} as R_L is reduced from a high value to a low value. The values of h_{11} and h_{22} contribute largely to the amount of change in R_{in}, as they contribute directly to the asymptote values of R_{in}.

To obtain the plot of input resistance versus the quantity $R_L h_{22}$, we must modify the numerator of Eq. (8.28). This can be done by multiplying the first term of the numerator by h_{22}/h_{22} and dividing the entire numerator by h_{11}. The result is

$$R_{in} = h_{11} \left[\frac{R_L h_{22} \left(\dfrac{\Delta^h}{h_{11} h_{22}} \right) + 1}{R_L h_{22} + 1} \right] \tag{8.40}$$

The plot of R_{in} versus $R_L h_{22}$ is shown in Fig. 8.9. This is quite similar in form to the plot of Fig. 8.8. We do see, however, that in terms of the quantity $R_L h_{22}$ the common-base connection does not show such a long unchanging region. The per cent changes of R_{in} are readily discernible from this plot.

As Eq. (8.33) indicates, the output resistance R_{out} is a function of the source resistance R_g. This equation shows that

$$\text{when } R_g = 0, \qquad R_{out} = \frac{h_{11}}{\Delta^h} \tag{8.41}$$

$$\text{when } R_g = \infty, \qquad R_{out} = \frac{1}{h_{22}} \tag{8.42}$$

The plot of R_{out} versus R_g for the 2N1414 is shown in Fig. 8.10. The output resistance for the common-base and common-collector connections increases as the source resistance increases. This is explained by the negative sign for the h_{21} parameter for both of these connections. The positive sign for h_{21} in the common-emitter connection makes the quantity h_{11}/Δ^h bigger than the quantity $1/h_{22}$. The output impedance of the common-emitter connection

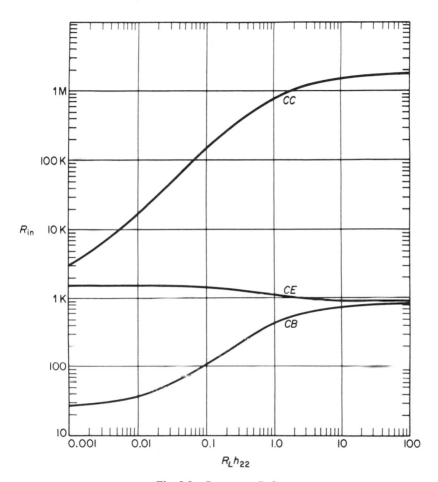

Fig. 8.9 R_in versus $R_L h_{22}$.

has the least variation of any connection. At low values of R_g the common-emitter and common-base output impedances approach the same value, and at high values of R_g the common-emitter and common-collector output impedances approach the same value. The typical 2N1414 does not show extensive variation of common emitter R_out as R_L is varied. As in the case of R_in versus R_L, it is just a coincidental situation for the h-parameters of a 2N1414. Other transistors can exhibit as much as four or five times variation as R_L is decreased from a very high to a very low value. Again, the magnitudes of h_{11} and h_{22} have large effects, as they contribute directly to the asymptote values.

In order to obtain the plot of output resistance versus some function of R_g normalized, let us modify the form of Eq. (8.33). By dividing both

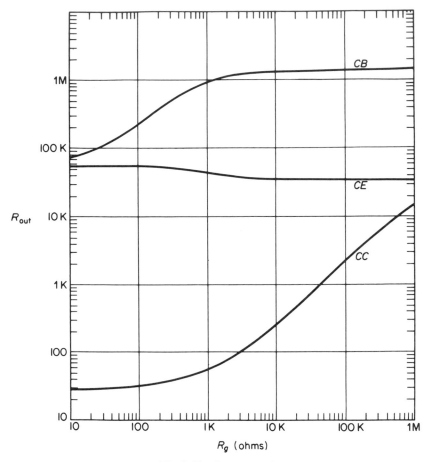

Fig. 8.10 R_{out} versus R_g.

numerator and denominator by h_{11} and by factoring h_{22} in the denominator, we obtain

$$R_{\text{out}} = \left(\frac{1}{h_{22}}\right)\left(\frac{\dfrac{R_g}{h_{11}} + 1}{\dfrac{R_g}{h_{11}} + \dfrac{\Delta^h}{h_{11}h_{22}}}\right) \tag{8.43}$$

We have retained the familiar term $\Delta^h/h_{11}h_{22}$, and now have our normalized parameter, R_g/h_{11}. The plot of R_{out} versus R_g/h_{11} appears as in Fig. 8.11. This is very similar in form to Fig. 8.10.

The power-gain attribute is the last one to be considered. This attribute is seen to be a function of R_L also. Equation (8.26) suggests that the power gain is zero for both $R_L = 0$ and $R_L = \infty$. Since for intermediate values of

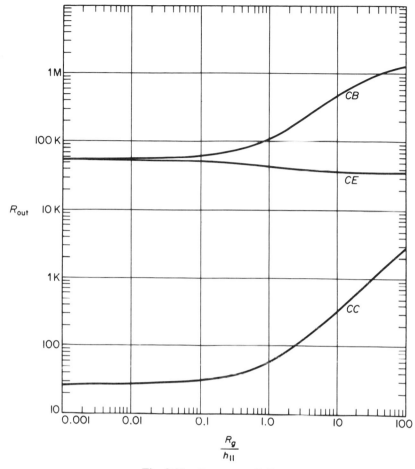

Fig. 8.11 R_{out} versus R_g/h_{11}.

R_L the device displays some measurable power gain, it is suspected that the power-gain attribute maximizes somewhere between the zero and infinite values of R_L. The actual value of R_L yielding the maximum power gain can be obtained in the following manner. First, complete the denominator of Eq. (8.26). Taking the derivative with respect to R_L, one obtains

$$\frac{dA_p}{dR_L} = R_L^2 h_{22}\Delta^h - h_{11} \tag{8.44}$$

Setting expression (8.44) equal to zero, we will obtain that value of R_L which makes the power gain a maximum. That value is

$$R_L = \sqrt{\frac{h_{11}}{h_{22}\Delta^h}} \tag{8.45}$$

Substituting Eq. (8.45) back into (8.26), we find that the maximum value of power gain from a transistor is

$$\max A_p = \frac{h_{21}^2}{[\sqrt{\Delta^h} + \sqrt{h_{11}h_{22}}]^2} \tag{8.46}$$

Recalling the definition of the attribute A_p, we must bear in mind that this gain figure represents maximized conditions for a given amount of power at the input terminals being amplified and transferred to the load R_L. The plot of power gain A_p versus load resistance R_L is shown in Fig. 8.12. Here

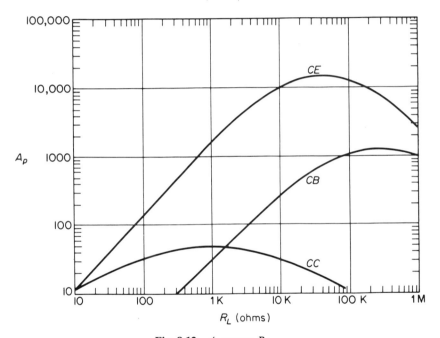

Fig. 8.12 A_p versus R_L.

we note that for any given load, the value of power gain in the common-emitter connection is greater than the power gain obtained in either the common-base or common-collector connections. At a value of $R_L = 1$ K, where the common collector maximizes at almost 17 db of power gain, the common emitter for the same value of load gives about 15 db more of gain. Likewise at $R_L = 300$ K, where the common-base gain is a maximum of 31 db, the common emitter gives 7.5 db more of gain for the same value of load. Only at very low loads does the common-collector approach the common-emitter capability. Likewise it is only at high loads that the common-base approaches the common-emitter capability.

Should there be interest in the plot of power gain versus the quantity $R_L h_{22}$, it can be obtained very easily. Recalling the definition of power gain as given by Eq. (8.25), we need only substitute Eqs. (8.20) and (8.37). That is,

$$A_p = A_i A_v$$

$$= \left(\frac{h_{21}}{R_L h_{22} + 1}\right) \left(\frac{h_{21}}{h_{11} h_{22}}\right) \left(\frac{R_L h_{22}}{R_L h_{22} \frac{\Delta^h}{h_{11} h_{22}} + 1}\right) \tag{8.47}$$

The resultant plot of power gain versus $R_L h_{22}$ is shown in Fig. 8.13. Again we observe the superiority of the common-emitter connection.

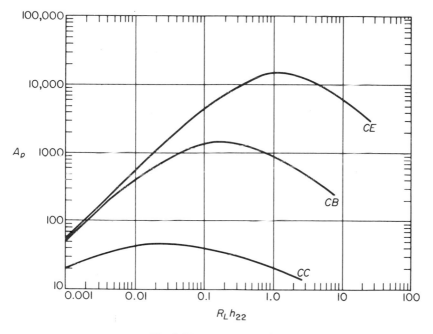

Fig. 8.13 A_p versus $R_L h_{22}$.

8.3. Further discussion of power gain. The power-gain attribute is, without doubt, the most significant figure of merit for a transistor. This is reasonable because in most of its applications the transistor is being used as a power amplifier. The power gain as we have thus far defined and considered it [Eqs. (8.25), (8.26), and ultimately Eq. (8.46)] indicates a transistor's ability to amplify a given amount of power once this power has been delivered to the input terminals of the transistor. A very realistic and practical question arises. How well matched is the transistor input to the impedance of the power source in the circuit, and how well are we using the power that is available for amplification? In developing our thinking in these matters we should always bear in mind that the transistor is a bilateral device. That is to say, happenings at the output make themselves felt at the input just as happenings at the input cause certain things to happen at the output. At this point in our dealings with the transistor, the most important evidence of the bilateral nature of the transistor is that the input resistance is a function of the load resistance, and that the output resistance is a function of the source impedance. The transistor itself, for any given operating point, has intrinsic abilities to amplify power. In making our plot of power gain versus load resistance, we are merely demonstrating that for the given intrinsic parameter levels $h_{11} h_{21} h_{12} h_{22}$ some particular value of load resistance matches the transistor output and hence is able to receive optimum power from the transistor.

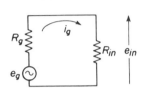

Fig. 8.14 Simple termination on power source e_g, R_g.

The concepts of impedance matching and optimized power transfer might well be reviewed at this point. Consider the circuit of Fig. 8.14. Here in its simplest form is a situation where a load R_{in} is being placed across a power source. Of interest is the maximum amount of power that we can actually get into R_{in}, and the value of R_{in} for which this maximum power-transfer condition exists. The power in the resistor R_{in} can be written

$$P_{\text{in}} = i_g^2 R_{\text{in}}$$

$$= \left(\frac{e_g}{R_g + R_{\text{in}}}\right)^2 R_{\text{in}} \tag{8.48}$$

Taking the derivative of Eq. (8.48) with respect to R_{in}, one obtains

$$\frac{dP}{dR_{\text{in}}} = \frac{e_g^2}{(R_g + R_{\text{in}})^3}(R_g - R_{\text{in}}) \tag{8.49}$$

Setting this last expression equal to zero, we will find the value of R_{in} for which the power in R_{in} is a maximum. That unique value of R_{in} is found to be

$$R_{\text{in}} = R_g \tag{8.50}$$

The maximum amount of power that is actually transferred from the power source is found to be

$$\max P_{\text{trans}} = \frac{e_g^2}{4R_g} \tag{8.51}$$

Note that this particular quantity of power is expressed in terms of R_g. The implication is that there is a maximum amount of power that any power source can transfer. This quantity is sometimes referred to as *available power*. Whether or not this increment of power actually is transferred depends on the value of the termination R_{in} with respect to the source impedance R_g.

Let us go back now to the point where we digressed from our discussion of the transistor. The maximizing of the power gain is effectively an optimizing of the power transfer between the output of the transistor and the load itself. The value of R_{in} that optimizes the power transfer at the transistor output also determines the value of input resistance at the input terminals [Eq. (8.28)]. The actual value of input resistance, as compared with the value of source impedance, determines how efficiently power is transferred from the source to the transistor input. This can be of great significance in practical circuitry. Total circuit gain is the true performance result.

In some situations, both the source and the load are fixed and cannot be adjusted to values that for a given transistor are the optimum for transfer of power into the input terminals and out of the output terminals. In other situations it may be that only the source is fixed in value. In any event, there is concern for the effectiveness of the circuit. In order to observe, for a given circuit, how efficiently the source and load are being matched, a new gain attribute called *transducer gain*, G_T, is employed. By definition, transducer gain is the ratio of actual power in the load divided by available power from the generator. Mathematically,

$$G_T = \frac{P_{load}}{P_{avail.\ at\ source}} \tag{8.52}$$

Substituting Eq. (8.21) for the power in the load and Eq. (8.51) for the power available from the source, we get

$$G_T = \frac{i_2^2 R_L 4 R_g}{e_g^2}$$
$$G_T = \left(\frac{i_2}{i_1}\right)^2 \frac{4 R_g R_L}{(R_g + R_{in})^2} \tag{8.53}$$

Substituting Eq. (8.20), the expression for current gain, and Eq. (8.28), the expression for input resistance R_{in}, it can be shown that Eq. (8.53) will reduce to

$$G_T = \frac{4 h_{21}^2 R_g R_L}{(R_g R_L h_{22} + R_L \Delta^h + R_g + h_{11})^2} \tag{8.54}$$

The maximum value that exists for transducer gain is that of the maximum transistor gain as given by Eq. (8.46). The value of R_L that optimized power transfer between the transistor and the load was given by Eq. (8.45) as

$$R_L = \sqrt{\frac{h_{11}}{h_{22}\Delta^h}} \qquad (8.45)$$

Substituting this value into the expression for R_{in}, Eq. (8.28),

$$R_{\text{in}} = \sqrt{\frac{h_{11}\Delta^h}{h_{22}}} \qquad (8.55)$$

We would find that if R_g and R_L had values as prescribed by Eqs. (8.55) and (8.45), respectively, total circuit performance would be optimized. That is, if Eqs. (8.55) and (8.45) were substituted into Eq. (8.54) for R_g and R_L respectively, the expression for transducer gain would then equal the maximum-power-gain expression as given in Eq. (8.46). If this ultimate in optimizing were desired, impedance-matching transformers would be required between source and input and output and load.

The student is encouraged, however, to review closely the curves presented, to grasp the significance in the practical aspects of the total picture. For example, for the common-emitter connection, the load can vary approximately two-to-one in both directions and the circuit is within 1 db of maximum power gain. Transcribing this increment to the input side, we note that within the R_L spread giving the 1-db variation from optimum, the input resistance can vary about two-to-one total. A multitude of similar observations are possible, using all the curves that are presented. An ability to grasp intuitively the total picture in transistor applications makes the difference between sensible design techniques and unwieldy and uneconomical efforts for precisely optimized designs.

8.4. Example: calculating circuit performance   A 2N1414 is operating in the circuit of Fig. 8.15. This circuit was developed in Chapter 6 for bias considerations and was reviewed again in Chapter 7 in the discussion of the modified h-parameters. Calculate (a) the power gain of the circuit and (b) the value of source impedance giving maximized power transfer at the input terminals, and (c) determine the gain lost due to the bias network as compared to the transistor alone.

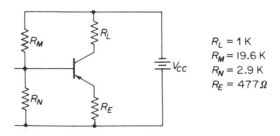

Fig. 8.15   Circuit for illustrative example of Sec. 8.4.

(a) From Example 1 in Sec. 7.10 the modified h-parameters due to the bias network are

$$h'_{21} = 4.47$$

$$h'_{11} = 2.25 \text{ K}$$

$$h'_{22} = 4.2(10^{-6}) \text{ mhos}$$

$$h'_{12} = 13.7(10^{-4})$$

Using these, we obtain from Eq. (8.26)

$$A_p = \frac{-h'^2_{21}R_L}{(R_L h'_{22} + 1)(R_L \Delta^{h'} + h'_{11})}$$

$$= -\frac{(4.47)^2(10^3)}{[10^3(4.2)(10^{-6}) + 1][10^3(33.3)(10^{-4}) + 2.25(10^3)]}$$

$$= -8.9 = 9.5 \text{ db}$$

(b) For optimized transfer of power at the input terminals we must match the source to the input resistance of the stage. By (8.28)

$$R_{\text{in}} = \frac{R_L \Delta^{h'} + h'_{11}}{R_L h'_{22} + 1}$$

$$= \frac{10^3(33.3)(10^{-4}) + 2.25 \text{ K}}{10^3(4.2)(10^{-6}) + 1}$$

$$= 2.25 \text{ K}$$

(c) From Fig. 8.12 we find that at $R_L = 1$ K, the typical 2N1414 has a power gain of 1400 or 31.5 db. Hence the bias network is causing us to lose 31.5 minus 9.5 or 22 db.

8.5. Circuit design using emitter by-pass capacitance. The example in Sec. 8.4 points up dramatically the extent to which gain can be lost in a design that has as its main objective the control of the operating point. The transistor with unmodified parameters could deliver a gain of 31.5 db but the circuit reviewed can give only 9.5 db. A circuit procedure that is incorporated to reduce bias losses is shown in Fig. 8.16. Here we note that a capacitor has been placed in parallel with the emitter resistor R_E. The value of such a capacitor is carefully selected so that at the frequency of operation of interest the capacitive reactance

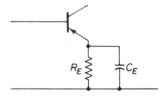

Fig. 8.16 Emitter-circuit modification to minimize gain losses.

is very small compared to R_E. From an a-c viewpoint, then, the emitter resistor is shorted to ground and need no longer be considered as a modifying element. From the d-c viewpoint, of course, the emitter resistance is still present and contributes to operating-point stability. The capacitor that we have just introduced is called a *by-pass capacitor*. In eliminating the modification of *h*-parameters due to R_E, the gain picture of a transistor circuit is improved.

EXAMPLE: Repeat the calculations of Sec. 8.4 with the addition of a by-pass capacitor such that the capacitive reactance is 1 Ω at 400 cycles.

(a) Since the modifying effects of R_E are eliminated, we need only consider a modification due to $R_M = 19.6$ K and $R_N = 2.9$ K. Using previous nomenclature,

$$R_S = \frac{R_M R_N}{R_M + R_N}$$

$$= \frac{(19.6\text{ K})(2.9\text{ K})}{19.6\text{ K} + 2.9\text{ K}} = 2.52\text{ K}$$

The reference *h*-parameters are those of the transistor itself:

$$h_{11e} = 1320 \text{ ohms}$$

$$h_{21e} = 44$$

$$h_{22e} = 28.2(10^{-6})\text{ mhos}$$

$$h_{12e} = 2.95(10^{-4})$$

For convenience in the calculations we can determine

$$\frac{R_S}{h_{11} + R_S} = \frac{2.52\text{ K}}{1320 + 2.52\text{ K}} = .657$$

By (7.71)

$$h'_{11} = \frac{h_{11} R_S}{h_{11} + R_S}$$
$$= 1320(.657) = 868 \text{ ohms}$$

By (7.70)

$$h'_{21} = \frac{h_{21} R_S}{h_{11} + R_S}$$
$$= 44(.657) = 28.9$$

By (7.73)

$$h'_{22} = h_{22} - \frac{h_{21} h_{12}}{h_{11} + R_S}$$
$$= 28.2(10^{-6}) - \frac{44(2.95)(10^{-4})}{3.84\text{ K}}$$
$$= (28.2 - 3.4)(10^{-6}) = 24.8(10^{-6})\text{ mhos}$$

By (7.74)

$$h'_{12} = \frac{h_{12} R_S}{h_{11} + R_S}$$
$$= 2.95(10^{-4})(.657) = 1.94(10^{-4})$$

By (7.93a)

$$\Delta^{h'} = h'_{11}h'_{22} - h'_{12}h'_{21}$$
$$= 868\,(24.8)(10^{-6}) - 1.94(10^{-4})(28.9)$$
$$= 159(10^{-4})$$

By (8.26)

$$A_p = \frac{-(28.9)^2(10^3)}{[10^3(24.8)(10^{-6}) + 1][10^3(159)(10^{-4}) + 868]}$$
$$= -924$$
$$= 29.66 \text{ db}$$

(b) By (8.28)

$$R_{in} = \frac{884}{1.024} = 862 \text{ ohms}$$

(c) The losses due to the bias network are reduced to 1.8 db when a by-pass capacitor is used in conjunction with R_E.

PROBLEMS

1. A transistor has the following h-parameters at $I_E = 1$ ma and $V_C = 5$ v:

$$h_{11b} = 42\ \Omega$$
$$h_{21b} = -.978$$
$$h_{22b} = 1.2(10^{-6}) \text{ mhos}$$
$$h_{12b} = 5(10^{-4})$$

Calculate the limit values of R_{in} and R_{out} for the common-base, common-emitter, and common-collector connections, as R_L is varied.

2. Compare the results of Problem 1 with the results plotted for a typical 2N1414 in Figs. 8.8 and 8.10. Compare h-parameter values for the common-emitter connection and comment on the results.

3. Using the common-emitter parameters from Problem 1, calculate the current gain, voltage gain, and power gain at $R_L = 10$ K.

4. What are the values of R_L giving maximum power gain for each connection of the transistor in Problem 1?

5. The transistor of Problem 1 is placed into the circuit of Fig. 8.17.
   (a) Calculate A_p.
   (b) Calculate P_{in}.
   (c) Calculate P_{out}.
   (d) Calculate transducer gain.
   (e) Calculate losses due to bias network.

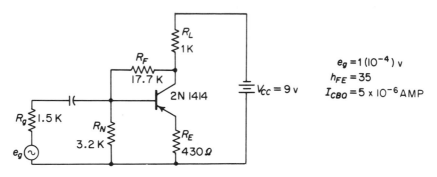

Fig. 8.17 Circuit for Problem 5.

6. Repeat Problem 5 when a by-pass with a capacitive reactance of 1 ohm is used to shunt the 430-ohm emitter resistor.

9

LOW-FREQUENCY

CASCADE

AMPLIFIERS

In the last chapter we studied the various circuit attributes of a single-stage amplifier. In practical applications, more often than not, we find that a single stage of amplification does not provide sufficient gain. Thus two, three, or even more stages must be operated in cascade in order to obtain the total circuit gain that is of interest. In coupling the output of any stage to the input of a succeeding stage, one problem is immediately apparent; d-c coupling is usually difficult to implement practically because the a-c conditions at the output of the one stage disturb the bias conditions at the input of the second stage. Although d-c coupling is ideally desirable, it is not frequently used. For the most part, then, in a-c amplifiers some form of reactive coupling such as transformers or capacitive networks can be used. The resultant circuit performance is strongly dependent on the type of coupling that is actually used. Circuit features and limitations for both coupling techniques will be discussed in the sections that follow.

9.1. General-case analysis procedures. Experience with transistor circuits is likely to fall into two categories: (1) an analysis of existing circuits and (2) the design of circuits to obtain specific performance requirements. The approaches used in analyzing cascade circuits are relatively simple. In the interest of making the design problems easier to solve, we will devote this section to the step-by-step considerations used in analyzing an existing cascade-amplifier circuit. A general-case possibility is shown in

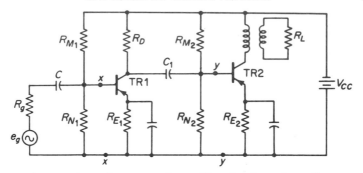

Fig. 9.1 General-case cascade amplifier showing RC coupling and transformer coupling.

Fig. 9.1. In this circuit, transistor 1 is connected to the input of transistor 2 (points YY) by means of the resistor R_D and the capacitor C_1. Hence such a coupling is called *RC coupling*. The total impedance connected to points YY is the one into which we want to develop a-c power. The resistor R_D is present because a path for d-c collector current is necessary. At the output of transistor TR2 we are connecting the load R_L into the collector by means of a transformer. Hence we call this *transformer coupling*. Assuming that at the frequency of interest the coupling capacitive reactances are negligible and that the emitter resistors are adequately bypassed, the circuit of Fig. 9.1 reduces to the equivalent circuit shown in Fig. 9.2. Using the nomenclature of Fig. 9.2, we can see that the power developed in R_L is truly the output power of interest. Likewise the power that is delivered to the input terminals of transistor TR1 (points XX) is truly the input power of interest. Writing these quantities mathematically, we obtain

$$P_{\text{out}} = i_L^2 R_L \tag{9.1}$$

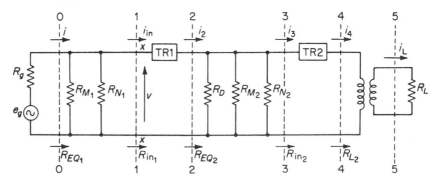

Fig. 9.2 A-C equivalent of circuit in Fig. 9.1. Notice numbered observation points of circuit analysis.

$$P_{\text{in}} = i_{\text{in}}^2 R_{\text{in}_1} \qquad (9.2)$$

The power gain of the system can be expressed as

$$A_p = \frac{P_{\text{out}}}{P_{\text{in}}} \qquad (9.3)$$

$$= \left(\frac{i_L}{i_{\text{in}}}\right)^2 \frac{R_L}{R_{\text{in}_1}} \qquad (9.4)$$

The value R_{in_1} depends on the effective load on TR1. This in turn involves R_{in_2}, which depends on the load on TR2. This, of course, is R_L reflected to the primary of the transformer. The overall current gain can also be shown to depend on the load on TR2. Thus, our analysis will begin at the output terminals and proceed back to the input terminals. Observation points of interest are numbered to make the analysis easier. Let us first work with the impedance transformations.

At point 4 we find

$$R_{L_2} = n^2 R_L \qquad (9.5)$$

where

$$n = \frac{n_p}{n_s} \qquad (9.6)$$

where n = turns ratio of the transformer
       n_p = primary turns
       n_s = secondary turns

At point 3 we obtain by Eq. (8.28)

$$R_{\text{in}_2} = \frac{R_{L_2}\Delta^h + h_{11}}{R_{L_2} h_{22} + 1} \qquad (9.7)$$

Note that the h-parameters to be used in Eq. (9.7) are those of transistor TR2. Moving on to point 2, we wish now to consider the effective load on transistor TR1. It is obvious from the circuit that the entire interstage circuitry existing between points 2 and 3 is connected to the output of TR1. This interstage circuitry is nothing more than R_D, R_{M_2}, R_{N_2}, and R_{in_2} all in parallel. Reducing these to a single value, we obtain

$$R_{EQ_2} = \frac{R_D R_{M_2} R_{N_2} R_{\text{in}_2}}{R_{M_2} R_{N_2} R_{\text{in}_2} + R_D R_{N_2} R_{\text{in}_2} + R_D R_{M_2} R_{\text{in}_2} + R_D R_{M_2} R_{N_2}} \qquad (9.8)$$

At point 1 we obtain by Eq. (8.28)

$$R_{\text{in}_1} = \frac{R_{EQ_2}\Delta^h + h_{11}}{R_{EQ_2} h_{22} + 1} \qquad (9.9)$$

Here the h-parameters are those of TR1.

The overall current gain is basically the product of the individual current gains through the system. That is,

$$\frac{i_L}{i_{\text{in}}} = \frac{i_L}{i_4} \frac{i_4}{i_3} \frac{i_3}{i_2} \frac{i_2}{i_{\text{in}}} \qquad (9.10)$$

At point 4

$$\frac{i_L}{i_4} = n \tag{9.11}$$

At point 3 we obtain by Eq. (8.20)

$$\frac{i_4}{i_3} = \frac{h_{21}}{R_{L_2} h_{22} + 1} \tag{9.12}$$

Between points 2 and 3 we actually have a loss circuit. Resistors R_D, R_{M_2}, and R_{N_2} divert portions of the total current i_2. Hence, i_3 is less than i_2. The power at point 3 is less than the power into the interstage at point 2. Realizing that the voltage is the same across all of these parallel resistors, we can write

$$i_2 R_{EQ_2} = i_3 R_{in_2}$$

$$\frac{i_3}{i_2} = \frac{R_{EQ_2}}{R_{in_2}} \tag{9.13}$$

This will, in fact, be a number less than unity. At point 1 we repeat the use of (8.20) to obtain

$$\frac{i_2}{i_{in}} = \frac{h_{21}}{R_{EQ_2} h_{22} + 1} \tag{9.14}$$

The product of Eqs. (9.11), (9.12), (9.13), and (9.14) is the total current gain as indicated by Eq. (9.10).

Once the pertinent input impedance and the overall current ratio have been calculated as in Eqs. (9.9) and (9.10), the actual power gain can be calculated by substitution in (9.4).

In order to determine the actual amount of power into terminals XX we must make one other set of calculations at point 00. Resistors R_{M_1}, R_{N_1}, and R_{in_1} are all in parallel and constitute the load on the power source. The equivalent of these three resistors can be written as

$$R_{EQ_1} = \frac{R_{M_1} R_{N_1} R_{in_1}}{R_{N_1} R_{in_1} + R_{M_1} R_{in_1} + R_{M_1} R_{N_1}} \tag{9.15}$$

Letting v be the value of voltage across R_{M_1}, R_{N_1}, and R_{in_1} in parallel, we can write

$$v = \left(\frac{R_{EQ_1}}{R_{EQ_1} + R_g} \right) e_g \tag{9.16}$$

Thus the actual power at terminals XX is

$$P_{in} = \frac{v^2}{R_{in_1}} \tag{9.17}$$

Substituting Eq. (9.16) into (9.7), we will obtain

$$P_{in} = \left(\frac{R_{EQ_1} e_g}{R_{EQ_1} + R_g} \right)^2 \frac{1}{R_{in_1}} \tag{9.18}$$

Once the power gain of the cascade amplifier is calculated by Eq. (9.4), the power output can be determined merely by multiplying this power-gain figure by the actual amount of power input as calculated in Eq. (9.18).

Several comments are in order relative to our analytical procedures. If the output transformer is lossless, the power at the primary is the same as the power at the secondary. Hence we usually transform the load impedance back to the primary and complete our design there. It is imperative, also, to be alert to the effective current amplification through a transformer by means of the turns-ratio manipulation as in Eq. (9.11). When a transformer is used between stages, this current-multiplying factor should not be overlooked.

9.2. Transformer coupling. As the name implies, this type of circuit uses a transformer as the coupling component between transistor stages. Because transformers can be obtained in a wide variety of primary-to-secondary turns ratios, it is permissible to match impedances to obtain maximum gain conditions. We shall learn later, however, that this is not always desirable from a frequency-response viewpoint. This matter will be reserved for consideration in a later chapter. In any circuit where we do wish to maximize the circuit gain we need only determine the values of input and output impedance for each transistor stage. An adjustment of turns ratio for the transformer will provide the necessary impedance matching and hence maximized power gain. The logical sequence of events in the design of a transformer-coupled amplifier might be as demonstrated in the following example:

EXAMPLE: A power source with an internal impedance of 2000 Ω, capable of delivering $5(10^{-4})$ v, is available. Our interest is the design of a two-stage amplifier such that maximum power gain exists in delivering power to a load of 1000 Ω. A d-c supply voltage of 6 v is available. Let stage 1 be a 2N1414 and stage 2 be a 2N1415. Their parameters are itemized as follows ($V_C = 5$ v, $I_E = 1$ ma):

2N1414	2N1415
$h_{22b} = .62$ μmhos	$h_{22b} = .55$ μmhos
$h_{11b} = 29$ Ω	$h_{11b} = 29$ Ω
$h_{12b} = 5.2(10^{-4})$	$h_{12b} = 5.7(10^{-4})$
$h_{21e} = 44$	$h_{21e} = 64$
$h_{FE} = 35$	$h_{FE} = 56$
$I_{CBO} = 6$ μa	$I_{CBO} = 6$ μa

Assume that the operating point for each transistor is to be $V_C = 5$ v and $I_C = 1$ ma, also that $V_B = .15$ v. In addition, let the operating-point stability be described by the limit conditions itemized as follows:

2N1414	2N1415
$h'_{FE} = 60$	$h'_{FE} = 80$
$I'_{CBO} = 12$ μa	$I'_{CBO} = 12$ μa
$I'_C = 1.2$ ma	$I'_C = 1.2$ ma

The final assumption relates to the transformers. Here let us consider that the transformers can be supplied with primaries with d-c resistance less than 400 Ω.

In organizing the approach to a solution, the first factor to consider is the attainment of the required operating-point stability. In addition, we must acknowledge the undersirable deterioration of gain due to the presence of emitter or voltage-feedback resistors. The undesirable effects of emitter resistance can be eliminated by the use of a by-pass capacitor. As we have mentioned, we place a capacitor in parallel with the emitter resistance. The value of the capacitor is such that at the frequency of interest the capacitive reactance is very small. Hence from the a-c viewpoint there is essentially no emitter resistance. From a d-c viewpoint the emitter resistance still does exist to accomplish its intended stabilizing function. Since gain is the main design requirement, we will use a by-pass capacitor in conjunction with the voltage-feedback bias circuit. The complete circuit will then look as shown in Fig. 9.3. If each emitter resistor is properly by-passed, the equivalent circuit of Fig. 9.3 becomes that of Fig. 9.4.

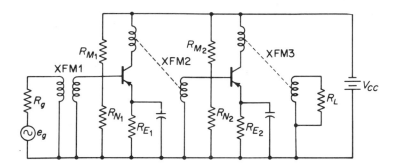

Fig. 9.3   Complete two-stage circuit using transformer coupling.

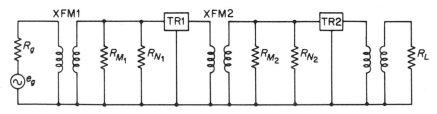

Fig. 9.4   Equivalent circuit of Fig. 9.3.

These preliminaries having been duly considered, the design proceeds with calculation of the bias networks and the a-c attributes of each stage. The bias network for TR2 is determined as follows.

By (6.21)

$$R_E = \frac{h_{FE}}{1 + h_{FE}} \left[\frac{V_{CC} - V_C - I_C R_L}{I_C - I_{CBO}} \right]$$

$$= \frac{56}{57} \left[\frac{6 - 5 - 10^{-3}(400)}{(1 - .006)(10^{-3})} \right]$$

$$= 590 \ \Omega$$

The calculation constants are

$$B = (I_C - I_{CBO})(1 + h_{FE})$$
$$= (1 - .006)(10^{-3})(57) = 56.7(10^{-3})$$

$$B' = (I'_C - I'_{CBO})(1 + h'_{FE})$$
$$= (1.2 - .012)(10^{-3})(81) = 96.2(10^{-3})$$

$$C = I_C - (1 + h_{FE})I_{CBO}$$
$$= 10^{-3} - 57(.006)(10^{-3}) = .658(10^{-3})$$

$$C' = I'_C - (1 + h'_{FE})I'_{CBO}$$
$$= 1.2(10^{-3}) - 81(.012)(10^{-3}) = .228(10^{-3})$$

$$E = B'h_{FE} - Bh'_{FE}$$
$$= 96.2(10^{-3})(56) - 57.6(10^{-3})(80) = 850(10^{-3})$$

$$F = Ch'_{FE} - C'h_{FE}$$
$$= .658(10^{-3})(80) - .228(10^{-3})(56) = 39.8(10^{-3})$$

$$G = B'C - BC'$$
$$= 96.2(.658)(10^{-6}) - 56.7(.228)(10^{-6}) = 50.4(10^{-6})$$

By (6.25)

$$R_{N_2} = \frac{V_{CC} E R_E}{(V_{CC} - V_B)F - G R_E}$$

$$= \frac{6(850)(10^{-3})(590)}{(6 - .15)(39.8)(10^{-3}) - 50.4(10^{-6})(590)}$$

$$= 14.9 \ \text{K}$$

By (6.22)

$$R_{M_2} = \frac{R_N[h_{FE}(V_{CC} - V_B) - B R_E]}{C R_N + B R_E + h_{FE} V_B}$$

$$= \frac{14.9(10^3)[56(6 - .15) - 56.7(10^{-3})590]}{.658(10^{-3})14.9(10^3) + 56.7(10^{-3})590 + 56(.15)}$$

$$= 84 \ \text{K}$$

Using a design frequency of 400 cycles and a desired capacitive reactance of $2 \, \Omega$,

$$C = \frac{1}{2\pi f X_C}$$

$$= \frac{1}{2\pi (400) 2}$$

$$= 200 \ \mu\text{f}$$

The bias network for TR1 is determined as follows. By (6.21)

$$R_E = \frac{35}{36}\left[\frac{6 - 5 - 10^{-3}(400)}{(1 - .006)(10^{-3})}\right]$$

$$= 590\ \Omega$$

The calculation constants for TR1 are

$$B = (1 - .006)(10^{-3})(36) = 35.8(10^{-3})$$

$$B' = (1.2 - .012)(10^{-3})(61) = 72.5(10^{-3})$$

$$C = 10^{-3} - 36(.006)(10^{-3}) = .784(10^{-3})$$

$$C' = 1.2(10^{-3}) - 61(.012)(10^{-3}) = .468(10^{-3})$$

$$E = 72.5(10^{-3})(35) - 35.8(10^{-3})(60) = 400(10^{-3})$$

$$F = .784(10^{-3})(60) - .468(10^{-3})(35) = 30.6(10^{-3})$$

$$G = 72.5(.784)(10^{-6}) - 35.8(.468)(10^{-6}) = 40(10^{-6})$$

By (6.25)

$$R_{N_1} = \frac{6(400)(10^{-3})590}{(6 - .15)30.6(10^{-6}) - 40(10^{-6})590}$$

$$= 9.1\text{ K}$$

By (6.22)

$$R_{M_1} = \frac{9.1(10^3)[35(5.85) - 35.8(10^{-3})590]}{.784(10^{-3})9.1(10^3) + 35.8(10^{-3})590 + 35(.15)}$$

$$= 50\text{ K}$$

Now that each bias network is designed, we turn our attention to the dynamic problems. In particular, we are concerned with the transistor impedance levels that give maximum gain. In Chapter 7 we calculated the common-emitter h-parameters for the 2N1414 at $V_C = 5$ v and $I_E = 1$ ma. They are

$$h_{22e} = 28.2\ \mu\text{mhos}$$

$$h_{12e} = 2.95(10^{-4})$$

$$h_{11e} = 1320\ \Omega$$

$$h_{21e} = 44$$

The pertinent h-parameters for the 2N1415 are

$$h_{22b} = .55\ \mu\text{mho}$$

$$h_{11b} = 29\ \Omega$$

$$h_{12b} = 5.7(10^{-4})$$

$$h_{21e} = 64$$

Converting these to the common-emitter equivalents, we proceed as follows. By (7.47)

$$h_{21b} = \frac{-h_{21e}}{1 + h_{21e}} = -\frac{64}{65} = -.985$$

$$\therefore\quad 1 + h_{21b} = .015$$

By (7.42)

$$h_{22e} = \frac{h_{22b}}{1 + h_{21b}} = \frac{.55(10^{-6})}{.015} = 36.7 \; \mu\text{mhos}$$

By (7.45)

$$h_{12e} = \frac{h_{11b}h_{22b} - h_{12b}(1 + h_{21b})}{1 + h_{21b}}$$

$$= \frac{29(.55)(10^{-6}) - 5.7(10^{-4})(.015)}{.015} = 4.96(10^{-4})$$

By (7.46)

$$h_{11e} = \frac{h_{11b}}{1 + h_{21b}} = \frac{29}{.015} = 1930 \; \Omega$$

At this point an element of practicality must be considered. The bias resistors R_M and R_N are seen as shunts to the inputs of each transistor. Some power will be lost in these shunt paths, and a deviation from the ideal transistor must be executed to minimize the loss. This can be done very conveniently using the modified h-parameters developed in Chapter 7. For TR1 the equivalent of R_{M_1} and R_{N_1} is

$$R_{S_1} = \frac{50(9.1)(10^6)}{59.1(10^3)} = 7.7 \; \text{K}$$

By (7.71)

$$h'_{11} = \frac{h_{11} R_{S_1}}{h_{11} + R_{S_1}} = \frac{1320(7.7)(10^3)}{1320 + 7700} = 1125 \; \Omega$$

By (7.70)

$$h'_{21} = \frac{h_{11} R_{S_1}}{h_{11} + R_{S_1}} = \frac{44(7.7 \; \text{K})}{9.02 \; \text{K}} = 37.6$$

By (7.73)

$$h'_{22} = h_{22} - \frac{h_{21} h_{12}}{h_{11} + R_{S_1}}$$

$$= 28.2(10^{-6}) - \frac{44(2.95)(10^{-4})}{9.02 \; \text{K}} = 26.76 \; \mu\text{mhos}$$

By (7.74)

$$h'_{12} = \frac{h_{12} R_{S_1}}{h_{11} + R_{S_1}} = \frac{2.95(10^{-4})7.7 \; \text{K}}{9.02 \; \text{K}} = 2.52(10^{-4})$$

By (7.93a)

$$\Delta^{h'} = h'_{11} h'_{22} - h'_{12} h'_{21}$$

$$= 1125(26.76)(10^{-6}) - 2.52(10^{-4})(37.6) = 205(10^{-4})$$

The actual input and output impedances for maximum gain in TR1 can now be calculated. By (8.55)

$$R_{\text{in}_1} = \left(\frac{h'_{11} \Delta^{h'}}{h'_{22}}\right)^{1/2}$$

$$= \left[\frac{1125(205)(10^{-4})}{26.76(10^{-6})}\right]^{1/2}$$

$$= 930 \; \Omega$$

By (8.45)

$$R_{L_1} = \left(\frac{h'_{11}}{h'_{22}\Delta^{h'}}\right)^{1/2}$$

$$= \left[\frac{1125}{26.76(10^{-6})205(10^{-4})}\right]^{1/2}$$

$$= 45.4 \text{ K}$$

For TR2 the modifying equivalent of R_{M_2} and R_{N_2} is

$$R_{S_2} = \frac{84(14.9)(10^6)}{98.9(10^3)} = 12.7 \text{ K}$$

By (7.71)

$$h'_{11} = \frac{h_{11}R_{S_2}}{h_{11}+R_{S_2}} = \frac{1930(12.7)\text{ K}}{1930+12.7\text{ K}} = 1670\ \Omega$$

By (7.70)

$$h'_{21} = \frac{h_{21}R_{S_2}}{h_{11}+R_{S_2}} = \frac{64(12.7\text{ K})}{14.6\text{ K}} = 55.7$$

By (7.73)

$$h'_{22} = h_{22} - \frac{h_{21}h_{12}}{h_{11}+R_{S_2}}$$

$$= 36.7(10^{-6}) - \frac{64(4.96)(10^{-4})}{14.6\text{ K}} = 34.53\ \mu\text{mhos}$$

By (7.74)

$$h'_{12} = \frac{h_{12}R_{S_2}}{h_{11}+R_{S_2}} = \frac{4.96(10^{-4})(12.7\text{ K})}{14.6\text{ K}} = 4.31(10^{-4})$$

By (7.93a)

$$\Delta^{h'} = h'_{11}h'_{22} - h'_{12}h'_{21}$$

$$= 1670(34.53)(10^{-6}) - 4.31(10^{-4})(55.7)$$

$$= 336(10^{-4})$$

Thus for TR2 the actual input and output impedances giving maximum gain are, by (8.55)

$$R_{\text{in}_2} = \left(\frac{h'_{11}\Delta^{h'}}{h'_{22}}\right)^{1/2}$$

$$= \left[\frac{1670(336)(10^{-4})}{34.53(10^{-6})}\right]^{1/2}$$

$$= 1274\ \Omega$$

and by (8.45)

$$R_{L_2} = \left(\frac{h'_{11}}{h'_{22}\Delta^{h'}}\right)^{1/2}$$

$$= \left[\frac{1670}{34.53(10^{-6})336(10^{-4})}\right]^{1/2}$$

$$= 37.9 \text{ K}$$

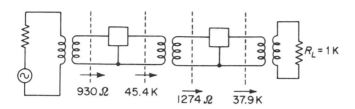

Fig. 9.5 Circuit form noting values of input and output impedance giving optimized gain. Effects of modified h's are included.

Knowing now the effective or modified input and output impedances for each transistor, we can reduce the equivalent circuit to the form of Fig. 9.5. Here we acknowledge that the real impedances must be matched by the coupling transformer to obtain maximum power gain. The turns ratios for each transformer are

$$\text{for XFM No. 3:} \qquad \frac{n_p}{n_s} = \left(\frac{37,900}{1000}\right)^{1/2} = 6.18$$

$$\text{for XFM No. 2:} \qquad \frac{n_p}{n_s} = \left(\frac{45,400}{1274}\right)^{1/2} = 5.95$$

$$\text{for XFM No. 1:} \qquad \frac{n_p}{n_s} = \left(\frac{2000}{930}\right)^{1/2} = 1.46$$

The total gain of the circuit can now be calculated. Since we have matched impedances to obtain optimized power gain, we will calculate power gain by using Eq. (8.46) and the modified h-parameters for each device. For TR1

$$
\begin{aligned}
A_{p_1} &= \frac{h_{21}^{'2}}{[(\Delta^{h'})^{1/2} + (h_{11}' h_{22}')^{1/2}]^2} \\
&= \frac{37.6^2}{\{[205(10^{-4})]^{1/2} + [(1125)(26.76)(10^{-6})]^{1/2}\}^2} \\
&= 14,140 = 41.5 \text{ db}
\end{aligned}
$$

For TR2

$$
\begin{aligned}
A_{p_2} &= \frac{55.7^2}{\{[336(10^{-4})]^{1/2} + [1670(34.53)(10^{-6})]^{1/2}\}^2} \\
&= 17,300 = 42.38 \text{ db}
\end{aligned}
$$

The total gain is $(A_{p_1})(A_{p_2})$ or $(A_{p_1}$ in db$) + (A_{p_2}$ in db$)$. The total circuit gain is 83.88 db or 244(10^6).

Our power source was a generator of $5(10^{-4})$ v with an internal impedance of 2000 Ω. Assuming a lossless transformer, the power given to TR1 as calculated on the primary side of XFM 1 is

$$P \text{ into TR1} = \left[\left(\frac{R_{in}''}{R_g + R_{in}''}\right)e_g\right]^2 \frac{1}{R_{in}''}$$

where $R''_{in} = R_{in_1}$ reflected to primary of XFM 1 = 2000 Ω.

$$\therefore \quad P_{in} = \left[\left(\frac{2\,K}{2\,K + 2\,K}\right)5(10^{-4})\right]^2 \frac{1}{2000}$$

$$= 31.2(10^{-12}) \text{ w}$$

The power delivered to the 1000-ohm load then is

$$P_L = (\text{total gain})(P_{in})$$

$$= 244(10^6)31.2(10^{-12})$$

$$= 7.63 \text{ mw}$$

Since we have optimized our design, we find perfect use of our generator. That is, the transducer gain is equal to the actual gain in our circuit.

The use of the modified h-parameters is the most direct way of designing, as it requires but two calculations—the total input and output impedances of the stage. The gain figure that results is for the transistor and the shunt resistances considered all together. This gain figure includes an effective-loss portion, which accounts for the presence of the shunt resistors. The method outlined would apply if the emitter resistor were not by-passed or if a current-feedback resistor were present. The magnitudes of the terminal impedances and the resultant gain would, however, vary drastically.

9.3. RC-coupled circuits—iterative case. Reference was made to an *RC*-coupled stage in the demonstration circuit of Fig. 9.1. In that particular circuit, the load of interest was the transistor stage connected to points YY. If this had been an output stage, then a resistor alone would have been connected to terminals YY. In either of these situations certain limitations prevail that restrict the flexibility of design and actual performance abilities. The most dramatic peculiarity of an *RC*-coupled circuit is the limitation in gain imposed by the low levels of impedance that are usually present at terminals YY. Consider, for a moment, the equivalent circuit of a single *RC*-coupled stage as shown in Fig. 9.6(b). Assume that the resistor R_D is

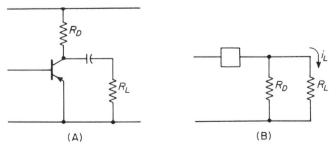

(A) (B)

Fig. 9.6 (A) Load connection for *RC* coupling. (B) A-C equivalent for output circuitry.

very much larger than R_L. The effective load then is equal to the resistor R_L alone. Let us at the same time consider a frequently occurring situation in which similar transistors, each operating at the *same d-c conditions*, are connected by means of *RC* coupling. If we again eliminate the effects of R_D at the output of each transistor, and if we also ignore the shunting effects of bias resistors at the input, we can generate an idealized equivalent circuit for the cascade circuit. Such an idealized equivalent circuit is shown in Fig. 9.7. We now have a situation where the input impedance of any one stage serves by a direct connection as the load on the preceding stage. By virtue of the assumptions made, and the similarity of stages, any one stage other than the last can be called an *iterative stage*. The peculiarities of such an iterative stage will be developed shortly. Each type of transistor connection will be considered separately.

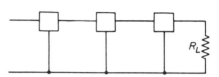

Fig. 9.7 Depiction of ideal iterative circuitry requires lossless inputs and outputs, similar d-c operating points.

The material discussed in Secs. 8.1 and 8.2 is pertinent and deserving of recollection. Recall particularly Figs. 8.8 and 8.9 in the range of R_L such that $R_L h_{22}$ is negligible as compared to unity (.01 or less is the order of magnitude to consider). This level of R_L is typical for *RC*-coupled amplifiers.

(a) For the common-base connection, the input impedance varies negligibly over the range of R_L, whereby $R_L h_{22}$ is less than .01. In fact the input impedance is almost the same as though the output were short-circuited, namely h_{11}. For the single-stage case we can write

$$R_{in} = h_{11} \tag{9.19}$$

A consideration of the other major circuit attributes yields the following statements for similar loading conditions in a single *RC*-coupled stage.

$$A_i = h_{21} \tag{9.20}$$

$$A_v = h_{21} \frac{R_L}{R_{in}} \tag{9.21}$$

Substituting Eq. (9.19) for R_{in},

$$A_v = h_{21} \frac{R_L}{h_{11}} \tag{9.22}$$

$$A_p = (h_{21})^2 \frac{R_L}{R_{in}} \tag{9.23}$$

Again substituting Eq. (9.19) for R_{in},

$$A_p = (h_{21})^2 \frac{R_L}{h_{11}} \tag{9.24}$$

It is important to note that the preceding equations were developed for the ideal case of a *lossless input and output*. The presence of R_D tends to reduce the effective value of R_L. The presence of the input components can be incorporated into a calculation of modified h-parameters. The modified h_{21} and h_{11} are less than those of the transistors alone. Usually the per cent reduction in the total load is greater than the per cent change in $(h_{21})^2/h_{11}$. Thus, the idealized equations suggest maximum values for the circuit attributes.

It is interesting now to determine the values of circuit attributes when the circuit of interest is an iterative one. We have commented that the load on such an iterative stage is the R_{in} of the succeeding stage. Hence, substituting Eq. (9.19) for R_L in Eqs. (9.22) and (9.24), we obtain for an iterative common-base stage:

$$A_v = h_{21} \tag{9.25}$$

$$A_p = (h_{21})^2 \tag{9.26}$$

As before,

$$A_i = h_{21} \tag{9.20}$$

For the common-base iterative stage, the current, voltage, and power gains are essentially equal to unity or zero decibels. For all intents and purposes the common-base connection, when appearing in an iterative chain, is useful only in transforming a low impedance to a high impedance.

(b) The considerations of a common-emitter circuit are qualitatively the same as those for a common-base circuit. This is permissible because, as Fig. 8.9 shows, the input impedance of a common-emitter stage does not change over the range of $R_L h_{22}$ less than .01. In fact, the input impedance of a common-emitter stage does not really change significantly for $R_L h_{22}$ values as high as .1. Hence all the equations developed for the common-base stage apply to the common-emitter stage. Because the forward-current gain of the common-emitter connection is considerably greater than unity, we observe for the iterative stage that the current gain, voltage gain, and power gain are of useful magnitudes.

(c) The common-collector stage exhibits a drastically changing input impedance for $R_L h_{22}$ less than .01. Thus a more detailed consideration of such a connection is in order. The exact equation for the input impedance of a circuit was given by Eq. (8.28); that is,

$$R_{\text{in}} = \frac{R_L \Delta^h + h_{11}}{R_L h_{22} + 1}$$

Since we are interested in the range where $R_L h_{22}$ is very much less than unity, Eq. (8.28) can properly be reduced to

$$R_{\text{in}} = R_L \Delta^h + h_{11} \tag{9.27}$$

Previous samples and problems have shown that for a common-collector connection

$$\Delta^h \cong h_{21} \qquad (9.28)$$

In addition

$$R_L h_{21} > h_{11} \qquad (9.29)$$

Substituting the results leading to Eq. (9.29) into (9.27), we find for a single *RC*-coupled common-collector stage that

$$R_{\text{in}} \cong R_L h_{21} \qquad (9.30)$$

Using Eq. (9.30) as the basis for considering the other major circuit attributes, we obtain for a single *RC*-coupled common-collector stage that

$$A_i \cong h_{21} \qquad (9.31)$$

$$A_v = 1 \qquad (9.32)$$

$$A_p \cong h_{21} \qquad (9.33)$$

The relatively low and relatively constant power gain in the low-R_L region is substantiated by the information in Fig. 8.12, which shows relatively small gain variation as $R_L h_{22}$ changes in the region of $R_L h_{22} = .01$.

The properties of the iterative common-collector stage are somewhat complicated by the rapidly changing input-impedance versus load-value relationship. For example, in a chain of n identical stages all but the last *two* are iterative if they are connected common-collector. All but the last *one* is iterative if they are connected common-base or common-emitter. Because a more exact solution is required, we must refer to Eq. (8.28) and substitute the quantity R_{in} for R_L. The solution will be the actual value of R_{in} for an iterative stage, and will take the form

$$h_{22} R_{\text{in}}^2 + (1 - \Delta^h) R_{\text{in}} + (-h_{11}) = 0 \qquad (9.34)$$

Since $\Delta^h \gg 1$ and $\Delta^h \gg 4 h_{11} h_{22}$, the solution to Eq. (9.34) is

$$R_{\text{in}} \cong \frac{h_{21}}{h_{22}} \qquad (9.35)$$

If now this value of impedance were substituted in Eq. (8.26), the general expression for power gain, we would find that for an iterative common-collector stage

$$A_p \cong 1 \qquad (9.36)$$

The reader is cautioned that he must be *fully* aware of the ground rules cited in obtaining Eqs. (9.19) through (9.26) for common-base and common-emitter stages whether single *RC* or iterative, and for Eqs. (9.27) through (9.36) for the common collector, either single *RC* or iterative. The key generality is that the load is such that $R_L h_{22}$ is negligible as compared to unity. In the type of circuit employing current or voltage feedback, the value of the modified output admittance increases drastically. Hence, an R_L that for the transistor alone gives an $R_L h_{22}$ product less than .01, might result in an $R_L h_{22}''$ product close to or greater than unity. The approximations and resultant equations just cited will no longer suffice: the exact equations must be used. The reader is directed to a full review of the facts before proceeding in any problem solution.

A review of the three connections suggests that the common-emitter connection is the most desirable for RC-coupled circuits.

Even though it provides lower gain than a transformer-coupled circuit, the RC coupled amplifier is widely used. Its major desirable features are: (1) the components themselves occupy less space than transformers, which is important when space is limited, (2) the components used are less costly, and (3) inherently a high degree of operating-point stability may be obtained.

9.4. RC-coupled circuits—general-case analysis. The RC coupled amplifier is quite critical from a design veiwpoint. General circuit attributes such as maximum gain, the actual amount of output power that can be developed, minimum distortion, and maximum circuit efficiency are traits that for practical purposes are not obtainable simultaneously. The designer, then, is alerted to a number of basic facts in the following discourse. The specific problem at hand will determine the sensible and proper approach.

A great deal of enlightenment results when we consider the manner in which an RC circuit operates. Refer to the circuit as shown in Fig. 9.8; dc current flows only through R_D. R_L is the load into which we want to deliver some quantity of useful a-c power. Yet, R_D and R_L in parallel are the *total* a-c load on the transistor. Following similar approaches used in the past in constructing circuit load lines, we may write for the d-c conditions around the collector loop (assuming $I_E = I_C$)

$$V_C = V_{CC} - I_C R_{\text{d-c}} \tag{9.37}$$

where

$$R_{\text{d-c}} = R_D + R_E \tag{9.38}$$

We have no immediate knowledge as to where to place the a-c load line. We know initially, however, that the total a-c performance is described by

$$V = I R_{\text{TOT}} \tag{9.39}$$

where

$$R_{\text{TOT}} = \frac{R_L R_D}{R_L + R_D} \tag{9.40}$$

and V = rms voltage across R_{TOT}
        I = rms current through R_{TOT}

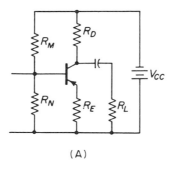

(A)

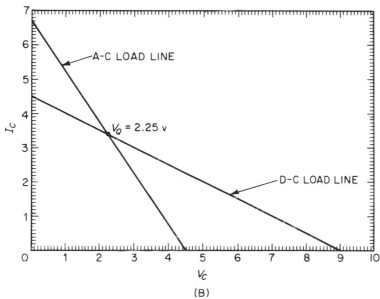

(B)

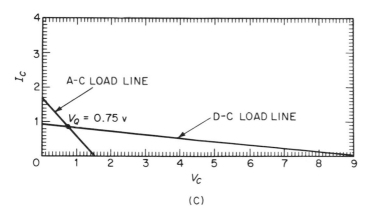

(C)

Fig. 9.8 (A) General-case RC-coupled circuit. (B) Typical placement of a-c and d-c load lines for circuit of Fig. 9-8(A) if $R_E = 0$, $R_D = 2$ K, $R_L = 1$ K, $V_{CC} = 9$ v. (C) Typical placement if $R_E = 0$, $R_D = 10$ K, $R_L = 1$ K, $V_{CC} = 9$ v.

We do know specifically that the a-c and d-c load lines will cross at the transistor operating point, determined by the bias circuitry. In order to show some circuit possibilities a d-c load of first 2 K and then 10 K is used in conjunction with an R_L of 1 K. Typical placements of the a-c load lines are shown in Fig. 9.8(b) and 9.8(c), respectively. As should have been expected, the slope for the a-c load line for the 2-K and 1-K combination is steeper than the slope of the 10-K and 1-K a-c load. Note also that a greater range of d-c operating currents is available when low values of d-c load are used.

Finally, note that the power developed in the load resistor can be expressed as the square of the rms load voltage divided by the load resistor itself. The rms voltage across the load is determined from the voltage swing associated with the a-c load line. Some general comments about design possibilities are now possible.

(a) If we are interested in maximum gain, we must attempt to make R_D as big as possible to minimize the loss in R_D. This, however, tends to limit the amount of power output, since the current and voltage swings are limited. Refer to the appearance of Fig. 9.8(c). Maximizing the gain also requires that we minimize the loss in the input circuit—hence we will be obtaining gain at the expense of operating-point stability. In addition, a large amount of distortion is likely to occur. This tends to make such an approach undesirable.

(b) If we are interested in obtaining a given amount of power output, we are typically in a situation of nonmaximized gain. The reason is that the necessary current and voltage swings across the load are likely to be obtained only as the slope of the d-c load line increases. In the situation where a maximum power output is desired with a minimum of distortion, the operating point will be found to be the center of the a-c load line. This latter matter applies also for the large-signal amplifiers to be discussed later.

(c) If minimum distortion is a main requirement, the operating point should be as high a current value as the required output power will permit. Such an operating point minimizes the variation of input impedance with changes in a-c current swing. Such a situation does, however, reduce the gain of the circuit.

(d) The last comment to be made relates to the operating point itself. Rarely, if ever, are we able to pick a specific operating point and design around it. In the usual approach, output power or gain is a more important requirement. The operating point comes about later, as the specific circuit components assume the values that satisfy the higher-priority requirements. When stability of the operating point becomes of interest, bridge resistor R_N, emitter resistance R_E, or feedback resistance R_F may appear in the circuit. These must be acknowledged in the preparation of the a-c load line and in the calculation of modified h-parameters.

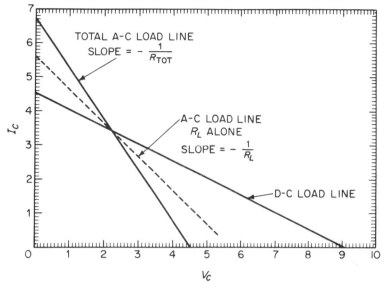

Fig. 9.9 Comparison of load-line slopes for R_{TOT} and R_L.

Improved understanding of *RC*-coupled circuit performance can be
obtained by studying the information presented in Fig. 9.9. Here we repeat
the d-c and total a-c load lines shown already in Fig. 9.8(b) for $R_L = 1$ K
and $R_D = 2$ K. In addition we show an a-c load line for R_L alone. Such a
load line is described by

$$V_L = I_L R_L \tag{9.41}$$

where V_L = rms voltage across R_L
   I_L = rms current through R_L

It is a basic matter that R_{TOT}, as described by Eq. (9.40), will be smaller
than R_L alone. Therefore, the slope of the total a-c load line is steeper than
the slope for the load line of R_L alone. As far as the transistor is concerned,
the load line for R_{TOT} defines the useful operating range. The significance
of this concept is demonstrated as follows. The power in R_L can be described
as

$$P_{\text{load}} = \frac{V_L^2}{R_L} \tag{9.42}$$

If we now define

$$V_m = V_L \sqrt{2} \tag{9.43}$$

We obtain

$$P_{\text{load}} = \frac{V_m^2}{2R_L} \tag{9.44}$$

To obtain the desired power in R_L, the total a-c load line must accommodate an a-c voltage swing with a peak value of V_m. If we relate, mathematically, the power requirements in R_L and the performance limitations of the total a-c load line as given by Eq. (9.39), it can be seen that

$$V = \frac{V_m}{\sqrt{2}} \qquad (9.45)$$

As before, V is the rms value of voltage appearing at any time across the total a-c load line. It can, and will, be shown that the best all-around design approach is to have the d-c load line cross the total a-c load line at a point midway on the total a-c load line. As applied to an ideal transistor, this establishes a situation whereby the voltage, V_m, which satisfies or establishes the power situation in R_L, becomes also the voltage value for the quiescent operating point. The three key equations for any ideal transistor operating RC-coupled are

load power: $\qquad P_{\text{load}} = \dfrac{V_m^2}{2R_L} \qquad (9.44)$

d-c load line: $\qquad V_C = V_{CC} - I_C R_{\text{d-c}} \qquad (9.37)$

total a-c load line: $\quad V_m = I_m R_{\text{TOT}} \qquad (9.46)$

Equation (9.46) was obtained by substituting Eq. (9.45) into Eq. (9.39) for V.

Before Eqs. (9.37) and (9.46) can be considered simultaneously to establish the operating point, certain aspects of R_E must be considered. As indicated in Eq. (9.38), the quantity $R_{\text{d-c}}$ is the sum of a collector resistance R_D and an emitter resistance R_E, should one appear in the circuit. It is certainly appropriate to use the total $R_{\text{d-c}}$ quantity for the d-c load line placement. The manner in which $R_{\text{d-c}}$ should be split for R_D and R_E allocations constitutes an interesting problem. Stability considerations may not be a design factor, and R_E can be made equal to zero. More often than not, the design is not so simple and stability factors must be considered. If R_E then is made too low in value, the bias network R_M and R_N at the input terminals will tend to be low in value, causing excessive losses in the input circuitry. If R_E is made too high in value, the collector resistor R_D will be low, causing excessive losses in the output circuitry. It has been shown elsewhere in the literature that a unique value of R_E exists that minimizes losses in both the input and output circuits simultaneously. Practice, however, will verify that the R_E value can vary somewhat from this unique value and still allow the circuit to be operating within 1.0 to 2.0 db of maximum ideal gain. As a practical approach in dividing $R_{\text{d-c}}$ into its R_E and R_D parts, it is acceptable to use as an R_E value a quantity that is 10 to 20 per cent of the total $R_{\text{d-c}}$ value. Such an R_E value yields near-optimum results. It will be shown in a later development that the use of current-feedback biasing generally eliminates the need for an R_E to exist at all.

Having obtained some enlightenment about the value of R_E, we can assume as a typical situation that

$$R_E = .15 R_{\text{d-c}} \tag{9.47a}$$

and

$$R_{\text{d-c}} = 1.18 R_D \tag{9.47b}$$

Acknowledging now that the d-c or quiescent voltage is to be equal to V_m, we can solve Eqs. (9.37) and (9.46) simultaneously for V_m, and include Eq. (9.47) to obtain

$$V_m = \frac{V_{cc} R_L}{1.18 R_D + 2.18 R_L} \tag{9.48}$$

A rearrangement of (9.48) yields

$$R_D = \frac{R_L}{1.18}\left(\frac{V_{cc}}{V_m} - 2.18\right) \tag{9.49}$$

In the situation where R_E is to be equal to zero, it can be shown that

$$V_m = \frac{V_{cc} R_L}{R_D + 2R_L} \tag{9.50}$$

$$R_D = R_L\left(\frac{V_{cc}}{V_m} - 2\right) \tag{9.51}$$

Equation (9.49) or (9.51) indicates the value of R_D that for a given required V_m results in an a-c d-c load line intersection midway on the a-c load line. Equation (9.48) or (9.50) gives the unique value of V_m that for a given R_L and $R_{\text{d-c}}$ represents the voltage value for the midpoint of the total a-c load line.

The attainment of close to optimized gain in an RC-coupled amplifier is not too difficult should this requirement have priority status. Close scrutiny of the governing mathematics, and the manipulation of a number of circuit designs, confirms the dominance of output losses when optimum gain is not obtained. We should strive to obtain an R_D value that is as high as the supply voltage and power requirements will allow. If we substitute the quantity R_D equal to $10R_L$ into Eq. (9.48), we find

$$V_m \simeq \frac{V_{cc}}{14} \tag{9.52}$$

Equation (9.52) indicates the near maximum ideal voltage swing for an RC-coupled circuit with minimized output losses. This condition is assumed to yield maximum circuit gain. Should a larger voltage swing be needed to satisfy a power requirement, less than ideal gain will be obtained.

Having discussed the generalities of an *ideal* transistor, and in particular the nature of circuit design in minimizing output losses, we turn now to the discussion of the real transistor in an *RC*-coupled circuit. Of special interest here are the attributes of saturation voltage and leakage, the temperature extremes of circuit operation, and the parameter variation between transistors. Let us look first at Fig. 9.10. Retaining the same concepts of interrelation for output power, d-c load line, and a-c load line, it is seen that the real-case quiescent operating point must be

$$V_Q = V_m + V_{SAT} \tag{9.53}$$

$$I_Q = I_m + I_{CEO} \tag{9.54}$$

where V_m, as before, is the voltage swing determining useful power output in the load resistor R_L, and where $I_{CEO} = (1 + h_{FE})I_{CBO}$. Equations (9.46) and (9.47) still apply:

$$V_m = I_m R_{TOT}, \qquad R_E = .15(R_{\text{d-c}}), \qquad R_{\text{d-c}} = 1.18 R_D$$

The equation for the d-c load line now becomes

$$V_c + V_{SAT} = V_{CC} - [I_C + I_{CEO}]R_{\text{d-c}} \tag{9.55}$$

Substituting Eq. (9.46) into Eq. (9.55) for I_C and utilizing the "*m*" subscripts throughout, we get

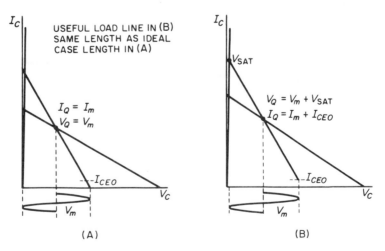

Fig. 9.10 (A) Load-line placement for ideal device. Note potential clip due to V_{SAT} and I_{CEO}. (B) Load-line placement for actual device.

$$V_m = \frac{R_L(V_{CC} - V_{\text{SAT}} - 1.18 R_D I_{CEO})}{1.18 R_D + 2.18 R_L} \tag{9.56}$$

Rearranging, we obtain

$$R_D = \frac{R_L(V_{CC} - 2.18 V_m - V_{\text{SAT}})}{1.18(V_m + R_L I_{CEO})} \tag{9.57}$$

In the event that R_E is equal to zero, it can be shown that

$$V_m = \frac{R_L(V_{CC} - V_{\text{SAT}} - R_D I_{CEO})}{R_D + 2R_L} \tag{9.58}$$

$$R_D = \frac{R_L(V_{CC} - 2V_m - V_{\text{SAT}})}{V_m + I_{CEO} R_L} \tag{9.59}$$

Equation (9.56) or (9.58) indicates the value of voltage swing that is half the length of the available a-c load line. Equation (9.53), of course, indicates the actual value of the quiescent voltage. Equation (9.57) or (9.59) indicates the value of R_D that for a given V_m places the intersection of the a-c and d-c load lines midway on the useful portion of the a-c load line.

9.5. Design example: *RC*-coupled amplifier. In order to demonstrate the application of the preceding material let us consider the requirement that the 2N1414 of the example in Sec. 9.2 deliver 1 mw to a 1 K load. A supply voltage of 9 v is available. In addition, let the bias circuitry be established by the requirement that a limit device with $h_{FE} = 60$ and $I_{CBO} = 8$ μa be capable of providing the 1 mw of power to the 1 K load. Assume that saturation voltage is .04 v. For a given $R_{\text{d-c}}$ the a-c load lines for a high- and low-current-gain device are shown in Fig. 9.11. The operating point tends to shift from operating point A to operating point A' as we change from a low- to a high-current-gain device. The high-gain unit, being closer to the coordinates and having a higher value of cutoff current, is the more critical of the two devices. It is appropriate to actually optimize the a-c design around the high-gain unit using the low-gain unit to design the d-c bias circuitry.

The design proceeds as follows. From (9.44)

$$V_m = \sqrt{2 R_L P_{\text{load}}}$$
$$= \sqrt{2(1 \text{ K})(1 \text{ mw})} = 1.4 \text{ V}$$

Proceeding directly to Eq. (9.57), we obtain

$$R_D = \frac{R_L(V_{CC} - 2.18 V_m - V_{\text{SAT}})}{1.18(V_m + R_L I_{CEO})}$$
$$= \frac{1 \text{ K } [9 - 2.18(1.4) - .04]}{1.18 \, [1.4 + 1 \text{ K } (61)(.008)10^{-3}]}$$
$$= 2.65 \text{ K}$$

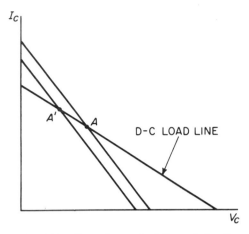

Fig. 9.11 General-case depiction of situation when d-c current gain changes in a given circuit; A is the low-gain Q point, and A′ is the high-gain Q point. Circuit is more nearly optimum for low-gain unit as shown here.

By (9.47b)
$$R_{\text{d-c}} = 1.18\,R_D = 3.13 \text{ K}$$
By (9.47a)
$$R_E = .15\,R_{\text{d-c}} = 470 \text{ }\Omega$$

The current swing for the total load is given by Eq. (9.46):

$$I_m = \frac{V_m}{R_{\text{TOT}}}$$
$$= \frac{1.4(3.65 \text{ K})}{2.65 \text{ K (1 K)}} = 1.93 \text{ ma}$$

The quiescent operating point for the high-limit device is, by (9.53),

$$V'_Q = V_m + V_{\text{SAT}}$$
$$= 1.4 + .04 = 1.44 \text{ v}$$

By (9.54)

$$I'_Q = I_m + I_{CEO}$$
$$= 1.93 + 61(.008) = 2.42 \text{ ma}$$

For the 2N1414 with its current gain $h_{FE} = 35$ and the leakage $I_{CBO} = 6$ μa the minimum acceptable operating point is

$$I_Q = I_m + I_{CEO}$$
$$= 1.93 + 36(.006) = 2.15 \text{ ma}$$

Substituting the quiescent current level back into Eq. (9.55) for the low-current gain device, we obtain

$$V_Q = V_m + V_{\text{SAT}} = 9 - [2.15(10^{-3})]3.13 \text{ K}$$
$$= 2.26 \text{ v}$$

The load lines for the high- and low-gain devices are drawn in Fig. 9.12. To assure that the low-current-gain operating point permits a voltage excur-

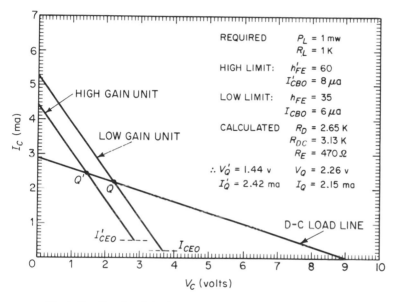

Fig. 9.12 Graphical depiction for illustrative problem of Sec. 9.5.

sion of the necessary value we can determine the cutoff voltage from Fig. 9.12 as 3.7 v. The increment of $3.7 - 2.26$ equaling 1.44 v is greater than the 1.4-v swing required. Thus our operating point of 2.26 v and 2.15 ma is acceptable for the low-limit device. The operating point of 1.44 v and 2.42 ma applies to the high-current-gain device. Notice that the placement of operating points considered the voltage swing as a limiting aspect for the high-gain device, and the current swing as a limiting aspect for the low-gain device.

Having placed the operating points at proper values, we can proceed to design the bias circuitry. For our reference transistor we have $h_{FE} = 35$, $I_{CBO} = 6$ μa, and $I_c = 2.15$ ma. For the high-gain device we have $h'_{FE} = 60$, $I'_{CBO} = 8$ μa, and $I'_c = 2.42$ ma. The calculation constants are

$$B = (I_C - I_{CBO})(1 + h_{FE})$$
$$= (2.15 - .006)(10^{-3})(36) = 77.3(10^{-3})$$

$$B' = (I'_C - I'_{CBO})(1 + h'_{FE})$$
$$= (2.42 - .008)(10^{-3})(61) = 147(10^{-3})$$

$$C = I_C - (1 + h_{FE})I_{CBO}$$
$$= 2.15(10^{-3}) - 36(.006)(10^{-3}) = 1.93(10^{-3})$$

$$C' = I'_C - (1 + h'_{FE})I'_{CBO}$$
$$= 2.42(10^{-3}) - (61)(.008)(10^{-3}) = 1.93(10^{-3})$$

$$E = B'h_{FE} - Bh'_{FE}$$
$$= 147(10^{-3})35 - 77.3(10^{-3})60 = 510(10^{-3})$$

$$F = Ch'_{FE} - C'h_{FE}$$
$$= 1.93(10^{-3})60 - 1.93(10^{-3})35 = 48.2(10^{-3})$$

$$G = B'C - BC'$$
$$= 147(10^{-3})1.93(10^{-3}) - 77.3(10^{-3})1.93(10^{-3}) = 135(10^{-6})$$

Since R_E was established at 470 Ω, we can proceed now to the bias resistors. By (6.25)

$$R_N = \frac{V_{CC}R_E E}{(V_{CC} - V_B)F - GR_E}$$
$$= \frac{9(470)510(10^{-3})}{(9 - .15)48.2(10^{-3}) - 135(10^{-6})470} = 5.9\text{ K}$$

By (6.23)

$$R_M = \frac{R_N[h_{FE}(V_{CC} - V_B) - BR_E]}{CR_N + BR_E + h_{FE}V_B}$$
$$= \frac{5.9\text{ K}[35(9 - .15) - 77.3(10^{-3})470]}{1.93(10^{-3})5.9(10^3) + 77.3(10^{-3})470 + 35(.15)}$$
$$= 29.4\text{ K}$$

The equivalent input shunt due to R_N and R_M becomes

$$R_S = \frac{R_M R_N}{R_M + R_N}$$
$$= \frac{29.4\text{ K }(5.9\text{ K})}{29.4\text{ K} + 5.9\text{ K}} = 4.9\text{ K}$$

To determine the circuit gain for the low-gain device we must acknowledge that its operating point is $V_C = 2.26$ v and $I_C = 2.15$ ma. We must accordingly determine the h-parameters for this operating point. From Fig. 7.7(a) at $I_E = 2.15$ ma, we find that the multipliers for each parameter are

$$h_{22b} \text{ multiplier} = 1.9$$
$$h_{11b} \text{ multiplier} = .4$$

$$h_{12b} \text{ multiplier} = 1.1$$
$$h_{21e} \text{ multiplier} = 1.15$$

From Fig. 7.7(b) at $V_C = 2.26$ v we find that the multipliers for each parameter are

$$h_{22b} \text{ multiplier} = 1.65$$
$$h_{11b} \text{ multiplier} = 1.04$$
$$h_{12b} \text{ multiplier} = 1.5$$
$$h_{21e} \text{ multiplier} = .94$$

The reference values of the h-parameters are

$$h_{11b} = 29 \ \Omega$$
$$h_{21e} = 44$$
$$h_{22b} = .62(10^{-6}) \text{ mhos}$$
$$h_{12b} = 5.2(10^{-4})$$

At 2.26 v and 2.15 ma then

$$h_{22b} = .62(10^{-6})(1.9)(1.65) = 1.94(10^{-6}) \text{ mhos}$$
$$h_{11b} = 29(.4)(1.04) = 12 \ \Omega$$
$$h_{12b} = 5.2(10^{-4})(1.1)(1.5) - 8.56(10^{-4})$$
$$h_{21e} = 44(1.15)(.94) = 47.5$$

By (7.47)

$$h_{21b} = \frac{-h_{21e}}{1 + h_{21e}}$$

$$= \frac{-47.5}{1 + 47.5} = -.98$$

$$\therefore \quad 1 + h_{21b} = .02$$

The common-emitter h-parameters at the operating point in question become, by (7.42)

$$h_{22e} = \frac{h_{22b}}{1 + h_{21b}} = \frac{1.94(10^{-6})}{.02} = 97(10^{-6}) \text{ mhos}$$

By 7.45

$$h_{12e} = \frac{h_{11b}h_{22b} - h_{12b}(1 + h_{21b})}{1 + h_{21b}}$$

$$= \frac{12(1.94)(10^{-6}) - 8.56(10^{-4})(.02)}{.02} = 3.1(10^{-4})$$

and by (7.46)

$$h_{11e} = \frac{h_{11b}}{1 + h_{21b}} = \frac{12}{.02} = 600 \ \Omega$$

The first modification of the h-parameters accounts for the presence of R_E. By (7.79)

$$h''_{11} = h_{11} + \frac{R_E(1 + h_{21})}{1 + R_E(h_{22})}$$

$$= 600 + \frac{470(48.5)}{1 + 470(97)10^{-6}} = 22.4 \text{ K}$$

By (7.78)

$$h''_{21} = \frac{h_{21}}{1 + R_E h_{22}}$$

$$= \frac{47.5}{1.0456} = 45.5$$

By (7.80)

$$h''_{22} = \frac{h_{22}}{1 + R_E h_{22}}$$

$$= \frac{97(10^{-6})}{1.0456} = 91.8(10^{-6})$$

By (7.81)

$$h''_{12} = \frac{h_{12} + h_{22} R_E}{1 + R_E h_{22}}$$

$$= \frac{3.1(10^{-4}) + 97(10^{-6})470}{1.0456} = 438(10^{-4})$$

The second modification of the h's acknowledges the presence of R_S shunting the input. By (7.70)

$$h'_{21} = \frac{h''_{21} R_S}{h''_{11} + R_S}$$

$$= \frac{45.5(4.9 \text{ K})}{22.4 \text{ K} + 4.9 \text{ K}} = 8.2$$

By (7.71)

$$h'_{11} = \frac{h''_{11} R_S}{h''_{11} + R_S}$$

$$= \frac{22.4 \text{ K}(4.9 \text{ K})}{27.3 \text{ K}} = 4 \text{ K}$$

By (7.73)

$$h'_{22} = h''_{22} - \frac{h''_{21} h''_{12}}{h''_{11} + R_S}$$

$$= 91.8(10^{-6}) - \frac{45.5(438)10^{-4}}{27.3 \text{ K}}$$

$$= 18.8(10^{-6})$$

In order now to determine the circuit gain we first recall that the total load as given by Eq. (9.40) is

$$R_{\text{TOT}} = \frac{R_L R_D}{R_L + R_D}$$

$$= \frac{1\text{ K }(2.65\text{ K})}{3.65\text{ K}} = 726\ \Omega$$

The general-case quantity $R_L h_{22}$ is now calculated specifically as

$$R_{\text{TOT}} h'_{22} = 726(18.8)10^{-6} = .0136$$

Since this quantity is less than the reference value of .1 previously cited, we may proceed to calculate the overall circuit gain by use of Eqs. (9.3) and (9.23) with the quantity R_{TOT} for the load:

$$A_p = (h'_{21})^2 \frac{R_{\text{TOT}}}{h'_{11}}$$

$$= (8.2)^2 \frac{726}{4000} = 12.2 = 10.86\text{ db}$$

In considering the total power, P_{tot}, in R_D and R_L as compared with the specific power P_{out} in R_L alone, it can be shown that

$$P_{\text{out}} = \frac{R_D}{R_D + R_L} P_{\text{tot}} \tag{9.60}$$

We can define a *useful power gain*, which is the ratio of P_{out} divided by P_{in}. This is nothing more than a practical interpretation of (9.23). Thus

$$\text{useful } A_p = (h_{21})^2 \frac{R_{\text{TOT}}}{h_{11}} \frac{R_D}{R_D + R_L} \tag{9.61}$$

For our example, the useful gain is

$$\text{useful } A_p = (8.2)^2 \frac{726}{4000} \frac{2.65\text{ K}}{3.65\text{ K}}$$

$$= 8.85 = 9.5\text{ db}$$

This is not really high-gain performance. Other bias circuits that yield higher gain are considered in the next sections.

9.6. *RC*-coupled circuit using current-feedback bias.   The modified combination current-voltage feedback circuit shown in Fig. 6.8 and repeated here as Fig. 9.13 is a natural for use in conjunction with *RC*-coupled amplifiers. Usually the value of R_D is great enough, and the value of operating voltage V_C small enough, to allow effective control of the operating point. The absence of a low-value shunt resistance between base and emitter means there is a minimized-loss situation at the input terminals. In addition, a calculation of the modified h-parameters will disclose only slight modification of the critical parameters, h_{11} and h_{21}. Finally, R_E can usually be selected to be equal to zero and still have effective bias control. This helps to yield

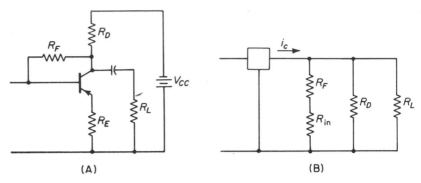

Fig. 9.13 (A) Schematic of *RC*-coupled circuit using modified combination current-voltage feedback biasing. (B) A-C equivalent circuit assuming that $R_E = 0$.

a high value of R_D, which helps in approaching the situation of minimized losses at the output.

The design approach for the current-feedback circuitry is only slightly more complicated than the bridge type-voltage feedback approach just discussed. The d-c analysis commences with a summation of voltages around the collector circuit. The result is similar to Eq. (6.34):

$$V_C = V_{CC} - (I_C + I_F)R_D - I_E R_E$$

For our particular purposes we will reduce R_E to be equal to zero, and incorporate the real-life aspects of saturation voltage and leakage current. The result is

$$V_Q = V_C + V_{\text{SAT}} = V_{CC} - (I_C + I_{CEO} + I_F)R_D \qquad (9.62)$$

since

$$I_F = \frac{V_C + V_{\text{SAT}} - V_B}{R_F} \qquad (9.63)$$

$$\therefore \quad V_Q = V_C + V_{\text{SAT}} = \frac{R_F[V_{CC} - R_D(I_C + I_{CEO})] + V_B R_D}{R_D + R_F} \qquad (9.64)$$

The total a-c load on the stage is shown in Fig. 9.13(b). Since the input impedance R_{in} of the transistor is small in comparison to R_F, we may express the total load as

$$R_{\text{TOT}} = \frac{R_F R_L R_D}{R_F R_L + R_F R_D + R_L R_D} \qquad (9.65)$$

The a-c performance is described then by

$$V_m = I_m R_{\text{TOT}} \qquad (9.66)$$

where R_{TOT} is given by (9.65). Substituting Eqs. (9.66) and (9.65) into Eq. (9.64), and utilizing "*m*" subscripts throughout, we obtain

$$V_m = \frac{R_L[R_F(V_{CC} - I_{CEO}R_D - V_{\text{SAT}}) - (V_{\text{SAT}} - V_B)R_D]}{R_D(R_F + 2R_L) + 2R_LR_F} \qquad (9.67)$$

Rearranging, we obtain

$$R_D = \frac{R_LR_F(V_{CC} - 2V_m - V_{\text{SAT}})}{V_m(R_F + 2R_L) + I_{CEO}R_LR_F + (V_{\text{SAT}} - V_B)R_L} \qquad (9.68)$$

Equation (9.67) indicates the value of voltage swing that is half the length of the available load line. Equation (9.53) indicates the actual value of quiescent voltage. Equation (9.68) indicates the value of R_D that for a given V_m places the intersection of the a-c and d-c load lines midway on the useful portion of the a-c load line. In either equation the value of R_F has to be known.

In those cases where we are designing to known transistors and known power requirements, an optimum load line situation results only for specific, compatible values of R_D and R_F. These may be determined by referring back to Eqs. (6.39), (6.40), and (6.41) and revising them to accommodate the situation of Fig. 9.12—namely, that R_E equals zero and R_N equals infinity. The results are

$$I_Q = \frac{h_{FE}(V_{CC} - V_B) + (1 + h_{FE})I_{CBO}(R_D + R_E)}{R_F + (1 + h_{FE})R_D} \qquad (9.69)$$

$$V_Q = V_m + V_{\text{SAT}} = \frac{R_F}{h_{FE}}[I_Q - (1 + h_{FE})I_{CBO}] + V_B \qquad (9.70)$$

The I_Q term in Eq. (9.70) is the same as the expression given in (9.69). The design procedure requires a consideration of the parameter spread on the transistors, and the operating-point limitations for each. The main consideration for the low-limit transistor is that the value of collector current be large enough to sustain the current swing in the total load. Substituting this value of operating current and low-limit transistor parameters into Eq. (9.69), we obtain

$$R_F = \frac{h_{FE}(V_{CC} - V_B) - BR_D}{C} \qquad (9.71)$$

For the high-limit transistor, the main consideration was operating voltage and the need to have a value large enough to accommodate the required output-voltage swing. Substituting values for the high-limit transistor into Eqs. (9.69) and (9.70) and then substituting (9.69) into 9.70 for I_Q, we obtain

$$R_F = \frac{(1 + h'_{FE})(V_m + V_{\text{SAT}} - V_B)R_D}{V_{CC} - V_m - V_{\text{SAT}} - (1 + h'_{FE})I'_{CBO}R_D} \qquad (9.72)$$

The typical situation would be to consider the *high-limit conditions more restrictive*. In this case, substitute (9.72) into (9.68) for R_F to obtain

$$R_D = \frac{R_L[(V_{CC} - 2V_m - V_{\text{SAT}})(1 + h'_{FE})(V_m + V_{\text{SAT}} - V'_B) - (2V_m + V_{\text{SAT}} - V_B)(V_{CC} - V_m - V_{\text{SAT}})]}{(V_m + I'_{CEO}R_L)(1 + h'_{FE})(V_m + V_{\text{SAT}} - V_B) - R_LI'_{CEO}(2V_m + V_{\text{SAT}} - V'_B)} \qquad (9.73)$$

Equation (9.73) yields the value of R_D that, for given transistor parameters and power requirements, will place the interception of the a-c and d-c load lines midway on the useful portion of the a-c load line. Having determined R_D, one substitutes this value back into Eq. (9.72) to establish the value of R_F.

9.7. Design example: *RC*-coupled amplifier using current-feedback bias.
Let us now apply current-feedback bias to the design we completed earlier using the bridge network and voltage-feedback resistor. Here we can resummarize that

$$V_m = 1.4 \text{ v}$$

$$h'_{FE} = 60$$

$$I'_{CBO} = 8 \text{ }\mu\text{a}$$

$$I'_{CEO} = (1 + h'_{FE})I'_{CBO} = .488(10^{-3}) \text{ amp}$$

By (9.73)

$$R_D=$$

$$\frac{R_L[(V_{CC}-2V_m-V_{SAT})(1+h'_{FE})(V_m+V_{SAT}-V'_B)-(2V_m+V_{SAT}-V_B)(V_{CC}-V_m-V_{SAT})]}{(V_m+I'_{CEO}R_L)(1+h'_{FE})(V_m+V_{SAT}-V_B)-R_LI'_{CEO}(2V_m+V_{SAT}-V'_B)}$$

$$= \frac{1 \text{ K} [(9 - 2.8 - .04)(61)(1.4 + 0.4 - .15) - (2.8 - .04 - .15)(9 - 1.4 - .04)]}{[1.4 + .488(10^{-3})](10^3)(61)(1.4 + .04 - .15) - 10^3[.488(10^{-3})](2.8 + .04 - .15)}$$

$$= 3.14 \text{ K}$$

By (9.72)

$$R_F = \frac{(1 + h'_{FE})(V_m + V_{SAT} - V_B)R_D}{V_{CC} - V_m - V_{SAT} - (1 + h'_{FE})I'_{CBO}R_D}$$

$$= \frac{61(1.4 + .04 - .15)(3.14 \text{ K})}{9 - 1.4 - .04 - .488(10^{-3})3.14(10^3)} = 40.8 \text{ K}$$

The quiescent operating voltage for our high-limit transistor is determined by Eq. (9.53):

$$V'_Q = V_m + V_{SAT} = 1.4 + 0.4 = 1.44 \text{ v}$$

To find the quiescent current for our high-limit transistor we use Eq. (9.69) to find

$$I'_Q = \frac{h'_{FE}(V_{CC} - V_B) + (1 + h'_{FE})I'_{CBO}(R_D + R_F)}{R_F + (1 + h'_{FE})R_D}$$

$$= \frac{60(9 - .15) + .488(10^{-3})(40.8 + 3.14) \text{ K}}{40.8 \text{ K} + 61(3.14) \text{ K}} = 2.36 \text{ ma}$$

The required current swing I_m is

$$I_m = \frac{V_m}{R_{TOT}}$$

By (9.65)

$$R_{\text{TOT}} = \frac{R_F R_L R_D}{R_F R_L + R_F R_D + R_L R_D} = 745 \ \Omega$$

$$\therefore \quad I_m = \frac{1.4}{745} = 1.88 \ \text{ma}$$

The construction of the d-c and a-c load lines intercepting at 1.44 v and 2.36 ma is shown in Fig. 9.14. The required current and voltage swings are obtained with the high-limit device. We must check now to determine whether the current swing required is obtained when the low-limit device is placed into the circuit. Using low-limit parameters in Eq. (9.69), we find

$$I_Q = \frac{h_{FE}(V_{CC} - V_B) + (1 + h_{FE})I_{CBO}(R_D + R_F)}{R_F + (1 + h_{FE})R_D}$$

$$= \frac{35(8.85) + 36(.006)\,10^{-3}(43.9 \ \text{K})}{40.8 \ \text{K} + 36(3.14)\ \text{K}} = 2.08 \ \text{ma}$$

This allows a usable swing in current of 2.08 ma minus .216 ma or 1.86 ma. If the usable swing for the low-limit device were greater than 1.88 ma, there would be no question as to the acceptability of the design. If the usable current swing were significantly less than 1.88 ma, a tighter current-gain spread would be required or a reduced power output would have to be accepted. For the results of our calculations, the usable current swing of 1.86 ma is close enough to the required swing of 1.88 ma to permit con-

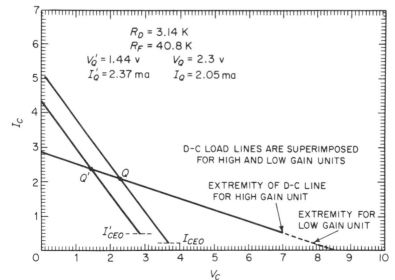

Fig. 9.14 Graphical depiction for illustrative problem using current feedback bias.

tinuance of the design procedure and analysis. For the low-gain device, we
find by (9.70)

$$V_Q = \frac{R_F}{h_{FE}}[I_Q - (1 + h_{FE})I_{CBO}] + V_B$$

$$= \frac{40.8\text{ K}}{35}[1.86(10^{-3})] + .15 = 2.33\text{ v}$$

The quiescent operating point for our low-gain device is 2.33 v and 2.08 ma.
These numbers are quite close to the values 2.26 v and 2.15 ma obtained for
this device when it was operating in the bridge-biased circuit. To determine
gain of the low-limit device in our current-feedback circuit, we will use the
previously determined h's, for the operating point of 2.26 v and 2.15 ma of
Sec. 9.5., i.e.,

$$h_{22e} = 97(10^{-6})\text{ mhos}$$

$$h_{12e} = 3.1(10^{-4})$$

$$h_{11e} = 600\ \Omega$$

$$h_{21e} = 47.5$$

The presence of the resistor R_F requires that the h-parameters be modified
in the following way. By (7.87)

$$h_{21}''' = \frac{h_{21}R_F}{R_F + h_{11}}$$

$$= \frac{47.5(40.8\text{ K})}{41.4\text{ K}} = 47.5(.986) = 46.9$$

By (7.88)

$$h_{11}''' = \frac{h_{11}(R_F)}{R_F + h_{11}}$$

$$= 600(.986) = 591\ \Omega$$

By (7.89)

$$h_{22}''' \cong h_{22} + \frac{1 + h_{21}}{R_F + h_{11}}$$

$$= 97(10^{-6}) + \frac{48.5}{41.4\text{ K}} = 1267(10^{-6})\text{ mhos}$$

By (7.90)

$$h_{12}''' \cong h_{12} + \frac{h_{11}}{R_F + h_{11}}$$

$$= 3.1(10^{-4}) + \frac{600}{41.4\text{ K}} = 148(10^{-4})$$

By (7.93a)

$$\Delta^{h'''} = h_{11}''' h_{22}''' - h_{12}''' h_{21}'''$$

$$= 591(1267)10^{-6} - 148(10^{-4})46.9$$

$$= 560(10^{-4})$$

Since the total load on our stage was 745 Ω, the quantity $R_{TOT}h_{22}'''$ becomes

$$R_{TOT}h_{22}''' = 745(1267)10^{-6}$$
$$= .945$$

Since this quantity is not less than .1, we must use the exact calculation for R_{in} as given by Eq. (8.28).

$$R_{in} = \frac{R_{TOT}\Delta^{h'''} + h_{11}'''}{R_{TOT}h_{22}''' + 1}$$

$$= \frac{745(560)10^{-4} + 591}{745(1267)10^{-6} + 1} = 326 \ \Omega$$

The total circuit gain is by Eq. (9.23):

$$A_p = (h_{21}''')^2 \frac{R_{TOT}}{R_{in}}$$

$$= (46.9)^2 \frac{745}{326}$$

$$= 5000 = 37 \ db$$

The useful power gain is calculated in conjunction with the concepts of Eqs. (9.60) and (9.61). Thus

$$\text{useful } A_p = (h_{21}''')^2 \frac{R_{TOT}}{R_{in}} \frac{R_D}{R_D + R_L}$$

$$= 5000 \frac{3.14}{4.14}$$

$$= 3800 = 35.8 \ db$$

In comparing the performance of the voltage-feedback circuit of Fig. 9.8 and the current-feedback circuit of Fig. 9.13, we see a distinct advantage in gain when the current-feedback circuit is used. This is explained by reduced output losses, less modification of the h_{21} parameter, and essentially no input-circuit losses. Another important advantage is the saving in components, namely two resistors and an electrolytic capacitor. Since all of these items are very favorable attributes, we should consider the current-feedback circuit as *preferred* if the resultant operating-point stability is acceptable.

9.8. Cascading RC-coupled stages.

In developing now an RC-coupled driving stage for a second RC-coupled stage we will find that we usually have greater design latitude. This situation ensues because, more often than not, the power requirements on the driving stage are very modest. This can be demonstrated by designing a driving stage for the current-feedback RC-coupled stage just designed in Sec. 9.7. The required power output was 1 mw. The useful power gain was calculated as 3800 times or 35.8 db. Thus the necessary power at the input can be calculated from Eq. (9.3); that is

$$P_{\text{in}} = \frac{P_{\text{out}}}{A_p}$$

$$= \frac{1\text{mw}}{3800}$$

$$= .264(10^{-6})\,\text{w}$$

Equations (9.44) will indicate what voltage swing will develop this power in the 326 ohm input impedance of the transistor. By (9.44)

$$V = \sqrt{2PR_{\text{in}}}$$

$$= \sqrt{2(.264)10^{-6}(326)} = .013\,\text{v}$$

This requirement certainly is not difficult to attain. One operating condition that comes to mind for the driving stage is to raise the quiescent-current level significantly in the hope that increased a-c current gain will provide increased gain. This, however, is likely not to occur because R_D would have to decrease, thereby increasing output losses. Also R_F would decrease, causing marked value changes for the modified h-parameters. The easiest solution is to make an identically designed stage. Note that we refrain from the use of the word *iterative* in this particular situation. Since the bias network is the same, the values of the modified h-parameters are the same. We need only determine the input impedance of our driving stage in order to determine the gain of this stage. Designating the input impedance (326 Ω) of our output stage as R_{in_2}, we may proceed to calculate the total load on our driving stage as

$$R_{\text{TOT}_1} = \frac{R_{D_1} R_{F_1} R_{\text{in}_2}}{R_{D_1} R_{F_1} + R_{D_1} R_{\text{in}_2} + R_{F_1} R_{\text{in}_2}} = 293\,\Omega$$

$$R_{\text{TOT}_1} h_{22}''' = 293(1267)10^{-6} = .371$$

Since $R_{\text{TOT}_1} h_{22}'''$ is greater than .1, then, by (8.28),

$$R_{\text{in}_1} = \frac{R_{\text{TOT}_1} \Delta^{h'''} + h_{11}'''}{R_{\text{TOT}_1} h_{22}''' + 1}$$

$$= \frac{293(5.6)10^{-2} + 591}{1.371} = 443\,\Omega$$

By (9.48)

$$\text{useful } A_p = h_{21}'''^{2} \frac{R_{\text{TOT}_1}}{R_{\text{in}_1}} \frac{R_{D_1}}{R_{\text{in}_2} + R_{D_1}}$$

$$= (46.9)^2 \frac{293}{443} \frac{3.14\,\text{K}}{3.466\,\text{K}}$$

$$= 1315 = 31.2\,\text{db}$$

The total useful gain of our two stages of *RC*-coupled amplifiers is 35.8 + 31.2 or 67 db.

The reader is encouraged to dwell on the practical significances of RC stages when feedback networks are used in the bias circuitry. In particular, the increased level of the modified output admittance h_{22}''' assumes significance in contributing to the gain level of the stage. For the problem used as the illustrative example, the magnitude of $R_L h_{22}'''$ for the output stage contributed a low input impedance and hence good gain. For the driver stage, the magnitude of $R_L h_{22}'''$ was lower and thus, by Eq. (8.28), the input impedance increased, causing reduced gain. Further cascading of identical stages would ultimately yield an iterative situation. This occurs when the $R_L h_{22}'''$ product is of the order of .5. This number of itself has no particular significance. We hope only to stimulate awareness of the occurrence of an iterative situation even in circuits with feedback. Use of exact equations is still recommended in dealing with such circuits to assure correct solutions.

PROBLEMS

1. What is the maximum power that can be developed in a load of 1 K when it is RC-coupled in a circuit that has minimized output-circuit losses? $V_{CC} = 9$ v.

2. What is the maximum ideal gain obtainable from three ideal-case common-emitter iterative stages?

3. It is desired to deliver a power of 1.5 mw to a load of 1 K with a transistor with a current gain h_{FE} of 55 and a leakage current I_{CBO} of 5 μa.
   (a) Design an optimized RC stage that uses current feedback. Assume V_{SAT} and V_B are negligible.
   (b) Using a 2N1414 with $h_{22b} = .62(10^{-6})$ mhos, $h_{11b} = 20$ ohms, $h_{12b} = 5.2$ (10^{-4}), and $h_{21e} = 44$ at 5 v and 1 ma, calculate the useful power gain when this device is used in the circuit of part (a).

4. It is desired to deliver 1 mw into a load of 1 K using two RC-coupled stages with current-feedback biasing. The limit transistor parameters (d-c) are

$$h_{FE}' = 45, \qquad h_{FE} = 25$$
$$I_{CBO}' = 6 \ \mu a, \qquad I_{CBO} = 5 \ \mu a$$

Use the a-c parameters of the 2N1414 device of Problem 3 as reference. Assume $V_{SAT} = .05$ v and $V_B = .15$ v.
   (a) Calculate the d-c collector load and the bias-resistor values.
   (b) Determine the operating-point values.
   (c) Draw the load-line depiction for the second stage.
   (d) Calculate the total useful circuit gain.

10

FREQUENCY EFFECTS

IN AUDIO AMPLIFIERS

The major matters in the design of low-frequency cascade amplifiers were discussed in Chapter 9. However, in discussing the reactive components used to couple stages or to by-pass emitter resistances we admittedly over-simplified by confining the analysis to a single frequency of operation. In reality, amplifiers such as those used in phonographs are expected to work satisfactorily over a frequency range that might extend from 50 to 25,000 cycles. We will learn in this chapter how the reactive circuit components serve to change the performance attributes of a transistor amplifier as frequency is varied. We will discover also that certain frequency-dependent transistor attributes cause performance variations in the audio-frequency range. Finally, we will discuss the various circuit techniques that can be employed to compensate for the degradations in performance introduced by both the transistor and the necessary reactive circuit components. Such compensation networks can be used to shape the frequency response of an amplifier to almost any desired form. Examples of practical amplifier circuits complete the chapter.

10.1. General-case frequency-dependent circuits. Before we actually study the specifics of reactive elements in transistor amplifiers, let us consider some nonspecific situations. Figure 10.1 illustrates graphically the variation of inductive and capacitive reactances as frequency is varied. The governing mathematical expression for Fig. 10.1(a) is

$$X_c = \frac{1}{2\pi f C} \tag{10.1}$$

222

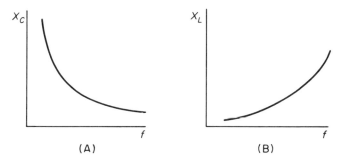

Fig. 10.1 (A) Variation of $X_c = (1/2\pi fC)$ versus f. (B) Variation of $X_L = 2\pi fL$ versus f.

where C = capacitance in farads
        X_c = capacitive reactance in ohms
        f = frequency in cycles

The governing mathematical expression for Fig. 10.1(b) is

$$X_L = 2\pi\, fL \qquad\qquad (10.2)$$

where L = inductance in henries
        X_L = inductive reactance in ohms
        f = frequency in cycles

Figure 10.2 shows an arbitrary circuit where a power source e_g, with its internal impedance R_g, is delivering power through a series capacitor C_1 to a load R_L, which is paralleled by a shunt capacitor C_2. The power in the load can be expressed as

$$P_{\text{load}} = \frac{e_L^2}{R_L} \qquad\qquad (10.3)$$

We have already been exposed to the situation in a circuit without reactance that maximum power transfer to the load occurs when $R_L = R_g$. This unique situation is not of immediate interest. We are more interested in the actual magnitude of e_L and how changes in frequency affect the value of e_L. Referring to the information of Fig. 10.1 and applying it to the circuit of Fig. 10.2, we can come up with several generalities. At low frequencies the reactance of each capacitor is large. The reactance X_{C_2} can be ignored, since a high-impedance shunt to R_L will not affect the value of e_L appearing across R_L. The reactance X_{C_1} appearing in series with R_L cannot be disregarded, because any voltage that is dropped across it leaves a reduced voltage value for e_L. The actual amount of voltage dropped in X_{C_1} depends on the value of X_{C_1},

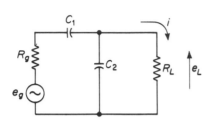

Fig. 10.2 General-case circuit with capacitance.

and this, of course, depends on the actual value of frequency f. At high frequencies the reactance of each capacitor will be small. The reactance X_{C_1}, then, can be ignored, since a series impedance of very small value will have negligible effect on the value of e_L appearing across R_L. The reactance X_{C_2}, which parallels the load R_L, cannot be ignored.

As frequency is increased, the combined impedance of C_2 and R_L in parallel gets smaller and smaller. The smaller this impedance, the lower the value of e_L that appears across R_L. At intermediate values of frequency it is reasonable to anticipate that neither C_1 nor C_2 causes undesirable degradations in the value of load voltage e_L. The exact frequency level at which both capacitors can be ignored depends on the relative values of the components in the circuit.

There seem to be, then, three specific ranges of frequency: a low range where the effects of C_1 are of interest, a mid range where neither C_1 nor C_2 is troublesome, and a high range where the effects of C_2 are of interest. Depending on frequency, the circuit of Fig. 10.2 will reduce to one of those shown in Fig. 10.3. These circuits omit either C_1 or C_2, or both, in conformance with the foregoing remarks. It is certainly of practical importance to obtain quantitative expressions for the value of e_L. We should anticipate a specific expression depending on the frequency range and equivalent circuit under consideration. A logical procedure is to express e_L in terms of the available source voltage, e_g.

The simplest circuit to analyze is the mid-frequency circuit shown in Fig. 10.3(b). By observation

$$i_L = \frac{e_g}{R_g + R_L} \tag{10.4}$$

$$e_L = i_L R_L \tag{10.5}$$

Substituting (10.4) into (10.5) for i_L, we find

$$e_L = \left(\frac{e_g}{R_g + R_L}\right) R_L \tag{10.6}$$

That is,

$$\frac{e_L}{e_g} = \frac{R_L}{R_g + R_L} \tag{10.7}$$

Equation (10.7) indicates that the ratio of e_L/e_g depends only on the relative values of R_g and R_L. Since there are no losses of voltage due to reactive components, the e_L/e_g ratio as given by Eq. (10.7) is a maximum-value condition for the circuit being considered.

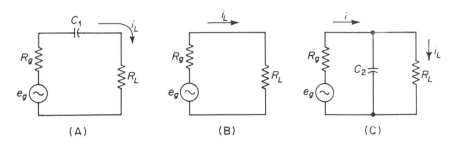

Fig. 10.3 Appropriate equivalents of Fig. 10.2 for (A) Low frequencies, $X_{C2} \gg R_L$; (B) Mid frequencies, $X_{C1} < R_L + R_g$, $X_{C2} > R_L$; (C) High frequencies, $X_{C1} \ll R_L + R_g$.

Let us now consider the low-frequency circuit of Fig. 10.3(a). The total series impedance is given by

$$Z = R_g + R_L - jX_{C_1} \tag{10.8}$$

We find then that

$$i_L = \frac{e_g}{R_g + R_L - jX_{C_1}} \tag{10.9}$$

Since Eq. (10.5) still applies, we would find by substituting (10.9) into (10.5) for i that

$$e_L = \left(\frac{e_g}{R_g + R_L - jX_{C_1}}\right) R_L \tag{10.10}$$

That is,

$$\frac{e_L}{e_g} = \frac{R_L}{R_g + R_L - jX_{C_1}} \tag{10.11}$$

$$= \frac{R_L}{[(R_g + R_L)^2 + (X_{C_1})^2]^{1/2}} \tag{10.12}$$

Equations (10.11) and (10.12) state just what the qualitative observations disclosed. As frequency decreases, the reactance X_{C_1} increases. As X_{C_1} increases, the denominators of Eqs. (10.11) and (10.12) get bigger, causing the e_L/e_g ratio to decrease.

As a numerical guide in comparing the relative performance of various component-value combinations, we need some analytical standard or reference. A commonly used figure of merit in evaluating frequency response is the so-called *half-power frequency*. This is the frequency at which, as frequency is changed from the mid range, the power in R_L is reduced to one-half the power that existed in R_L at mid frequencies. Symbolically, the low-frequency half-power point is called f_L. Equations (10.11) and (10.12) indicate how the value of e_L at low frequency compares to e_g. It is useful to create an expression that shows how the low-frequency value of e_L compares with the mid-frequency value of e_L. If we designate the e_L in Eq. (10.7) as $e_{L(\text{mid})}$ and the e_L in Eq. (10.12) as $e_{L(\text{low})}$, and then divide Eq. (10.12) by (10.7), we obtain

$$\frac{e_{L(\text{low})}}{e_{L(\text{mid})}} = \frac{R_g + R_L}{[(R_g + R_L)^2 + X_{C_1}^2]^{1/2}}$$

$$= \frac{1}{\left[1 + \left(\dfrac{X_{C_1}}{R_g + R_L}\right)^2\right]^{1/2}} \tag{10.13}$$

Equation (10.3) reminds us that power depends on the square of the load voltage e_L. At the half-power point, the ratio $e_{L(\text{low})}/e_{L(\text{mid})}$ must be equal to $1/\sqrt{2}$ or 0.707. Inspection of the denominator of Eq. (10.13) reveals that the condition for half power in R_L occurs at a frequency such that the quantity X_{C_1} is equal to the total series resistance, that is, the quantity $R_g + R_L$. We can say

$$f_L = \frac{1}{2\pi C_1(R_g + R_L)} \tag{10.14}$$

Speaking in terms of decibels, the half-power point can be described as the frequency at which the power is down 3 db from the mid-range value. Equations (10.11) or (10.12) can be used to obtain the e_L at any frequency of interest.

Consider now the high-frequency circuit of Fig. 10.3(c). The effective load impedance is the parallel combination of C_2 and R_L. This can be expressed as

$$Z_L = \frac{R_L(-jX_{C_2})}{R_L - jX_{C_2}} \tag{10.15}$$

where Z_L = effective load impedance.

For this circuit

$$i = \frac{e_g}{R_g + Z_L} \tag{10.16}$$

$$e_L = iZ_L \tag{10.17}$$

Substituting (10.15) and (10.16) into (10.17), we obtain

$$e_L = \frac{e_g}{R_g - \dfrac{jR_LX_{C_2}}{R_L - jX_{C_2}}}\left(\frac{-jR_LX_{C_2}}{R_L - jX_{C_2}}\right)$$

$$= e_g\left[\frac{-jR_LX_{C_2}}{R_gR_L - jX_{C_2}(R_g + R_L)}\right] \tag{10.18}$$

Dividing through by X_{C_2} and multiplying numerator and denominator by j we get

$$e_L = e_g \left(\frac{R_L}{R_g + R_L + j\dfrac{R_g R_L}{X_{C_2}}} \right) \tag{10.19}$$

That is,

$$\frac{e_L}{e_g} = \frac{R_L}{R_g + R_L + j\dfrac{R_g R_L}{X_{C_2}}} \tag{10.20}$$

$$= \frac{R_L}{\left[(R_g + R_L)^2 + \left(\dfrac{R_g R_L}{X_{C_2}}\right)^2 \right]^{1/2}} \tag{10.21}$$

Equation (10.21) indicates that as frequency increases, making X_{C_2} smaller, the denominator gets bigger, making the e_L/e_g ratio smaller. To obtain an expression indicating how the high-frequency value of e_L compares with the mid-frequency value of e_L, we designate the e_L in Eq. (10.21) as $e_{L(high)}$ and divide Eq. (10.21) by (10.7). The result is

$$\frac{e_{L(high)}}{e_{L(mid)}} = \frac{R_g + R_L}{\left[(R_g + R_L)^2 + \left(\dfrac{R_g R_L}{X_{C_2}}\right)^2 \right]^{1/2}}$$

$$= \frac{1}{\left[1 + \left(\dfrac{R_g R_L}{X_{C_2}(R_g + R_L)}\right)^2 \right]^{1/2}} \tag{10.22}$$

The high-frequency half-power point of any circuit is called f_H. At this half-power point, the ratio $e_{L(high)}/e_{L(mid)}$ must be equal to $1/\sqrt{2}$. Inspection of the denominator of Eq. (10.22) reveals that half power in R_L occurs at a frequency such that X_{C_2} equals the quantity $R_g R_L/(R_g + R_L)$. Note that the quantity $R_g R_L/(R_g + R_L)$ is essentially the series-circuit resistance. We can say then that

$$f_H = \frac{R_g + R_L}{2\pi C_2 R_g R_L} \tag{10.23}$$

The composite performance characteristic of the network shown in Fig. 10.2 can be shown graphically as in Fig. 10.4. Performance in the low-, mid-, and high-frequency ranges noted is described by Eqs. (10.12), (10.7), and (10.21), respectively.

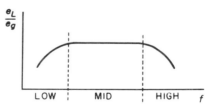

Fig. 10.4   Performance versus f for Fig. 10.2.

There may be times when an analysis involving current ratios is more appropriate. This might occur if the power source happened to present itself as a current generator in parallel with the effective source impedance. Such a situation is shown in Fig. 10.5(a). The evaluation of performance of this circuit would involve the calculation of the current ratio i_L/i_g. Probably the

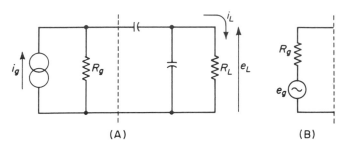

Fig. 10.5 (A) Current generator source. (B) Voltage generator source. For both diagrams $e_g = i_g R_g$.

easiest procedure is to replace the current source with its voltage-source equivalent. That is, the open-circuit source voltage e_g can be expressed as

$$e_g = i_g R_g \tag{10.24}$$

The quantity R_g would include the contribution of any resistor directly in parallel with it, should one exist in the circuit under consideration. The voltage equivalent is shown in Fig. 10.5(b). We would proceed exactly as we had before, with a separate consideration of low, mid, and high ranges of frequency. The equivalent circuits would be exactly the same as those shown in Figs. 10.3(a), (b), and (c). Recall the information of Eqs. (10.5) and (10.24):

$$e_L = i_L R_L \tag{10.5}$$

$$e_g = i_g R_g \tag{10.24}$$

We need only substitute these equations into Eqs. (10.7), (10.12), and (10.21) to get the desired current ratios. For the mid-frequency equivalent circuit,

$$\frac{i_L}{i_g} = \frac{R_g}{R_g + R_L} \tag{10.25}$$

For the low-frequency equivalent circuit,

$$\frac{i_L}{i_g} = \frac{R_g}{[(R_g + R_L)^2 + X_{C_1}^2]^{1/2}} \tag{10.26}$$

For the high-frequency equivalent circuit,

$$\frac{i_L}{i_g} = \frac{R_g}{\left[(R_g + R_L)^2 + \left(\frac{R_g R_L}{X_{C_2}}\right)^2 \right]^{1/2}} \tag{10.27}$$

Studying the form of these equations, it will be seen that

$$\frac{i_{L(\text{low})}}{i_{L(\text{mid})}} = \frac{1}{\left[1 + \left(\frac{X_{C_1}}{R_g + R_L}\right)^2 \right]^{1/2}} \tag{10.28}$$

This, of course, is the same as the expression for voltage ratio given by Eq. (10.13). The low frequency for half power is the same as that given by Eq. (10.14). In like manner it can be shown that

$$\frac{i_{L(\text{high})}}{i_{L(\text{mid})}} = \frac{1}{\left\{1 + \left[\dfrac{R_g R_L}{X_{C_2}(R_g + R_L)}\right]^2\right\}^{1/2}} \quad (10.29)$$

This is similar to the voltage-ratio expression given by Eq. (10.22). The high frequency for half power is the same as that given by Eq. (10.23).

The one other reactance likely to be encountered in our transistor circuits is the inductance associated with interstage coupling transformers. Since this inductance parallels the load, let us consider as a nonspecific circuit the one shown in Fig. 10.6. The source is shown as a current generator in 10.6(a), and as an equivalent voltage generator in 10.6(b). At high frequencies the

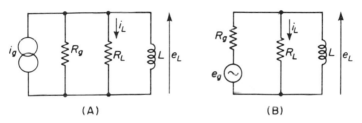

Fig. 10.6 General case of L shunting R_L. (A) Current generator source. (B) Voltage generator source. The relation $e_g = i_g R_g$ applies.

reactance X_L is high and does not affect the value of load voltage e_L. As frequency is reduced to low values, the reactance X_L diminishes. The combined impedance of R_L and X_L in parallel then gets smaller and smaller, thereby reducing the load voltage. We need then consider two equivalent circuits. A single circuit shown in Fig. 10.7(a) applies for the mid- and

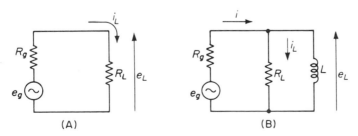

Fig. 10.7 Appropriate equivalents of Fig. 10.6 for: (A) mid and high frequencies, $X_L \gg R_L$. (B) low frequencies, $X_L < R_L$.

high-frequency ranges, where X_L can be ignored. The circuit of Fig. 10.7(b) should be used to analyze performance at lower frequencies.

For mid frequencies, the voltage ratio and current ratio are given by Eqs. (10.7) and (10.25), respectively. For low frequencies, the total load impedance is

$$Z_L = \frac{R_L(jX_L)}{R_L + jX_L} \tag{10.30}$$

The circuit current is

$$i = \frac{e_g}{R_g + Z_L} \tag{10.31}$$

The load voltage is

$$e_L = iZ_L \tag{10.32}$$

Substituting (10.30) and (10.31) into (10.32), it can be shown that

$$\frac{e_L}{e_g} = \frac{R_L}{\left[(R_g + R_L)^2 + \left(\frac{R_g R_L}{X_L}\right)^2\right]^{1/2}} \tag{10.33}$$

Similarly

$$\frac{i_L}{i_g} = \frac{R_g}{\left[(R_g + R_L)^2 + \left(\frac{R_g R_L}{X_L}\right)^2\right]^{1/2}} \tag{10.34}$$

Following the procedure of definitions developed originally for the circuits involving capacitors,

$$\frac{i_{L(low)}}{i_{r(mid)}} = \frac{e_{L(low)}}{e_{L(mid)}} = \frac{1}{\left\{1 + \left[\frac{R_g R_L}{(R_g + R_L)X_L}\right]^2\right\}^{1/2}} \tag{10.35}$$

$$f_L = \frac{R_g R_L}{2\pi L(R_g + R_L)} \tag{10.36}$$

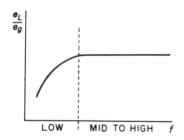

Fig. 10.8 Performance vs f for Fig. 10.6.

Half power in R_L occurs at the frequency where the quantity X_L equals the quantity $R_g R_L/(R_g + R_L)$. This latter quantity is essentially the total circuit series resistance. Note that the quantity R_L would include and might consist entirely of the impedance reflected from the secondary of the transformer. The performance characteristic of the network of Fig. 10.6 is shown graphically in Fig. 10.8.

10.2. Specific analysis—transistors at low frequency. General-situation circuits have been introduced to help the reader visualize the procedures in analyzing frequency-dependent circuits. Equations have been derived to show mathematically how the various components contribute to performance variations with frequency. We will now consider the specifics of a transistor circuit. We must know how the transistor interacts with the various circuit components if we are to properly control the variables that dominate the frequency response of transistor audio amplifiers. The transistor itself presents no reactive attribute to contribute to low-frequency performance degradation. Three specific circuit components that do contribute to low-frequency performance degradation are (a) interstage coupling transformers, (b) interstage coupling capacitors, and (c) emitter by-pass capacitors.

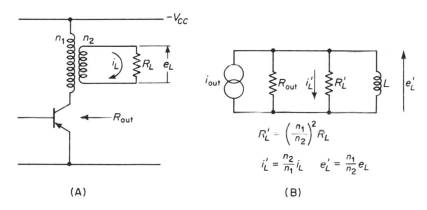

(A)   (B)

Fig. 10.9 (A) Transistor circuit with transformer coupled load. (B) Equivalent circuit applicable for analyzing frequency effects.

Consider first the circuit shown in Fig. 10.9. Here the load R_L is being transformer-coupled to the collector of the transistor. This is quite similar to the general-case situation. It can be shown from (10.33) that

$$\frac{e'_L}{e_{\text{out}}} = \frac{R'_L}{\left[(R_{\text{out}} + R'_L)^2 + \left(\frac{R_{\text{out}} R'_L}{X_L}\right)^2\right]^{1/2}} \qquad (10.37)$$

From (10.34)

$$\frac{i'_L}{i_{\text{out}}} = \frac{R_{\text{out}}}{\left[(R_{\text{out}} + R'_L)^2 + \left(\frac{R_{\text{out}} R'_L}{X_L}\right)^2\right]^{1/2}} \qquad (10.38)$$

From (10.35)

$$\frac{i'_{L(\text{low})}}{i'_{L(\text{mid})}} = \frac{e'_{L(\text{low})}}{e'_{L(\text{mid})}} = \frac{1}{\left\{1 + \left[\dfrac{R_{\text{out}} R'_L}{(R_{\text{out}} + R'_L) X_L}\right]^2\right\}^{1/2}} \tag{10.39}$$

From (10.36)

$$f_L = \frac{R_{\text{out}} R'_L}{2\pi L (R_{\text{out}} + R'_L)} \tag{10.40}$$

where

$$e'_L = \frac{n_1}{n_2} e_L \tag{10.41}$$

$$i'_L = \frac{n_2}{n_1} i_L \tag{10.42}$$

$$R'_L = \left(\frac{n_1}{n_2}\right)^2 R_L \tag{10.43}$$

R_{out} = output impedance of transistor

L = inductance of transformer primary

Here we observe that the low-frequency response of a transistor amplifier depends jointly on L, R_{out}, and R'_L as defined. Proper attention must be paid the relative values of these impedances to assure the desired low-frequency response.

Consider now an *RC*-coupled circuit as shown in Fig. 10.10(a). The equivalent circuit is shown in Fig. 10.10(b). Note that the *effective* source impedance is R_{out} and R_D in parallel. The *effective* load impedance is the resistance R_{in_2}, where R_{in_2} is the input impedance of the following stage. Knowing these specific facts for the transistor circuit, we can substitute directly into the general-case equations for an *RC*-coupled stage.

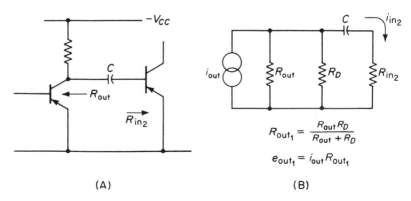

(A)   (B)

Fig. 10.10 (A) Transistor circuit with *RC*-coupled load. (B) Equivalent circuit applicable for analyzing frequency effects.

From (10.12)

$$\frac{e_{\mathrm{in}_2}}{e_{\mathrm{out}_1}} = \frac{R_{\mathrm{in}_2}}{[(R_{\mathrm{out}_1} + R_{\mathrm{in}_2})^2 + (X_C)^2]^{1/2}} \tag{10.44}$$

From (10.26)

$$\frac{i_{\mathrm{in}_2}}{i_{\mathrm{out}}} = \frac{R_{\mathrm{out}_1}}{[(R_{\mathrm{out}_1} + R_{\mathrm{in}_2})^2 + (X_C)^2]^{1/2}} \tag{10.45}$$

From (10.13 or 10.28)

$$\frac{i_{\mathrm{in}_2(\mathrm{low})}}{i_{\mathrm{in}_2(\mathrm{mid})}} = \frac{e_{\mathrm{in}_2(\mathrm{low})}}{e_{\mathrm{in}_2(\mathrm{mid})}} = \frac{1}{\left[1 + \left(\dfrac{X_C}{R_{\mathrm{out}_1} + R_{\mathrm{in}_2}}\right)^2\right]^{1/2}} \tag{10.46}$$

From (10.14)

$$f_L = \frac{1}{2\pi C (R_{\mathrm{out}_1} + R_{\mathrm{in}_2})} \tag{10.47}$$

where

$$R_{\mathrm{out}_1} = \frac{R_D R_{\mathrm{out}}}{R_D + R_{\mathrm{out}}} \tag{10.48}$$

$$e_{\mathrm{out}_1} = i_{\mathrm{out}} R_{\mathrm{out}_1} \tag{10.49}$$

More often than not the impedance R_{out} is much larger than R_D, and the last series of equations simplifies accordingly. The complete equations, however, should be retained as the references.

The third reactance that affects the low-frequency response of transistor amplifiers is the emitter by-pass capacitor C_E. A general-case situation is shown in Fig. 10.11(a). Here we show a transistor stage incorporating an emitter resistor R_E, with a by-pass capacitor C_E. The output coupling of this particular stage is not of immediate importance, nor is the means by which power is given to the input of this stage; this will be confirmed shortly. We show, then, as an equivalent circuit the configuration in Fig. 10.11(b).

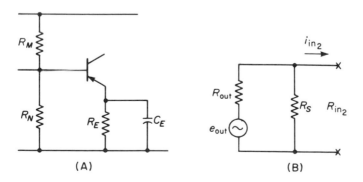

Fig. 10.11 (A) Bias network with an emitter by-pass capacitor. (B) Equivalent circuit configuration at input. R_{in_2} depends on frequency.

Our interest is in the transfer of power from the output of a preceding stage to the input of the stage in question, which is referred to by subscripts 2. In particular we are interested in the power in R_{in_2}. The input impedance of any stage is determined with the help of Eq. (8.28), which states

$$R_{in_2} = \frac{R_L \Delta^h + h_{11}}{R_L h_{22} + 1} \tag{10.50}$$

A few observations and recollections are helpful at this time. The bias resistors are not being considered a part of the input resistance R_{in_2}. At some mid range of frequencies the capacitor C_E succeeds in shorting out the quantity R_E. As frequency is reduced, the reactance X_{C_E} becomes larger. There is then less effective by-passing of R_E. At such lower frequencies the quantities h_{11}, h_{22}, and Δ^h should be appropriately modified to account for the presence of an emitter impedance Z_E, which is the impedance of R_E and C_E in parallel. At any frequency, the emitter impedance is

$$Z_E = \frac{R_E(-j X_{C_E})}{R_E - j X_{C_E}} \tag{10.51}$$

where

$$X_{C_E} = \frac{1}{2\pi f C_E} \tag{10.52}$$

Multiplying both numerator and denominator of Eq. (10.51) by the quantity j, we obtain

$$Z_E = \frac{R_E X_{C_E}}{X_{C_E} + j R_E} = \frac{R_E}{1 + j\omega R_E C_E} \tag{10.53}$$

Equation (10.50) would then become

$$R_{in_2} = \frac{R_L \Delta^{h'} + h_{11}''}{R_L h_{22}'' + 1} \tag{10.54}$$

Thinking back to the material on modified h-parameters, we can recall that for the typical values of emitter resistance that might be used, the values of h_{21}'' and h_{22}'' will hardly differ from the values of the transistor itself. The values of modified h_{11}'' and h_{12}'' are significantly larger than the values of these parameters for the transistor itself. It can be shown that the modified $\Delta^{h''}$ is approximately equal to the value for the transistor alone. The value of input impedance, as given by Eq. (10.54) for the particular circuit on hand, depends on the value of R_L. It is necessary to consider circuits such as RC-coupled amplifiers, where R_L is small, separately from circuits where R_L is made large to obtain maximum gain.

If R_L is small, Eq. (10.54) will reduce to

$$R_{in_2} = h_{11}'' \tag{10.55}$$

Substituting Eq. (7.79) for h_{11}'' in Eq. (10.55), we obtain

$$R_{\text{in}_2} = h_{11} + \frac{Z_E(1 + h_{21})}{1 + Z_E h_{22}} \qquad (10.56a)$$

Since the quantity $Z_E h_{22}$ is always small, we can say

$$R_{\text{in}_2} = h_{11} + (1 + h_{21})Z_E \qquad (10.56b)$$

Substituting Eq. (10.51) into (10.56b),

$$R_{\text{in}_2} = h_{11} - \frac{j(1 + h_{21})R_E X_{CE}}{R_E - jX_{CE}} \qquad (10.57)$$

The effective load on the source is the parallel combination of R_{in_2} and R_S. Let us label this effective load R_{in_2}', where

$$R_{\text{in}_2}' = \frac{R_S R_{\text{in}_2}}{R_S + R_{\text{in}_2}} \qquad (10.58)$$

The expressions that indicate performance as a function of frequency use the procedure already established. It is somewhat less rigorous to deal with the current expressions. We say as a general, all-frequency case

$$\frac{i_{\text{in}_2}}{i_{\text{out}}} = \left(\frac{R_{\text{out}}}{R_{\text{out}} + R_{\text{in}_2}'}\right)\left(\frac{R_{\text{in}_2}'}{R_{\text{in}_2}}\right) \qquad (10.59)$$

where R_{in_2}' is given in Eq. (10.58). Substituting now Eq. (10.58) for R_{in_2}' in (10.59), we obtain as our general expression

$$\frac{i_{\text{in}_2}}{i_{\text{out}}} = \frac{R_{\text{out}} R_S}{R_{\text{out}} R_S + (R_{\text{out}} + R_S)R_{\text{in}_2}} \qquad (10.60)$$

At the mid range, the reactance X_{CE} is intentionally made small in comparison to R_E. Equation (10.57) will then reduce to

$$R_{\text{in}_2} = h_{11} - j(1 + h_{21})X_{CE} \qquad (10.61a)$$

In practical use X_{CE} is of the order of 1–3 ohms at the mid-frequency design point. At mid and high frequency, Eq. (10.61a) reduces to

$$R_{\text{in}_2} \cong h_{11} \qquad (10.61b)$$

Substituting the conditions of (10.61b) in (10.60) we can say

$$\frac{i_{\text{in}_2(\text{mid})}}{i_{\text{out}}} = \frac{R_{\text{out}} R_S}{R_{\text{out}} R_S + h_{11}(R_{\text{out}} + R_S)} \qquad (10.62)$$

Designating the i_{in_2} quantity of Eq. (10.60) as $i_{\text{in}_2(\text{low})}$ and taking the ratio of Eqs. (10.60) and (10.62) with substitution of (10.57) for R_{in_2} it can be shown that

$$\frac{i_{\text{in}_2(\text{low})}}{i_{\text{in}_2(\text{mid})}} = \frac{[R_{\text{out}}R_S + h_{11}(R_{\text{out}} + R_S)](R_E - jX_{CE})}{\begin{array}{l}[R_{\text{out}}R_S + h_{11}(R_{\text{out}} + R_S)]R_E \\ \quad - jX_{CE}\{R_{\text{out}}R_S + (R_{\text{out}} + R_S)[h_{11} + R_E(1 + h_{21})]\}\end{array}} \qquad (10.63)$$

As a legitimate approximation we can say

$$\frac{i_{\text{in}_2(\text{low})}}{i_{\text{in}_2(\text{mid})}} \cong \frac{1}{1 - jX_{C_E}\dfrac{h_{11} + \dfrac{R_{\text{out}}R_S}{R_{\text{out}} + R_S} + (1 + h_{21})R_E}{R_E\left(h_{11} + \dfrac{R_{\text{out}}R_S}{R_{\text{out}} + R_S}\right)}} \tag{10.64}$$

The low-frequency half-power point occurs when

$$X_{C_E} = \frac{R_E\left(h_{11} + \dfrac{R_{\text{out}}R_S}{R_{\text{out}} + R_S}\right)}{h_{11} + \dfrac{R_{\text{out}}R_S}{R_{\text{out}} + R_S} + (1 + h_{21})R_E} \tag{10.65}$$

where X_{C_E} is given by Eq. (10.52). That is,

$$f_L = \frac{h_{11} + \dfrac{R_{\text{out}}R_S}{R_{\text{out}} + R_S} + (1 + h_{21})R_E}{2\pi C_E R_E\left(h_{11} + \dfrac{R_{\text{out}}R_S}{R_{\text{out}} + R_S}\right)} \tag{10.66}$$

The form of Eqs. (10.65) and (10.66) may not be quite as obvious as one might wish. If we multiply the numerator and denominator of the second term of Eq. (10.57) by the quantity $(1 + h_{21})$, we get

$$-j\frac{(1 + h_{21})^2 R_E X_{C_E}}{(1 + h_{21})(R_E - jX_{C_E})} \tag{10.67}$$

The form of the quantity in (10.67) suggests that at the input terminals of the transistor the emitter resistor appears multiplied by the quantity $(1 + h_{21})$ and the by-pass capacitor appears divided by the quantity $(1 + h_{21})$. The equivalent circuit for the circuit in Fig. 10.11 can be shown in detail as in Fig. 10.12. Inspection of this circuit confirms that the half-power frequency makes the reactance due to $C_E/(1 + h_{21})$ equal to the total series resistance.

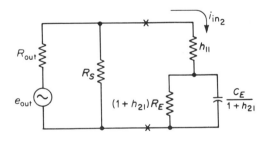

Fig. 10.12 Complete equivalent depiction of input circuitry of Fig 10.11 to include C_E per the development of Eq. (10.67). Diagram relates to low R_L value circuits.

This is precisely the content of Eqs. (10.65) and (10.66). One final practical comment. Typical circuit values are usually such that

$$(1 + h_{21})R_E \gg h_{11} + \frac{R_{out}R_S}{R_{out} + R_S}$$

This condition allows Eq. (10.65) to reduce to

$$X_{C_E} \cong \frac{h_{11} + \dfrac{R_{out}R_S}{R_{out} + R_S}}{1 + h_{21}} \tag{10.68}$$

Equation (10.66) becomes then

$$f_L \cong \frac{1 + h_{21}}{2\pi C_E \left(h_{11} + \dfrac{R_{out}R_S}{R_{out} + R_S} \right)} \tag{10.68a}$$

Equation (10.68) suggests that the actual value of emitter resistance is not of significance in the low-frequency performance of a transistor amplifier. Of greater importance are the impedances R_{out} of the generator and R_S due to a bias network which shunts the input terminals of the transistor. These components plus the capacitor C_E are the most significant elements controlling low-frequency performance.

If now we consider a high load, we should properly consider the effects of $R_L h_{22}$. We have mentioned that h_{22}'' is essentially the same as h_{22}; also that $\Delta^{h''}$ is essentially the same as Δ^h. At lower frequencies, where X_{C_E} is not negligible in comparison to R_E, we write

$$R_{in_2} = \frac{R_L\Delta^h + h_{11} - j \dfrac{(1 + h_{21})X_{C_E}R_E}{R_E - jX_{C_E}}}{R_L h_{22} + 1} \tag{10.69a}$$

$$= \frac{R_L\Delta^h + h_{11}}{R_L h_{22} + 1} - j \frac{1 + h_{21}}{R_L h_{22} + 1}\left(\frac{X_{C_E}R_E}{R_E - jX_{C_E}} \right) \tag{10.69b}$$

From Eq. (10.69b) an equivalent circuit such as Fig. 10.13 is drawn. The series resistance is the first term of Eq. (10.69b), that is the quantity

$$\frac{R_L\Delta^h + h_{11}}{R_L h_{22} + 1}$$

The emitter resistance appears multiplied by the quantity $(1 + h_{21})/(R_L h_{22} + 1)$, and the by-pass capacitor appears divided by the quantity $(1 + h_{21})/(R_L h_{22} + 1)$. As a short-cut approach, we should anticipate that at the half-power frequency, the capacitive reactance in the circuit of Fig. 10.13 is equal to the total series resistance. The solution is

$$X_{C_E} = \frac{R_E \left(\dfrac{R_L\Delta^h + h_{11}}{R_L h_{22} + 1} + \dfrac{R_{out}R_S}{R_{out} + R_S} \right)}{\dfrac{1 + h_{21}}{R_L h_{22} + 1}R_E + \dfrac{R_L\Delta^h + h_{11}}{R_L h_{22} + 1} + \dfrac{R_{out}R_S}{R_{out} + R_S}} \tag{10.70}$$

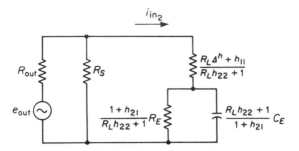

Fig. 10.13 Complete equivalent depiction of input circuitry of Fig. 10.11 to include C_E per the development of Eq. (10.69)—relates to high value R_L circuits.

where X_{C_E} as before is given by Eq. (10.52). The expression for the frequency value is

$$f_L = \frac{\dfrac{1 + h_{21}}{R_L h_{22} + 1} R_E + \dfrac{R_L \Delta^h + h_{11}}{R_L h_{22} + 1} + \dfrac{R_{out} R_S}{R_{out} + R_S}}{2\pi C_E R_E \left(\dfrac{R_L \Delta^h + h_{11}}{R_L h_{22} + 1} + \dfrac{R_{out} R_S}{R_{out} + R_S} \right)}$$ (10.71)

The general expression for frequency response would be

$$\frac{i_{in_2(low)}}{i_{in_2(mid)}} = \cfrac{1}{1 - jX_{C_E} \left[\cfrac{\dfrac{1 + h_{21}}{R_L h_{22} + 1} R_E + \dfrac{R_L \Delta^h + h_{11}}{R_L h_{22} + 1} + \dfrac{R_{out} R_S}{R_{out} + R_S}}{R_E \left(\dfrac{R_L \Delta^h + h_{11}}{R_L h_{22} + 1} + \dfrac{R_{out} R_S}{R_{out} + R_S} \right)} \right]}$$ (10.72)

In most circuit applications, the quantity $(1 + h_{21})R_E/(R_L h_{22} + 1)$ is larger than the other terms of the preceding equations. Equation (10.70) will reduce to

$$X_{C_E} \simeq \frac{\dfrac{R_L \Delta^h + h_{11}}{R_L h_{22} + 1} + \dfrac{R_{out} R_S}{R_{out} + R_S}}{\dfrac{1 + h_{21}}{R_L h_{22} + 1}}$$ (10.73)

Eq. (10.71) becomes than

$$f_L \simeq \frac{\dfrac{1 + h_{21}}{R_L h_{22} + 1}}{2\pi C_E \left(\dfrac{R_L \Delta^h + h_{11}}{R_L h_{22} + 1} + \dfrac{R_{out} R_S}{R_{out} + R_S} \right)}$$ (10.73a)

When we introduced this material on the emitter by-pass capacitor, we commented that the frequency effects of the interstage coupling capacitor or transformer can be ignored. This is permissible because the reactive factors in the emitter can cause more serious performance degradation than the coupling reactances. Proper design can, of course, compensate for these tendencies.

Designs usually require adequate capacitance to assure that performance does not fall off too soon. This justifies our treating coupling capacitance and by-pass capacitance separately. An approach dealing with both capacitances would reveal an f_L lower than that obtained by treating each capacitance on a separate basis. Thus in Eq. (10.47), where we deal with the cutoff due to coupling capacitance, any ineffectiveness of C_E would make R_{in_2} larger and the resultant f_L smaller. Likewise, in (10.66), where we study the cutoff due to C_E, an inclusion of C_1 would make the effective source larger. This would make the denominator of (10.66) larger and f_L smaller. If R_S were smaller than R_{out}, this observation would not hold. The former situation is, however, most likely. It is not likely that a minimum control be imposed on f_L, and thus in practical circuits it is not necessary to consider both reactances simultaneously.

The capacitor factors contributing to low-frequency performance are summarized in the following series of examples.

10.3. Example: coupling-capacitor effects on performance. As a numerical setup for our present examples, let us recall the circuit of Sec. 9.5 and the values of circuit elements and parameters determined for the low-gain 2N1414:

$$R_M = 29.4 \text{ K}$$
$$R_N = 5.9 \text{ K}$$
$$R_E = 470 \text{ }\Omega$$
$$R_D = 2.65 \text{ K}$$
$$R_L = 1 \text{ K}$$

The operating point is

$$V_Q = 2.26 \text{ v}$$
$$I_Q = 2.15 \text{ ma}$$

At this operating point,

$$h_{22e} = 97(10^{-6}) \text{ mhos}$$
$$h_{12e} = 3.1(10^{-4})$$
$$h_{11e} = 600 \text{ }\Omega$$
$$h_{21e} = 47.5$$

Let us assume perfect by-passing of R_E and calculate the value of C_1 that will assure that the half-power point does not occur at a frequency greater than 30 cps. Assume a source impedance of 3 K. The applicable circuit is shown in Fig. 10.14. Since R_E is by-passed, we cannot use the modified *h*-parameters calculated back in Sec. 9.5. We must calculate new *h*-parameters showing only the effect of R_S. The steps in determining R_{in_2} of our stage follow.

$$R_S = \frac{R_M R_N}{R_M + R_N}$$

$$= \frac{29.4\,\mathrm{K}\,(5.9\,\mathrm{K})}{35.3\,\mathrm{K}} = 4.9\,\mathrm{K}$$

$$\frac{R_S}{h_{11} + R_S} = \frac{4.9\,\mathrm{K}}{600 + 4.9\,\mathrm{K}} = .89$$

By (7.70)

$$h'_{21} = \frac{h_{21} R_S}{h_{11} + R_S}$$

$$= 47.5(.89) = 42.4$$

By (7.71)

$$h'_{11} = \frac{h_{11} R_S}{h_{11} + R_S}$$

$$= 600(.89) = 534\,\Omega$$

By (7.74)

$$h'_{12} = \frac{h_{12} R_S}{h_{11} + R_S}$$

$$= 3.1(10^{-4})(.89) = 2.76(10^{-4})$$

By (7.73)

$$h'_{22} = h_{22} - \frac{h_{12} h_{21}}{h_{11} + R_S}$$

$$= 97(10^{-6}) - \frac{3.1(10^{-4})47.5}{5.5\,\mathrm{K}} = 94.3(10^{-6})$$

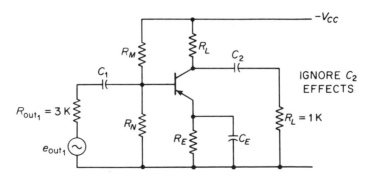

Fig. 10.14　Circuit for illustrative examples of Secs. 10.3 and 10.4.

We find then, that

$$R_L h'_{22} = 1\,K\,(94.3)\,10^{-6}$$
$$= .0943$$

Since $R_L\,h_{22}$ is less than .1, we can say

$$R_{\text{in}_2} \cong h'_{11}$$
$$= 534\,\Omega$$

Since we know R_{out_1} is 3 K, we need only substitute into Eq. (10.47).

$$C = \frac{1}{2\pi f (R_{\text{out}_1} + R_{\text{in}_2})} = \frac{1}{2\pi\,(30)\,(3000 + 534)} = 1.5\,\mu f$$

A nearest whole value of 2 μf gives an $f_L = 22.6$ cps.

10.4. Example: by-pass capacitor effects on performance.   Let us ignore the presence of the coupling capacitor C_1 in Fig. 10.14 and study the effects of the by-pass capacitor C_E. We will use the transistor parameters listed for Sec. 10.3. Let us begin by calculating the C_E that makes $X_{C_E} = 2$ ohms at 1000 cycles. By (10.52)

$$C_E = \frac{1}{2\pi f X_{C_E}} = \frac{1}{2\pi\,(1000)\,2} = 8\,\mu f$$

Using Eq. (10.66), we can now determine the f_L due to C_E alone. Prior calculations showed $R_S = 4.9$ K. Therefore

$$\frac{R_{\text{out}}\,R_S}{R_{\text{out}} + R_S} = \frac{3\,K\,(4.9\,K)}{7.9\,K} = 1.86\,K$$

Thus by (10.66)

$$f_L = \frac{h_{11} + \dfrac{R_{\text{out}}\,R_S}{R_{\text{out}} + R_S} + (1 + h_{21})\,R_E}{2\pi\,C_E\,R_E\left(h_{11} + \dfrac{R_{\text{out}}\,R_S}{R_{\text{out}} + R_S}\right)}$$

$$= \frac{534 + 1860 + 43.4\,(470)}{2\pi\,8\,(10^{-6})\,(470)\,(534 + 1860)}$$

$$= \frac{22.8\,K}{56.4} = 404 \text{ cps}$$

This is quite an interesting result. Having picked a C_E that seemed more than adequate as a by-pass at mid frequencies, we notice very rapid degradation in performance as frequency is decreased. This demonstrates how the emitter by-pass is more effective than coupling capacitance in affecting low-frequency performance. To find the value of C_E necessary to keep f_L from being greater than 30 cps, let us solve Eq. (10.66) for C_E using $f_L = 30$ cps.

$$C_E = \frac{h_{11} + \dfrac{R_{\text{out}} R_S}{R_{\text{out}} + R_S} + (1 + h_{21}) R_E}{2\pi f_L R_E \left(h_{11} + \dfrac{R_{\text{out}} R_S}{R_{\text{out}} + R_S}\right)}$$

$$= \frac{22.8\,\text{K}}{2\pi (30)(470)(534 + 1860)}$$

$$= \frac{22.8\,\text{K}}{212(10^6)} = 107\,\mu\text{f}$$

10.5. Specific analysis—transistors at high frequency. Having discussed the factors that contribute to the degradation of performance at low frequencies, we now consider the factors that affect circuit performance at high frequencies. Two specific matters deserve comment: (a) the barrier capacitance at the reverse-biased collector-base junction, and (b) the deterioration of forward-current gain in a transistor as frequency increases. In this latter matter we will incorporate the effects of the diffusion capacitance at the forward-biased emitter-base junction of a transistor.

Back in Chapter 2 we talked of the charge difference that exists across a diode junction under either equilibrium or back-bias conditions. This charge difference was likened to that which exists on the plates of a parallel-plate capacitor. The capacitance across a back-bias junction was named the *barrier capacitance*. In a common-base connection of a transistor, the collector and base terminals that serve as the output connections are back-biased. There will be, then, some amount of capacitance across the junction depending on the magnitude of the back-biasing collector-base voltage. For a transistor, this barrier capacitance across the collector-base junction is symbolized as C_{ob}. Since this capacitance is voltage-dependent, it is necessary to note the collector voltage at which the magnitude of C_{ob} is specified when it appears on a transistor specification sheet. It is also helpful to know how capacitance varies with voltage. This variation depends on the type of construction for the device. Since transistors are most frequently used in the common-emitter connection, we must refer C_{ob} to the collector-emitter terminals. The resultant common-emitter output capacitance is symbolized as C_{oe}, where

$$C_{oe} = (1 + h_{21e}) C_{ob} \tag{10.74}$$

For any typical *RC*-coupled amplifier, as shown in Fig. 10.10(a), a high-frequency equivalent circuit including C_{oe} is shown in Fig. 10.15. Converting to a voltage-generator source, where the effective source impedance is R_{out} and R_D in parallel, we observe that the equivalent circuit is the same as

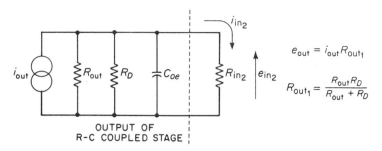

Fig. 10.15 Equivalent circuit of an *R-C* output including barrier capacitance C_{oe} (for high-frequency analysis).

the general-case situation shown in Fig. 10.3(c). Using the general-case equations on a direct-substitution basis, we obtain from (10.21)

$$\frac{e_{\text{in}_2}}{e_{\text{out}}} = \frac{R_{\text{in}_2}}{\left[(R_{\text{out}_1} + R_{\text{in}_2})^2 + \left(\frac{R_{\text{out}_1} R_{\text{in}_2}}{X_{C_{oe}}}\right)^2\right]^{1/2}} \tag{10.75}$$

From (10.27)

$$\frac{i_{\text{in}_2}}{i_{\text{out}}} = \frac{R_{\text{out}_1}}{\left[(R_{\text{out}_1} + R_{\text{in}_2})^2 + \left(\frac{R_{\text{out}_1} R_{\text{in}_2}}{X_{\iota_{oe}}}\right)^2\right]^{1/2}} \tag{10.76}$$

From (10.22) or (10.29)

$$\frac{e_{\text{in}_2(\text{high})}}{e_{\text{in}_2(\text{mid})}} = \frac{i_{\text{in}_2(\text{high})}}{i_{\text{in}_2(\text{mid})}} = \frac{1}{\left[1 + \left(\frac{R_{\text{out}_1} R_{\text{in}_2}}{X_{C_{oe}}(R_{\text{out}_1} + R_{\text{in}_2})}\right)^2\right]^{1/2}} \tag{10.77}$$

From 10.23

$$f_H = \frac{R_{\text{out}_1} + R_{\text{in}_2}}{2\pi C_{oe} R_{\text{out}_1} R_{\text{in}_2}} \tag{10.78}$$

This analysis verifies that at high frequencies the half-power frequency is that which causes the output reactance to equal the total series resistance. The total series resistance is in this case the parallel equivalent of the effective output and input impedances.

The next factor that may affect performance at the high end of the audio spectrum is the deterioration of forward-current gain as frequency increases. This is explained by recalling how transistors operate. The most important fact is that the carriers injected from the emitter into the base merely diffuse through the base. Each semiconductor material, whether N-type or P-type, has a known diffusion constant indicative of the rate at which injected particles will diffuse. Since every transistor has a finite base width, there is also a predictable time required for injected particles to diffuse from the emitter-base junction to the collector voltage line. This time period is called *transit time*. At low frequencies the time period of input signals is long in comparison to transit time, and the charge flow reaching the collector is indicative of normal charge injection and carrier recombination in the base region.

In Chapter 2 we spoke of the diffusion capacitance across the junction of a forward-biased diode. Such a capacitance exists between emitter and base in a transistor. The charge across this capacitor cannot change instantaneously. This is of special significance as far as the base region is concerned. As frequency increases, the time period of the input signal reduces to approach the transit time, and the base can no longer keep up with changing quantities of charge being injected by the emitter. There is then some cancellation of input charges in the base region, and fewer charges are received at the collector. A reduction is evident in the forward-current gain in the transistor. If frequency is made very high, the effective forward-current gain reduces to zero.

For many transistors some reduction of common-emitter current gain occurs within the audio-frequency range. A transistor's specification sheet gives information to enable us to determine the effects, if any, that occur within this range. This information is the so-called *small-signal forward-current-gain cutoff frequency*—the frequency at which the forward-current gain has decreased 3 db or is equal to .707 of the low-frequency value. There is a cutoff frequency for each of the common-base and common-emitter forward-current gains. The symbol for the common-base cutoff frequency is f_{hfb} and that for common-emitter cutoff frequency is f_{hfe}. The expression for common-base current gain at any frequency is

$$h_{21b(\text{high})} = \frac{h_{21b}}{1 + j\dfrac{f}{f_{hfe}}} \tag{10.79}$$

where h_{21b} = low-frequency small-signal value
f = frequency of interest

The expression for common-emitter current gain at any frequency is

$$h_{21e(\text{high})} = \frac{h_{21e}}{1 + j\dfrac{f}{f_{hfe}}} \tag{10.80}$$

where h_{21e} = low-frequency small-signal value
f = frequency of interest

The relation between the common-base and common-emitter cutoff frequencies is given by

$$f_{hfe} = \frac{f_{hfb}}{1 + h_{21e}} \tag{10.81}$$

It is important to appreciate the meanings of the values of the parameters involved in Eq. (10.81). As implied, the value of the common-base cutoff frequency is provided by the manufacturer on a specification sheet. The typical measurement circuit utilizes a current generator at the input terminals. The value of common-emitter cutoff frequency as calculated could be duplicated in an appropriate measurement circuit involving a current generator at the input terminals. Developing the matter of the common-emitter cutoff further, it can be shown that the value of f_{hfe} as calculated by Eq. (10.81) is a minimum value for the *apparent* cutoff value that a transistor can display in an operating circuit. Recall, for the moment, the equivalent circuit for a forward-biased diode shown in Fig. 2.21(b) and repeated in Fig. 10.16(a).

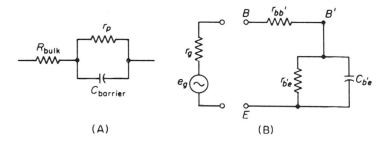

(A)   (B)

Fig. 10.16   (A) Equivalent circuit of forward-biased diode. (B) Equivalent circuit of forward-biased emitter-base regions in common-emitter connection.

In converting this equivalent circuit to apply to the forward-biased base-emitter regions of a transistor connected in the common-emitter circuit, we provide without elaboration the equivalent circuit shown in Fig. 10.16(b). The resistance $r_{bb'}$ is called the *extrinsic base resistance*, and represents the bulk a-c resistance of the base region. The quantity $r_{b'e}$ represents the a-c impedance of the forward-biased base-emitter diode. This parameter can be expressed mathematically as

$$r_{b'e} = (1 + h_{21e}) \frac{26}{I_E} \tag{10.82}$$

where $I_E \approx I_C$ is the operating point in milliamperes. The quantity $C_{b'e}$ represents the diffusion capacitance. This quantity is related to other pertinent quantities by

$$C_{b'e} = \frac{1}{2\pi f_{hfe} r_{b'e}} \tag{10.83}$$

where $C_{b'e}$ is the diffusion capacitance in farads
     f_{hfe} is given by Eq. (10.81)
     $r_{b'e}$ is given by Eq. (10.82)

The dynamic behavior of the transistor depends on the resultant useful voltage that appears between points B' and E. The diffusion capacitance is in parallel with these terminals and will therefore contribute to performance degradation at high frequencies. Acknowledging the presence of $r_{bb'}$ in series with the source R_g, we may substitute into the general-case equations to obtain from (10.21)

$$\frac{e_{b'e}}{e_g} = \frac{r_{b'e}}{\left[(R_g + r_{bb'} + r_{b'e})^2 + \left(\frac{(R_g + r_{bb'})r_{b'e}}{X_{C_{b'e}}} \right)^2 \right]^{1/2}}$$ (10.84)

From (10.27)

$$\frac{i_{b'e}}{i_g} = \frac{R_g + r_{bb'}}{\left[(R_g + r_{bb'} + r_{b'e})^2 + \left(\frac{(R_g + r_{bb'})r_{b'e}}{X_{C_{b'e}}} \right)^2 \right]^{1/2}}$$ (10.85)

From (10.22) or (10.29)

$$\frac{e_{b'e(high)}}{e_{b'e(mid)}} = \frac{i_{b'e(high)}}{i_{b'e(mid)}} = \frac{1}{\left[1 + \left(\frac{(R_g + r_{bb'})r_{b'e}}{X_{C_{b'e}}(R_g + r_{bb'} + r_{b'e})} \right)^2 \right]^{1/2}}$$ (10.86)

From (10.23)

$$f_H = \frac{R_g + r_{bb'} + r_{b'e}}{2\pi C_{b'e}(R_g + r_{bb'})(r_{b'e})}$$ (10.87)

$$= f_{hfe}\left(\frac{R_g + r_{bb'} + r_{b'e}}{R_g + r_{bb'}} \right)$$ (10.88)

Look now at Eq. (10.88). We observe that if the source is a current source, that is, R_g is a high impedance, the quantity $(R_g + r_{bb'})$ is much larger than $r_{b'e}$ and the equation reduces to the form of Eq. (10.83). In practical circuits, however, R_g is more realistically apt to be smaller than the value that would make the source a current source. The total resistance in series with $C_{b'e}$ becomes smaller than $r_{b'e}$ and the effective cutoff frequency increases in value. The variation of both common-base and common-emitter current gains with frequency, as given by Eqs. (10.79) and (10.80), respectively, is shown in Fig. 10.17. The contributions of source impedance in determining

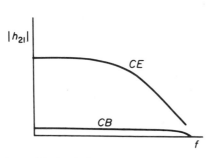

Fig. 10.17 Variation of h_{21e} and h_{21b} versus f.

the apparent value of common-emitter cutoff frequency can be demonstrated best by the example that follows.

10.6. Example: transistor parameters at high frequency. A transistor has a common-base cutoff frequency of 1 megacycle and a common-emitter current gain of 99 when operated at 1 ma. Calculate (a) the common-emitter cutoff frequency, (b) the value of current gain at this frequency, (c) the apparent value of common-emitter cutoff frequency when R_g equals 2 K. The magnitude of $r_{bb'}$ is 85 ohms. We can proceed as follows.

(a) By (10.81)

$$f_{hfe} = \frac{f_{hfb}}{1 + h_{21e}}$$

$$= \frac{1\,\text{Mc}}{1 + 99} = 10\,\text{Kc}$$

(b) From the definition of cutoff frequency we know that at this frequency the current gain has reduced to .707 of the low-frequency value; therefore

$$h_{21e(\text{high})} = .707\,h_{21e}$$

$$= .707(99) = 70$$

(c) Before calculating the apparent values of cutoff frequency we must calculate $r_{b'e}$. By (10.82)

$$r_{b'e} = (1 + h_{21e})\frac{26}{I_E}$$

$$= (1 + 99)\frac{26}{1} = 2600\,\Omega$$

By (10.88)

$$f_H = f_{hfe}\left(\frac{R_g + r_{bb'} + r_{b'e}}{R_g + r_{bb'}}\right)$$

$$= 10\,\text{Kc}\left(\frac{2\text{K} + 85 + 2.6\text{K}}{2.085\,\text{K}}\right) = 22.4\,\text{Kc}$$

10.7. Frequency response of multistage amplifier. We have discussed each factor that contributes to performance variation in an amplifier as frequency is changed. It is reasonable to anticipate that some of these factors are more critical than others, and that the analysis or design of an amplifier will require the simultaneous consideration of many factors. It is quite helpful, then, to determine at any frequency the increments of contribution for each operative factor. Equations (10.79) and (10.80) have the useful form that we desire. Equations (10.40), (10.47), (10.66), (10.78), and (10.88) give the half-power frequencies due to coupling transformers, coupling capacitors, emitter by-pass capacitors, output capacitance, and transit time, respectively. By substituting each of these itemized equations back into its source equation [Eqs. (10.39), (10.46), (10.65), (10.77), and (10.86), respectively] we obtain equations of the form

$$\frac{e_{\text{low}}}{e_{\text{mid}}} = \frac{i_{\text{low}}}{i_{\text{mid}}} = \frac{1}{\left[1 + \left(\frac{f_L}{f}\right)^2\right]^{1/2}} \qquad (10.89)$$

$$\frac{e_{\text{high}}}{e_{\text{mid}}} = \frac{i_{\text{high}}}{i_{\text{mid}}} = \frac{1}{\left[1 + \left(\frac{f}{f_H}\right)^2\right]^{1/2}} \qquad (10.90)$$

The performance variations are most conveniently expressed in decibels. Since the impedance levels involved in the current or voltage ratios are constant, our decibel calculation is obtained by multiplying by 10 the log of the square of the current or voltage ratio. That is,

$$\text{db loss at low frequency} = 10 \log \frac{1}{1 + \left(\frac{f_L}{f}\right)^2} \qquad (10.91)$$

$$\text{db loss at high frequency} = 10 \log \frac{1}{1 + \left(\frac{f}{f_H}\right)^2} \qquad (10.92)$$

Note that the increments of decibels represent increments of power relative to the mid-range performance value. Note further that the contribution of each factor is obtained merely by substituting the appropriate half-power frequency into Eqs. (10.91) and (10.92). Design charts that convert frequency ratios to decibels in accordance with the content of Eqs. (10.91) and (10.92) are shown in Figs. 10.18(a) and 10.18(b), respectively.

10.8. Example: performance of multistage circuit.   To show how several factors might be handled simultaneously, let us analyze the circuit of Fig. 10.19(a) as an example, and determine the circuit performance at 30 and 20,000 cycles. The basic circuit shown is that of the self-bias circuit design in Sec. 9.7. The important information applicable to both transistors is

$$
\begin{aligned}
&I_C = 2.08 \text{ ma} & &h_{22}''' = 1267(10^{-6}) \text{ mhos} \\
&h_{21} = 47.5 & &h_{12}''' = 148(10^{-4}) \\
&h_{21}''' = 46.9 & &\Delta^{h'''} = 560(10^{-4}) \\
&h_{11}''' = 591 \ \Omega
\end{aligned}
$$

From the manufacturer's data sheet we shall use $C_{ob} = 40$ pf and $f_{hfb} = 1$ Mc; and we assume that $r_{bb'} = 85$ ohms. At mid frequencies the total useful power gain A_p of the two stages was 67 db. To determine the total power

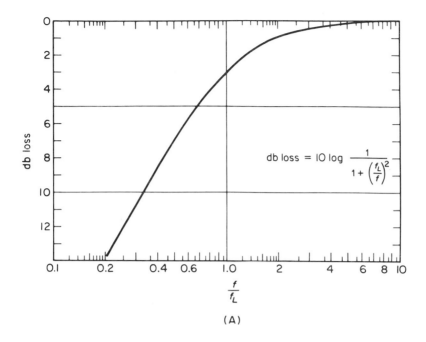

$$\text{db loss} = 10 \log \frac{1}{1+\left(\frac{f_L}{f}\right)^2}$$

(A)

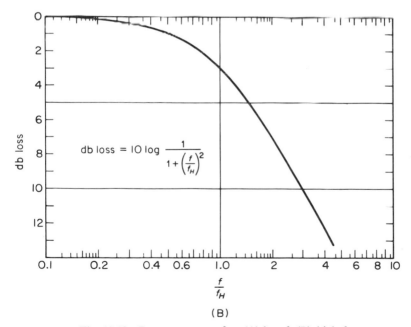

$$\text{db loss} = 10 \log \frac{1}{1+\left(\frac{f}{f_H}\right)^2}$$

(B)

Fig. 10.18   Response curves for: (A) low f; (B) high f.

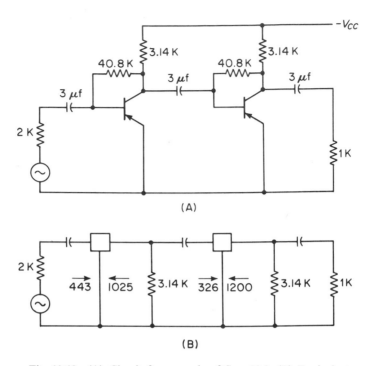

Fig. 10.19 (A) Circuit for example of Sec. 10.8. (B) Equivalent circuit showing key impedances.

gain at 30 and 20,000 cycles, we must calculate the high-frequency losses due to transit-time effects, the high-frequency losses due to output capacitance, and the low-frequency losses due to coupling capacitance.

(a) Consider first the high-frequency effect of transit time. By (10.81)

$$f_{hfe} = \frac{f_{hfb}}{1 + h_{21e}} = \frac{1\,\mathrm{Mc}}{1 + 47.5} = 20.6\,\mathrm{Kc}$$

By 10.82

$$r_{b'e} = (1 + h_{21e})\frac{26}{I_E} = (1 + 47.5)\frac{26}{2.08} = 605\,\Omega$$

For TR1, $R_g = 2\mathrm{K}$; therefore by (10.88)

$$f_H = f_{hfe}\left(\frac{R_g + r_{bb'} + r_{b'e}}{R_g + r_{bb'}}\right)$$

$$= 20.6\left(\frac{2\mathrm{K} + 85 + 605}{2\mathrm{K} + 85}\right)$$

$$= 26.5\,\mathrm{Kc}$$

The power loss in stage one due to transit-time effects at 20 Kc is, by (10.92),

$$\text{db loss} = 10 \log \frac{1}{1 + \left(\dfrac{f}{f_H}\right)^2}$$

$$= 10 \log \frac{1}{1 + \left(\dfrac{20}{26.5}\right)^2}$$

$$= 10 \log \frac{1}{1.57} = 10 \, (9.8 - 10)$$

$$= -2 \, \text{db}$$

Before we can calculate the transit time loss at the input of TR2, we must calculate the effective impedance presented by the output of TR1. By (8.33)

$$R_{\text{out}} = \frac{R_g + h_{11}'''}{R_g h_{22}''' + \Delta^{h''}}$$

$$= \frac{2\text{K} + 591}{2\text{K}(1267)10^{-6} + 560(10^{-4})} = 1025 \, \Omega$$

By (10.48)

$$R_{\text{out}_1} = \frac{R_D R_{\text{out}}}{R_D + R_{\text{out}}}$$

$$= \frac{3.14\text{K}(1.025\,\text{K})}{4.165\,\text{K}} = 772 \, \Omega$$

Since this is the effective source working into the input of TR2, we may use Eq. (10.88) to say for TR2

$$f_H = f_{hfe} \left(\frac{R_{\text{out}_1} + r_{bb'} + r_{b'e}}{R_{\text{out}_1} + r_{bb'}} \right)$$

$$= 20.6 \, \text{Kc} \left(\frac{772 + 85 + 605}{772 + 85} \right) = 35.2 \, \text{Kc}$$

The power loss in stage two due to transit-time effects at 20 Kc is

$$\text{db loss} = 10 \log \frac{1}{1 + \left(\dfrac{f}{f_H}\right)^2}$$

$$= 10 \log \frac{1}{1 + \left(\dfrac{20}{35.2}\right)^2} = 10 \log \frac{1}{1.323}$$

$$= 10(9.88 - 10) = -1.2 \, \text{db}$$

(b) The common-emitter output capacitance for each transistor is calculated by (10.74) to be

$$C_{oe} = (1 + h_{21e}) C_{ob} = (1 + 47.5)40 = 1940 \, \rho\text{f}$$

At the interstage involving the output of TR1, we use $R_{\text{out}_1} = 772\,\Omega$ and $R_{\text{in}_2} = 326\,\Omega$ to obtain, by (10.78),

$$f_H = \frac{R_{\text{out}_1} + R_{\text{in}_2}}{2\pi C_{oe} R_{\text{out}_1} R_{\text{in}_2}}$$

$$= \frac{772 + 326}{2\pi (1940)(10^{-12})(772)(326)} = 360\,\text{Kc}$$

There is no discernible performance degradation at 20 Kc due to output capacitance of TR1.

To check the output of TR2 we must calculate the output impedance of stage two. Using 772 ohms as the source for TR2, we find by (8.33)

$$R_{\text{out}} = \frac{R_g + h_{11}'''}{R_g h_{22}''' + \Delta^{h'''}}$$

$$= \frac{772 + 591}{772(1267)\,10^{-6} + 560(10^{-4})} = 1200\,\Omega$$

By (10.48)

$$R_{\text{out}_2} = \frac{R_D + R_{\text{out}}}{R_D R_{\text{out}}} = \frac{3.14\,\text{K}\,(1.2\,\text{K})}{4.34\,\text{K}} = 868\,\Omega$$

At the output of TR2, then, (10.78) appropriately altered yields

$$f_H = \frac{R_{\text{out}_2} + R_L}{2\pi C_{oe} R_{\text{out}_2} R_L}$$

$$= \frac{868 + 1000}{2\pi (1940)(10^{-12})(868)(1000)} = 177\,\text{Kc}$$

There is no discernible performance degradation at 20 Kc due to output capacitance of TR2. The total power loss at 20 Kc is the sum of the transit time losses or 3.2 db.

(c) The only low-frequency factors are the coupling capacitors C_1, C_2, and C_3. At the input of TR1, where $R_{\text{in}_1} = 443\,\Omega$, we have by (10.47)

$$f_L = \frac{1}{2\pi C(R_g + R_{\text{in}_1})}$$

$$= \frac{1}{2\pi (3)(10^{-6})(2000 + 443)} = 21.7\,\text{cps}$$

The power loss due to C_1 at 30 cycles is by (10.91)

$$\text{db loss} = 10 \log \frac{1}{1 + \left(\dfrac{f_L}{f}\right)^2}$$

$$= 10 \log \frac{1}{1 + \left(\dfrac{21.7}{30}\right)^2}$$

$$= -1.8\,\text{db}$$

At the input of TR2, we have $R_{\mathrm{out}_1} = 772 \,\Omega$, and $R_{\mathrm{in}_2} = 326 \,\Omega$. Therefore

$$f_L = \frac{1}{2\pi C(R_{\mathrm{out}_1} + R_{\mathrm{in}_2})}$$

$$= \frac{1}{2\pi (3)(10^{-6})(772 + 326)} = 48.2 \,\mathrm{cps}$$

The power loss due to C_2 at 30 cycles is

$$\mathrm{db\ loss} = 10 \log \frac{1}{1 + \left(\dfrac{f_L}{f}\right)^2}$$

$$= 10 \log \frac{1}{1 + \left(\dfrac{48.2}{30}\right)^2}$$

$$= -5.5 \,\mathrm{db}$$

At the coupling to the load, we have $R_{\mathrm{out}_2} = 868 \,\Omega$, and $R_L = 1\,\mathrm{K}$. Thus

$$f_L = \frac{1}{2\pi C(R_{\mathrm{out}_2} + R_L)}$$

$$= \frac{1}{2\pi (3)(10^{-6})(868 + 1000)}$$

$$= 28.4 \,\mathrm{cps}$$

The power loss due to C_2 at 30 cycles is

$$\mathrm{db\ loss} = 10 \log \frac{1}{1 + \left(\dfrac{f_L}{f}\right)^2}$$

$$= 10 \log \frac{1}{1 + \left(\dfrac{28.4}{30}\right)^2}$$

$$= -2.8 \,\mathrm{db}$$

The total power loss at 30 cycles is the sum of the individual losses or 10.1 db. The low-frequency falloff could readily have been prevented if larger coupling capacitor values had been chosen.

In circuits containing transformers or by-pass capacitors, approaches similar to those just reviewed would be used. It is relatively straightforward, then, to determine the frequency response of any multistage circuit. Conversely, a little experience will show which impedance level or reactive element should be manipulated to obtain a desired frequency response.

10.9. Basic principles of controlling frequency response. We have noted the various reasons for frequency-dependent performance degradation in a transistor amplifier. Very often it is desired to vary the frequency response

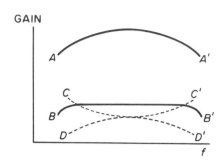

GAIN

Fig. 10.20 Samples of frequency responses possible from an uncompensated reference *AA'*. *AA'* is maximum gain achievable at any frequency.

in some prescribed fashion. Thus it might be of interest to attenuate the mid-frequency performance in relation to either the high- or low-frequency range or both. In other situations it might be of interest merely to control the performance in a particular range. We might accomplish such goals by the use of negative feedback. Since negative feedback reduces the gain, we should anticipate that frequency response can be controlled by controlling the amount of negative feedback applied to the circuit. Figure 10.20 is a graphical presentation of some of the frequency-response possibilities mentioned thus far. Curve *AA'* represents the basic amplifier characteristic. Curve *BB'* represents a situation where linear performance is desired over an extensive frequency range. Curves *CC'*, *CD'*, *DC'*, and *DD'* are some possibilities of controlling the performance in a particular frequency range compared to other frequency ranges. In any of the controlled conditions there is always a frequency-response-versus-gain compromise to be acknowledged. A discussion of the methods of controlling frequency response follows.

First let us discuss negative feedback. The basic fact here is that some fraction of an output current or voltage is fed back to the input so as to be out of phase with the input. A complete discussion of feedback concepts is highly mathematical, especially in the cases where multistage feedback is used, because we must calculate modified *h*-parameters if we pursue the approaches previously discussed. It is easy to calculate numerically the values of modified *h*-parameters and then substitute into the expressions for circuit attributes to obtain numerical criteria of circuit performance; in fact we have already done so in a number of our illustrative examples. It is quite another and cumbersome matter to derive expressions for circuit attributes in terms of the modified *h*-parameters. We choose to discuss the generalities of feedback techniques with the help of some simplified mathematical procedures. These simplified procedures are very common in servomechanism circuitry.

Consider the block diagram shown in Fig. 10.21. Here we are characterizing the active amplifier in terms of voltage gain A_v. Voltage feedback is being applied to the input, out of phase with the input, through network B_v. In situations where the feedback network is passive we may define B_v as the *voltage-feedback* factor. This quantity represents the amount or per cent of the output voltage that is fed back to the input. Mathematically

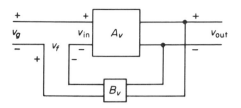

Fig. 10.21   Block diagram of voltage feedback network.

$$B_v = \frac{v_f}{v_{\text{out}}} \qquad (10.93)$$

For the basic amplifier without feedback

$$A_v = \frac{v_{\text{out}}}{v_{\text{in}}} \qquad (10.94)$$

In the case of a power source that is a *voltage* source we can also say

$$A_v = \frac{v_{\text{out}}}{v_g} \qquad (10.95)$$

When feedback is applied, the total voltage condition at the input requires a summation of the individual voltages.

$$v_g = v_{\text{in}} - v_f \qquad (10.96)$$

To find the performance of the total amplifier with feedback, we substitute (10.96) into (10.95) to obtain

$$A'_v = \frac{v_{\text{out}}}{v_{\text{in}} - v_f} \qquad (10.97)$$

where A'_v = voltage gain with feedback. Substituting (10.93) for v_f and dividing numerator and denominator by v_{in}, we obtain

$$A'_v = \frac{A_v}{1 - B_v A_v} \qquad (10.98)$$

For common-emitter amplifiers there is an inherent 180° phase shift between input and output; that is, A_v is a negative quantity. The absolute value of (10.98) is

$$A'_v = \frac{A_v}{1 + B_v A_v} \qquad (10.99)$$

Consider now the block diagram shown in Fig. 10.22. Here we characterize the active amplifier in terms of current gain A_i. Current feedback is being applied to the input, out of phase with the input through network B_i, where B_i is the *current-feedback factor*. This quantity represents the amount or per cent of output current that is fed back to the input. Mathematically

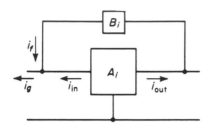

Fig. 10.22 Block diagram of current feedback network.

$$B_i = \frac{i_f}{i_{out}} \qquad (10.100)$$

For the basic amplifier without feedback

$$A_i = \frac{i_{out}}{i_{in}} \qquad (10.101)$$

In the case of a power source that is a current source, we can also say

$$A_i = \frac{i_{out}}{i_g} \qquad (10.102)$$

When feedback is applied, the total current condition at the input requires a summation of the individual currents. We find that

$$i_g = i_{in} + i_f \qquad (10.103)$$

To find the performance of the total amplifier with feedback, we substitute (10.103) into (10.102) to obtain

$$A_i' = \frac{i_{out}}{i_{in} + i_f} \qquad (10.104)$$

where $A_i' =$ current gain with feedback. Substituting (10.100) for i_f, and dividing numerator and denominator by i_{in}, we obtain

$$A_i' = \frac{A_i}{1 + B_i A_i} \qquad (10.105)$$

Equations (10.99) and (10.105) state specifically the variation of voltage gain or current gain as a function of the specific feedback factor and the basic amplifier-gain attribute. A general-case equation would be

$$A' = \frac{A}{1 + BA} \qquad (10.106)$$

Analysis of any given circuit will indicate the type of feedback that is most effective. When voltage sources are involved, voltage feedback is appropriate. Since the feedback voltage appears in series with the source voltage, this type of feedback is called *series feedback*. When current sources are involved, current feedback is appropriate. Since the feedback current parallels the source current in driving the input, this type of feedback is called *shunt feedback*.

Besides affecting gain, negative feedback increases the frequency response of an amplifier. The general-case equations applicable are

$$f_L' = \frac{f_L}{1 + BA} \qquad (10.107)$$

$$f_H' = f_H(1 + BA) \qquad (10.108)$$

where f'_L = low-frequency half-power point with feedback
      f'_H = high-frequency half-power point with feedback

10.10. Specifics of negative-feedback circuits.   The simplest of single-stage negative-feedback circuits have already been presented in the discussions of d-c operating-point stability. The principles discussed in conjunction with the d-c effects apply also to the a-c effects and can in fact be described by the procedures just discussed in Sec. 10.9. We have also calculated the modified h-parameters and resultant circuit attributes for circuits incorporating the series and shunt feedback elements. Some of the pertinent matters will be reviewed here as they apply to the matter of amplifier frequency response.

Consider the circuit of Fig. 10.23(a). The voltage feedback to the input depends on the magnitude of R_E. The actual voltage-feedback factor, B_v, can be written as

$$B_v = \frac{v_f}{v_{\text{out}}} = \frac{R_E}{R_L} \tag{10.109}$$

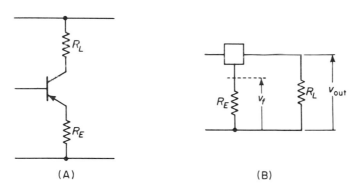

(A)   (B)

Fig. 10.23   (A) Circuit for voltage feedback. (B) Equivalent circuit.

The voltage gain in the amplifier in the presence of feedback can be expressed as

$$A'_v = \frac{A_v}{1 + \dfrac{R_E A_v}{R_L}} \tag{10.110}$$

One may question the legitimacy of considering only the voltage gain in the analysis of the amplifying abilities of the amplifier. It will be helpful to review the equations for the h-parameters as modified by the presence of R_E, and the resultant values of circuit-performance properties. From the material in Chapter 7 we should know that h_{11} is the most significantly

changing h-parameter as R_E is added to a circuit. As far as the circuit properties are concerned we observe that as R_E is added, current gain tends to
remain unchanged, voltage gain decreases, input resistance increases, and
output resistance increases. The voltage gain is dominant in affecting the
gain traits of the stage.

If current feedback is to be considered, we must refer to the circuit shown
in Fig. 10.24(a). To determine the actual amount of current feedback,
observe the presentation of Fig. 10.24(b). Following similar approaches used
in the past we can say

$$B_i = \frac{i_f}{i_c} = \frac{R_L}{R_F + R_L + R_{\text{in}}} \qquad (10.111)$$

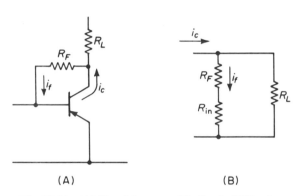

(A)   (B)

Fig. 10.24   (A) Circuit for current feedback. (B) Equivalent circuit.

Since R_{in} is usually much smaller than the sum of R_L and R_F, we can reduce
Eq. (10.111) to

$$B_i = \frac{i_f}{i_c} = \frac{R_L}{R_F + R_L} \qquad (10.112)$$

The current gain in the amplifier in the presence of feedback can be expressed
as

$$A_i' = \frac{A_i}{1 + \dfrac{R_L A_i}{R_F + R_L}} \qquad (10.113)$$

We are justified in considering only the current-gain attribute because of
the following. The most significantly changing h-parameter is h_{22} as R_F is
added to a circuit. For the circuit then as the R_F resistor is added, voltage
gain tends to remain unchanged, and current gain, input resistance, and out-

put resistance decrease. The current-gain atrribute is the dominant trait in controlling gain as feedback is applied.

The effectiveness of single-stage feedback is difficult to appraise by use of short-cut formulation. This condition exists because the input and output impedances do not both change the same amount. There is a need, then, to relate magnitudes of input and output impedance to the source and load impedances, respectively. This is the only proper way to evaluate the transfer of power from the source to the load. Thus it is best in a single-stage amplifier to use the more complete computational procedures in order to correctly calculate total amplifier performance.

Multiple-stage feedback is more effective than single-stage feedback. Since the total current gain or voltage gain of several stages is greater than the current gain or voltage gain of either of the individual stages, the multistage-feedback factor need not be so large to obtain a given end result. There are many possibilities for application of feedback around more than one stage. Proper attention must be paid, however, to the phasing between sampled and reference signals. Two of the most popular multistage approaches are shown in Fig. 10.25. In both situations shunt feedback is applied. In the circuit of Fig. 10.25(a) the feedback current is proportional to the output current, and the current-feedback factor is

$$B_i = \frac{R_E}{R} \tag{10.114}$$

In the circuit of Fig. 10.25(b) the feedback current is proportional to the output voltage, and the current-feedback factor is

$$B_i = \frac{R_L}{R} \tag{10.115}$$

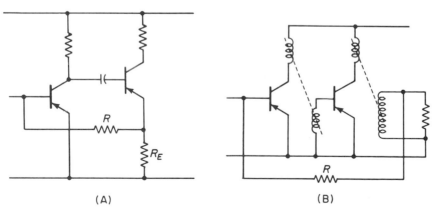

(A)   (B)

Fig. 10.25 Popular multistage feedback circuits. (A) Feedback current proportional to I_{out}. (B) Feedback current proportional to V_{out}.

In this circuit the output connection must be such that negative and not positive feedback is applied.

In each of the circuits of Fig. 10.25 the main effects of the feedback are the reduction of overall current gain and the reduction in input impedance in the stage receiving the feedback. Since the feedback resistor is very large as compared to the reference impedances R_E or R_L, as the case may be, the voltage gain of the amplifier is unaffected. The reduction in input impedance of the stage receiving the feedback will follow exactly the reduction of overall current gain as feedback is applied. The reference equation for current gain is (10.105), where the expressions for B_i are as given by Eqs. (10.114) and (10.115). The equation for input impedance in a circuit with feedback is

$$R'_{\text{in}} = \frac{R_{\text{in}}}{1 + B_i A_i} \qquad (10.116)$$

10.11. Tone-control circuits—bass boost. When frequency-response characteristics similar to CC', CD', DC', or DD' are required, frequency-dependent tone-control circuits involving reactive components are used. More often than not the reactive element is a capacitor. The frequency-dependent circuit may be a negative-feedback circuit similar to those already discussed, or it may appear in some form in the coupling circuitry between stages. A popular single-stage feedback circuit used to attenuate the mid-range relative to the low range is shown in Fig. 10.26. This is called a *bass boost* circuit. Noting that the total feedback impedance is $R - jX_C$, the current-feedback factor as given by Eq. (10.112) becomes

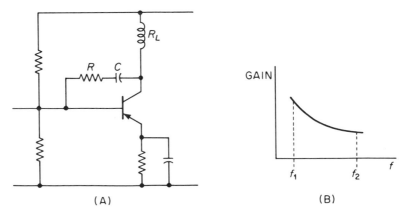

(A)   (B)

Fig. 10.26 (A) Circuit for attenuating mid and high frequencies relative to low frequency. (B) Generated response curve for (A).

$$B_t = \frac{R_L}{R_L + R - jX_C} \qquad (10.117)$$

We must get some idea of the actual amounts of power lost in an amplifier when we use the servomechanism-oriented expressions in applying feedback. Let us rewrite Eq. (10.106) as follows:

$$\frac{A}{A'} = 1 + BA \qquad (10.118)$$

The ratios of the current- or voltage-gain attributes are truly indicative of the power gain lost owing to feedback. The amount of feedback can be expressed in decibels as follows

$$\text{power loss} = 20 \log (1 + BA) \qquad (10.119)$$

Equation (10.119) is helpful in relating the shape of the frequency response as shown in Fig. 10.26(b) to the values of the feedback elements that should be used. At the frequency f_1 we might express the gain with feedback as A'_{f_1}, where

$$A'_{f_1} = \frac{A}{1 + B_{f_1} A} \qquad (10.120a)$$

where B_{f_1} is the current- or voltage-feedback factor at f_1. At the frequency f_2, we might express the gain with feedback as A'_{f_2}, where

$$A'_{f_2} = \frac{A}{1 + B_{f_2} A} \qquad (10.120b)$$

where B_{f_2} is the current- or voltage-feedback factor at f_2. The performance at f_1 relative to f_2 is expressed as

$$\frac{A'_{f_1}}{A'_{f_2}} = \frac{1 + B_{f_2} A}{1 + B_{f_1} A} \qquad (10.121)$$

The actual difference in performance expressed in decibels is

Δ db, f_1 relative to f_2

$$= 20 \log \frac{1 + B_{f_2} A}{1 + B_{f_1} A} \qquad (10.122)$$

The final comment about the circuit of Fig. 10.26 is that here we are using the feedback in the a-c sense only. Another array of components is being used to provide the d-c biasing of the transistor stage.

Another popular circuit useful in attenuating the mid range relative to

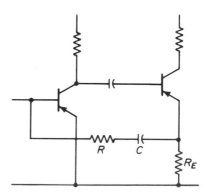

Fig. 10.27 Attenuation of mid and high frequencies in RC-coupled circuits.

the low range is one involving shunt feedback around two stages as shown in Fig. 10.27. The analysis of this circuit is quite similar to that for shunt feedback for the single stage just mentioned. The only specific concept involves the expression for the current-feedback factor. For this circuit we have

$$B_i = \frac{R_E}{R - jX_C} \tag{10.123}$$

Since this circuit is so similar in principle to the single-stage shunt feedback, no further comments are really necessary.

10.12. Design example: bass-boost tone control.   The following example illustrates feedback principles for boosting bass response.

A transistor is to be operated so that its gain at 1000 cycles is 15 db down from its gain at 10 cycles. In addition the gain at 10 cycles should be no less than 1 db down from the performance of the basic amplifier. The gain at frequencies greater than 1000 cycles is not critical, but gain losses are not intended beyond the 1000-cycle point. Shunt feedback similar to that of Fig. 10.26 is to be used. The basic current gain of the stage is 50 when $R_L = 3$ K. The solution procedure incorporates the following.

Assume that the impedance of the capacitor predominates as the feedback impedance at the low frequency. Then, when confirming the attainment of required decibel change in proceeding to the higher frequency, pick an R such that the feedback impedance does not change appreciably at frequencies greater than the 1000-cycle check point. At 10 cycles the power loss is to be held to 1 db. Thus, by (10.119),

$$20 \log (1 + B_{f_1} A) = 1 \text{ db}$$
$$\therefore \quad 1 + B_{f_1} A = 1.12$$
$$\therefore \quad B_{f_1} A = .12$$

However, at f_1

$$B_{f_1} = \frac{R_L}{X_C}$$

$$X_C = \frac{R_L A}{.12} = 1.25 \text{ megohms}$$

$$C = .0127 \mu\text{f} \qquad (\text{using } f = 10 \text{ cps})$$

A near value of $C = .012 \ \mu\text{f}$ would be acceptable. The next matter is the 15-db change in performance in going from 10 to 1000 cycles. By (10.122)

$$20 \log \frac{1 + B_{f_2} A}{1 + B_{f_1} A} = 15 \text{ db}$$

$$\log \frac{1 + B_{f_2}A}{1 + B_{f_1}A} = .75$$

$$\frac{1 + B_{f_2}A}{1 + B_{f_1}A} = 5.62$$

We know, however, that $1 + B_{f_1}A = 1.12$. Therefore

$$1 + B_{f_2}A = (1.12)(5.62) = 6.3$$

At f_2,

$$B_{f_2} = \frac{R_L}{R_L + R - jX_C}$$

Therefore

$$R_L + R - jX_C = \frac{R_L A}{5.3}$$
$$= 28.3\,\text{K}$$

At 1000 cycles $X_C = 13$ K. A little manipulation reveals that an R value of 22 K is acceptable. At a frequency of 10,000 cycles the effects of C are neglible in the feedback path. The power change in going from 1000 to 10,000 cycles can be checked by using (10.122) again:

$$\frac{A_{1,000}}{A_{10,000}} = 20 \log \frac{1 + \frac{3}{25}\,50}{1 + \frac{3}{28.3}\,50}$$

$$= 20 \log \frac{7.0}{6.3}$$

$$= .9\,\text{db}$$

This is acceptable.

10.13. Tone-control circuits—treble boost.   Single-stage shunt feedback incorporating capacitors can be made to attenuate the mid-frequency range relative to the high-frequency range. Such a circuit is called a *treble boost* circuit and is shown in Fig. 10.28. At the mid range the reactance X_C is high, causing the component of current i_1 that is fed back to the input to be greater than the value of this component at higher frequencies where X_C has more of a shunting effect.

Our analysis begins by noting that the feedback impedance Z_F is the sum of R_2 in series with the parallel equivalent of C and R_1. Thus we can say

$$\frac{i_f}{i_c} = \frac{R_L}{R_L + R_2 + \frac{R_1(-jX_C)}{R_1 - jX_C}} \tag{10.124}$$

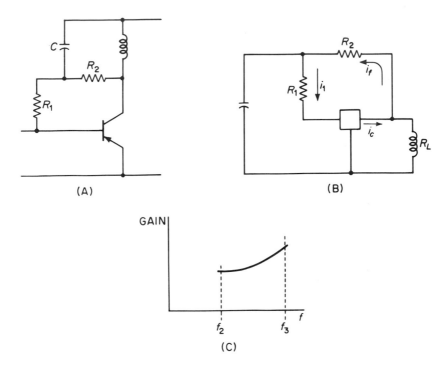

Fig. 10.28 (A) Circuit for attenuating low and mid frequencies relative to high frequency. (B) Alternate depiction of (A). (C) Generalized response curve for (A).

The current-feedback factor of interest is

$$B_i = \frac{i_1}{i_c} \tag{10.125}$$

$$\frac{i_1}{i_f} = \frac{-jX_C}{R_1 - jX_C} \tag{10.126}$$

Multiplying (10.126) by (10.124) and tidying the form, we obtain

$$B_i = \frac{i_1}{i_c} = \frac{R_L}{(R_1 + R_2 + R_L) + j\dfrac{R_1(R_L + R_2)}{X_C}} \tag{10.127}$$

10.14. Design example: treble-boost tone control. Let us demonstrate the practical use of Eq. (10.127) in an example requiring the design of a treble-boost circuit. The requirements might be such that the gain of a transistor at 1000 cycles is to be 4 db down from the gain at 20,000 cycles. In addition, the gain at 20,000 cycles is to be within 1 db of the basic amplifier. The basic current gain of the stage is 50 when $R_L = 3$ K. The solution procedure incorporates the following. Assume that the magnitude of X_C at 1000 cycles is large in comparison to R_1. The current-feedback factor as given by (10.127) reduces to

$$B_{f_z} = \frac{R_L}{R_1 + R_2 + R_L} \qquad (10.128)$$

At the 1000-cycle point the gain in relation to the basic amplifier is 4 db relative to 20,000 cycles plus 1 db relative to the basic amplifier. By (10.119)

$$20 \log (1 + B_{f_z}A) = 5 \text{ db}$$

$$1 + B_{f_z}A = 1.78$$

Thus

$$\frac{R_L}{R_L + R_1 + R_2} = \frac{.78}{50}$$

$$R_1 + R_2 \cong 190 \text{ K}$$

Look now at the denominator of (10.127). It can be shown that the value of the total term is essentially equal to the value of the larger term until the smaller term exceeds a value that is about 20 per cent of the larger term. That is to say, if

$$C = A + jB$$

For

$$B < .2A$$

$$C \cong A$$

Thus, for our example, if the imaginary term is to be negligible in relation to the real term at 1000 cycles, the smallest permissible value of X_C is given by

$$\frac{R_1(R_L + R_2)}{X_C} = 38 \text{ K}$$

The proper choice of value for R_1 and R_2 is not immediately apparent. Generally an R_1 value which is 5 to 10 per cent of the $(R_1 + R_2)$ quantity is acceptable. Numerical adjustments in this R_1 value might sometimes be required. Let us select an R_1 value which is 8 per cent of the $(R_1 + R_2)$ quantity of 190 K or 15 K. Therefore

$$X_C = \frac{15 \text{K} (3 \text{K} + 175 \text{K})}{38 \text{K}}$$

$$= 70 \text{K at 1000 cycles.}$$

Thus $C = 2.28(10^{-9})$ f. And thus at 20,000 cps

$$X_C = \frac{1}{2\pi \, 20(10^3)2.28(10^{-9})} = 3.1\,\text{K}$$

From Eq. (10.127) at the frequency of 20,000 cycles we find

$$B_{f_3} = \frac{3\,\text{K}}{(15\,\text{K} + 175\,\text{K} + 3\,\text{K}) + j\dfrac{15\,\text{K}(3\,\text{K} + 175\,\text{K})}{3.1\,\text{K}}}$$

$$= \frac{3\,\text{K}}{193\,\text{K} + j860\,\text{K}} = \frac{3\,\text{K}}{885\,\text{K}}$$

$$= .0034$$

The gain loss at 20,000 cycles can now be calculated. By Equation (10.119)

$$\text{loss} = 20 \log (1 + B_{f_3}A)$$
$$= 20 \log (1 + .17)$$
$$= 20 \, (.067) = 1.34 \, \text{db}$$

This is acceptable.

10.15. Combined bass-treble control using feedback. In concluding our discussion of feedback circuits, let us consider a situation where the mid-range performance must relate to both bass and treble requirements simultaneously. A popular single-stage shunt feedback circuit is shown in Fig. 10.29(a). The equivalent circuit is shown in Fig. 10.29(b). The single-stage feedback concepts already discussed are now applied simultaneously. At low and mid ranges the reactance of X_{C_1} should be high so that the active feedback network is R_1, R_2, and C_2. At high frequencies the reactance of X_{C_2} should be small so that the active feedback network is R_1, R_2, and C_1. We begin by noting that

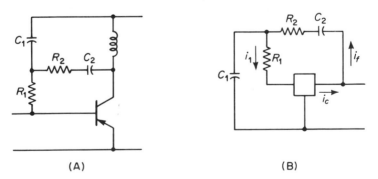

(A)   (B)

Fig. 10.29 (A) Circuit to attenuate mid frequencies relative to both high and low frequency. (B) Alternate depiction.

$$Z_F = R_2 - jX_{C_2} - \frac{jX_{C_1}R_1}{R_1 - jX_{C_1}} \tag{10.129}$$

$$\frac{i_f}{i_c} = \frac{R_L}{R_L + R_2 - jX_{C_2} - \dfrac{jX_{C_1}R_1}{R_1 - jX_{C_1}}} \tag{10.130}$$

The current-feedback factor of interest is

$$B_i = \frac{i_1}{i_c} \tag{10.131}$$

$$\frac{i_1}{i_f} = \frac{-jX_{C_1}}{R_1 - jX_{C_1}} \tag{10.132}$$

Multiplying (10.132) by (10.130) we obtain

$$B_i = \frac{i_1}{i_c}$$

$$= \frac{R_L}{(R_1 + R_2 + R_L) + j\dfrac{R_1(R_L + R_2)}{X_{C_1}} + \dfrac{X_{C_2}(R_1 - jX_{C_1})}{X_{C_1}}} \tag{10.133}$$

Equation (10.133) is indicative, then, of the performance of the circuit shown in Fig. 10.29.

10.16. Design example: combination control using feedback. As a problem illustrating the design of a circuit incorporating the suppression of mid frequencies relative to both lows and highs, consider the following. A transistor is to operate such that the gain at 1000 cycles is 15 db down from the gain at 10 cycles, and is 6 db down from the gain at 20,000 cycles. The gain at 10 cycles should be within 1 db of the basic amplifier. The basic current gain of the stage is 50 when $R_L = 3$ K. It is appropriate to start at the low end, ignoring completely the presence of C_1. We obtain results similar to the problem cited in Section 10.12. That is, when $C_2 = .012 \ \mu f$ and $R_1 + R_2 = 22$ K, the desired low-frequency result is obtained. In order to establish the correct values of C_1 and R_1, we look at the requirements of the f_3 point of 20,000 cycles. We want the gain at 20,000 cycles to be 6 db greater than the gain at 1000 cycles. A prior calculation has shown that at frequencies greater than 1000 cycles, the diminution of X_{C_2} to a negligible value could cause an additional .9 db loss in gain. The presence of X_{C_1}, however, can conceivably shunt R_1 fast enough to compensate for the X_{C_2} variation. Let us design strictly for 6 db at 20 Kc relative to 1 Kc. We have found by the earlier problem that

$$1 + B_{f_2}A = 6.3$$

Here we want

$$20 \log \frac{1 + B_{f_2} A}{1 + B_{f_3} A} = 6 \text{ db}$$

i.e.

$$\frac{1 + B_{f_2} A}{1 + B_{f_3} A} = 2$$

and

$$1 + B_{f_3} A = \frac{6.3}{2} = 3.15$$

$$B_{f_3} = \frac{2.15}{50} = .043$$

Substituting this into (10.33), and omitting the third term of the denominator because of its small contribution, we obtain

$$B_i = \frac{R_L}{(R_1 + R_2 + R_L) + j \dfrac{R_1(R_L + R_2)}{X_{C_1}}}$$

i.e.

$$.043 = \frac{3 \text{ K}}{25 \text{ K} + j \dfrac{R_1(R_L + R_2)}{X_{C_1}}}$$

In order that this equation hold true, the magnitude of the denominator must be 70 K. Thus at 20 Kc,

$$25 \text{ K} + j \frac{R_1(R_L + R_2)}{X_{C_1}} = 70 \text{ K}$$

$$\therefore \quad j \frac{R_1(R_L + R_2)}{X_{C_1}} = 65 \text{ K}$$

Knowing this relation we can establish the values of R_1, R_2, and C_1. If $R_1 = 2$ K, then $X_{C_1} = 710 \, \Omega$ and $C_1 = .0112 \, \mu\text{f}$. Should space permit use of a paper capacitor we would select $C_1 = .012$, for which X_{C_1} at 20,000 cycles equals 650 ohms. The magnitude of X_{C_1} at 1000 cps is 13.2 K. This is sufficiently large relative to the R_1 value of 2 K to cause inconsequential shunting effects. A check-out of the component values selected yields a performance such that the gain at 1000 cycles is 15 db down relative to 10 cycles and 6.25 db down relative to 20,000 cycles.

10.17. Tone control with coupling circuitry.   Besides the various feedback circuits discussed, we should mention the usefulness of coupling networks in controlling frequency response. In the Fig. 10.30(a) circuit the $R_2 C_2$ network serves to suppress the mid and high range relative to the low range,

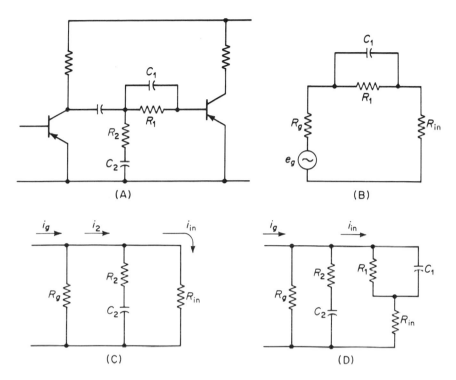

Fig. 10.30 (A) Circuit showing frequency control with elements in the coupling network. (B) Equivalent circuit for control of high frequencies and attenuation of mid and low frequencies. (C) Equivalent circuit for control of low frequencies and attenuation of mid and high frequencies. (D) Combination control.

while the $R_1 C_1$ network suppresses the low and mid range relative to the high range. Figure 10.30(b) shows the equivalent circuit of $R_1 C_1$ alone. In the frequency range where C_1 is active we can write

$$\frac{e_{in}}{e_g} = \frac{R_{in}}{R_g + R_{in} - j \dfrac{R_1 X_{C_1}}{R_1 - j X_{C_1}}} \qquad (10.134)$$

$$= \frac{R_{in}}{R_g + R_{in} + \dfrac{R_1}{1 + j\omega C_1 R_1}} \qquad (10.135)$$

At the mid range, the quantity X_{C_1} is large and we have

$$\frac{e_{in(mid)}}{e_g} = \frac{R_{in}}{R_g + R_{in} + R_1} \qquad (10.136)$$

At the high range the quantity X_{C_1} is a short around R_1 and we have

$$\frac{e_{\text{in(high)}}}{e_g} = \frac{R_{\text{in}}}{R_g + R_{\text{in}}} \tag{10.137}$$

The ratio of Eqs. (10.137) and (10.136) is indicative of the performance variation between the mid and high frequencies of interest. We obtain

$$\frac{A_{f_3}}{A_{f_2}} = 20 \log \frac{R_{\text{in}} + R_g + R_1}{R_{\text{in}} + R_g} \tag{10.138}$$

This gives the value of R_1 that would satisfy the performance requirements. The values of C_1 are established by the procedures used thus far.

In Fig. 10.30(c) we see the equivalent circuit for the R_2C_2 network. It can be shown that

$$\frac{i_{\text{in}}}{i_g} = \frac{R_g}{R_g + R_{\text{in}} + \dfrac{R_g R_{\text{in}}}{R_2 - jX_{C_2}}} \tag{10.139}$$

At mid frequencies the magnitude of X_{C_2} should be small compared to R_2; thus

$$\frac{i_{\text{in(mid)}}}{i_g} = \frac{R_g}{R_g + R_{\text{in}} + \dfrac{R_g R_{\text{in}}}{R_2}} \tag{10.140}$$

At low frequencies we want X_{C_2} large so that negligible current flows in the R_2C_2 path. This is obtained if

$$\frac{R_g R_{\text{in}}}{R_2 + jX_{C_2}} < R_g + R_{\text{in}} \tag{10.141}$$

By substituting the conditions of (10.141) into (10.139), we obtain

$$\frac{i_{\text{in(low)}}}{i_g} = \frac{R_g}{R_g + R_{\text{in}}} \tag{10.142}$$

The ratio of Eqs. (10.142) and (10.140) indicates the performance variation between the mid and low frequencies of interest.

$$\frac{A_{f_1}}{A_{f_2}} = 20 \log \frac{R_g(R_{\text{in}} + R_2) + R_{\text{in}} R_2}{R_2(R_g + R_{\text{in}})} \tag{10.143}$$

Equation (10.143) enables us to obtain the value of R_2 that satisfies the basic performance requirements. It is easy to proceed to obtain the value of C_2 that will operate with R_2 to satisfy the limit conditions required in Eqs. (10.140) and (10.141).

If we were to shape both the high- and low-frequency regions in relation to the mid range, we should consider the equivalent circuit of Fig. 10.30(d). It can be shown that

$$\frac{i_{in}}{i_g} = \frac{R_g}{R_{in} + R_g - \dfrac{jR_1 X_{C_1}}{R_1 - jX_{C_1}} + \dfrac{R_g R_{in}}{R_2 - jX_{C_2}} - \dfrac{jR_1 R_g X_{C_1}}{(R_1 - jX_{C_1})(R_2 - jX_{C_2})}} \tag{10.144}$$

At low frequencies X_{C_1} and X_{C_2} are large by comparison with R_1 and R_2, respectively. Therefore

$$\frac{i_{in(low)}}{i_g} = \frac{R_g}{R_{in} + R_g + R_1} \tag{10.145}$$

At mid frequencies, X_{C_1} should still be large compared to R_1, while X_{C_2} is small compared to R_2. Equation (10.144) reduces to

$$\frac{i_{in(mid)}}{i_g} = \frac{R_g}{(R_{in} + R_1)\left(1 + \dfrac{R_g}{R_2}\right) + R_g} \tag{10.146}$$

At high frequencies X_{C_1} and X_{C_2} are small compared to R_1 and R_2, respectively. We find then that

$$\frac{i_{in(high)}}{i_g} = \frac{R_g}{R_{in}\left(1 + \dfrac{R_g}{R_2}\right) + R_g} \tag{10.147}$$

The ratio of Eq. (10.145) to (10.146) indicates the performance variation between the mid and low frequencies of interest.

$$\frac{A_{f_1}}{A_{f_2}} = 20 \log \frac{(R_{in} + R_1)\left(1 + \dfrac{R_g}{R_2}\right) + R_g}{R_{in} + R_g + R_1} \tag{10.148}$$

The ratio of Eq. (10.147) to (10.146) indicates the performance variation between the mid and high frequencies of interest.

$$\frac{A_{f_3}}{A_{f_2}} = 20 \log \frac{(R_{in} + R_1)\left(1 + \dfrac{R_g}{R_2}\right) + R_g}{R_{in}\left(1 + \dfrac{R_g}{R_2}\right) + R_g} \tag{10.149}$$

The requirements of the high-frequency range are usually the most restrictive. It is not likely that we can hold the low-frequency performance to a given amount relative to the uncompensated amplifier and still fulfill the high-frequency requirements. The low- and high-frequency requirements appropriately require simultaneous solution. A little intuition, however, applied to Eq. (10.149) alone gives results that are close enough to be acceptable.

10.18. Design example: coupling circuitry tone control. As an example consider a situation in which we desire to have the gain at 1000 cycles down 15 db from the gain at 10 cycles and 6 db down from the gain at 20,000 cycles. Compute the values of R_1 and R_2 (Fig. 10.30) that satisfy the performance requirements. Let $R_{in} = 1.5$ K and $R_g = 2$ K. Looking first at (10.149), we note by inspection that

$$20 \log \frac{(R_{in} + R_1)\left(1 + \dfrac{R_g}{R_2}\right) + R_g}{R_{in}\left(1 + \dfrac{R_g}{R_2}\right) + R_g} = \frac{A_{f_3}}{A_{f_2}} = 6\,\mathrm{db}$$

$$\therefore \quad \frac{(1.5\mathrm{K} + R_1)\left(1 + \dfrac{2\mathrm{K}}{R_2}\right) + 2\mathrm{K}}{1.5\mathrm{K}\left(1 + \dfrac{2\mathrm{K}}{R_2}\right) + 2\mathrm{K}} = 2$$

A fair estimation of R_1 is 1.5 K. Substituting this back into 10.148 we obtain

$$20 \log \frac{(R_{in} + R_1)\left(1 + \dfrac{R_g}{R_2}\right) + R_g}{R_{in} + R_g + R_1} = \frac{A_{f_1}}{A_{f_2}} = 15\,\mathrm{db}$$

$$\frac{(1.5\mathrm{K} + 1.5\mathrm{K})\left(1 + \dfrac{2\mathrm{K}}{R_2}\right) + 2K}{1.5\mathrm{K} + 2\mathrm{K} + 1.5} = 5.6$$

$$\therefore \quad R_2 = 260\,\Omega$$

Substituting the values of R_1 and R_2 back into Eq. (10.149), we find that the actual amount of treble boost is 5.4 db. This is acceptable. The calculation of the capacitance values is relatively straightforward in accordance with the considerations brought to light in preceding examples.

10.19. Summary. This chapter has discussed the factors affecting the performance of transistors in the audio-frequency spectrum. It is helpful to reduce the material into two separate categories. In the first we consider the performance capabilities of the transistor itself and its circuit as frequency varies. We note that output capacitance and transit time effects may cause performance degradation at high frequencies. At low frequencies the transistor itself has no undesirable attributes. We observe instead that circuit elements such as interstage coupling transformers and capacitors and emitter by-pass capacitors are responsible for low-frequency performance degradations. We need only select proper values for these reactive components to obtain the greatest gain-performance characteristic possible for the given circuit function. In the second category we consider the shaping of the performance characteristic to specified requirements. We may want, then, bass or treble boost either separately or simultaneously. This obtained by frequency-dependent feedback circuitry or by frequency-dependent loss circuits deliberately built into the interstage coupling networks.

Simplified mathematical approaches were incorporated in the feedback material. The material in this chapter is really only an introduction to the truly vast subject of feedback circuitry. Subjects such as the reactive aspects of transistor parameters (current gain and terminal impedances for example) or the mathematical treatise of the gain-stability attributes of a transistor vs frequency might be discussed. Such subjects are however well beyond the scope of this text. Sometimes the performance vs frequency characteristic is properly executed as indicated in this chapter, and one might find that the gain-stability attributes of the transistor being used cause the actual circuit to be unstable. Since the design considerations for such a problem are not discussed in this chapter, one can either change the transistor being used or reduce the amount of circuit feedback. The reader should be alert to the possibility of such problems in multistage feedback circuits.

In both feedback and interstage control approaches one should be satisfied with solutions giving results that are within acceptable tolerances of the required result. Compromises must always be made to accommodate the use of standard-value components and to obtain stable performance. Detailed equations state performance characteristics for the feedback and interstage approaches. The manipulation of these equations at the critical frequencies of interest incorporates some common-sense approaches. The material in the chapter presents a broad and more than adequate introduction for solving the problems of frequency-dependent circuit performance.

PROBLEMS

1. Refer back to the example in Sec. 10.8. It is desired to limit the coupling loss due to C_2 to .5 db at 30 cycles. Compute the necessary value of C_2.

2. A transistor has $f_{hfb} = .8$ Mc, $h_{21e} = 99$, and $r_{bb'} = 100$ ohms. Make a plot of apparent f_{hfe} versus R_g.

3. Consider again the example in Sec. 10.8. If C_1, C_2, and $C_3 = 5$ μf, and $R_g = 4$ K, compute the total circuit losses at 20 and 25,000 cycles.

4. It is desired to supply 3 db of current feedback around a single stage where $R_L = 4$ K and $A_i = 50$. Compute R_F.

5. Derive Eq. (10.127).

6. Consider the circuit of Fig. 10.27. The current gain of the two stages is 2000. $R_E = 100$ ohms. Determine values of R and C for which the performance at 1000 cycles will be 15 db down from the performance at 10 cycles. Try to limit the gain loss at 10 cycles to 1 db relative to the compensated amplifier.

7. Derive Eq. (10.144).

8. For the problem in Sec. 10.18 compute the performance loss at 10 cycles relative to the uncompensated amplifier.

9. Design a compensation network similar to Fig. 10.30 such that the performance at 1000 cycles is 14 db down relative to 10 cycles and 8 db down relative to 20,000 cycles. $R_g = 3$ K, $R_{in} = 1$ K. Calculate appropriate capacitance values. Calculate also the performance loss at 10 cycles relative to the uncompensated amplifier.

10. Fulfill the requirements of Problem 9 by a circuit similar to Fig. 10.24. $A_i = 50$ when $R_L = 3$ K.

11

LOW-FREQUENCY

LARGE-SIGNAL

AMPLIFIERS

The amplifier circuits we have discussed thus far were classed as low-frequency small-signal amplifiers. The major attribute of such circuits is usually power gain. In dealing with such circuits we were able to use a small-signal equivalent circuit. We had at our disposal a number of circuit-attribute equations, all of which incorporated various small-signal *h*-parameters. In this chapter we introduce a new type of transistor circuit. The operational mode involves large rather than small amplitudes of signal currents and voltages. Such amplifiers are generally classed as *large-signal* or *power amplifiers*. Such amplifiers find use as output stages in audio amplifiers or as part of industrial control circuits. Since large-amplitude signals are involved, we can no longer use the small-signal equivalent circuit for circuit analysis. We will discuss in this chapter the major attributes of large-signal circuits, the transistor limitations that must be acknowledged, and the approaches used in analyzing and designing various types of large-signal amplifiers.

11.1. Large-signal amplifiers—basic considerations. As opposed to the small-signal amplifier, where maximized power gain is the objective most sought for, a large-signal amplifier has three specific functional objectives: (1) the delivery of maximum output power (2) with minimum distortion (3) at the best possible battery efficiency. As might be expected, all three conditions are not likely to be achieved simultaneously. The analytical approaches that we develop will provide insight into intelligent courses of compromise.

We have already implied that no specific equivalent circuit is applicable for the device in large-signal operation. We revert then to a graphical load-line approach. The basic concepts of load lines have already been discussed in Chapter 2 for diode circuits and again in Chapter 9 with respect to small-signal RC-coupled amplifier circuits. Load lines as we apply them now serve the same purposes as before.

The current-voltage relationships for the transistor and its d-c load and for the transistor and its a-c load can be visualized by superposition of d-c and a-c load lines, respectively, on the output characteristic of the transistor. Consider, for example, the circuit of Fig. 11.1(a). Here load resistor R_L is

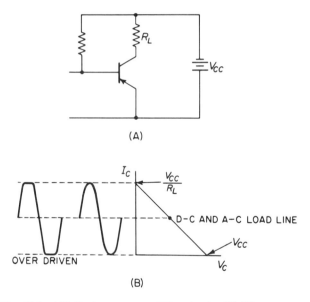

Fig. 11.1　(A) Basic power amplifier circuit. (B) Placement of a-c load line on output characteristic—acceptable and clipped or overdriven waveforms are shown.

connected directly in series with the collector of an ideal transistor, and we have the unique situation that R_L serves as both the d-c and a-c load on the transistor. In order to locate the d-c load line we sum the d-c voltages around the collector loop.

$$V_c = V_{cc} - I_c R_L \qquad (11.1)$$

The horizontal intercept is V_{cc} and the vertical intercept is V_{cc}/R_L. The slope of the d-c load line is $-1/R_L$. In considering the a-c aspects of current and voltage across R_L, we note that the a-c current and voltage are related by

$$V = IR_L \qquad (11.2)$$

where $V =$ a-c load voltage, rms
        $I =$ a-c load current, rms

The slope of the a-c load line is the same as that of the d-c load line or $-1/R_L$. Having located the a-c load line, we must locate on it a reference or operating point that will permit the attainment of one or another of the large-signal objectives. If maximum power output is the main objective, the logical operating point for an ideal transistor would be midway on the a-c load line. Equal swings in current or voltage can then be obtained in each direction from this point. The entire length of the load line is being used to advantage. If the input signal becomes too large, the amplifier is said to be *overdriven*. In this situation the input signal tends to work the amplifier beyond the limits of the available load line. Since the load-line length is fixed as a function of supply voltage and load-resistor magnitude, the peaks of the output-current and output-voltage waveforms become *clipped*. The appearance of the clipped waveform is shown in Fig. 11.1(b). Clipping is undesirable from a distortion viewpoint. Figure 11.1(b) indicates a desirable goal in large signal amplifiers; distortion or clipping should appear simultaneously at the output-waveform peaks as the amplifier is overdriven. This is a verification that the operating point has been chosen correctly to give maximized output power with minimized waveform distortion.

A basic categorization of large-signal amplifiers yields two specific types of operation: *Class A* and *Class B*. There are numerous differences between the two classes of amplifiers. The major distinction is that in a Class A amplifier the battery power is independent of the level of the rms output power, while in a class B amplifier the battery power used depends directly on the magnitude of the rms output power. Class B amplifiers yield higher maximum efficiencies then Class A amplifiers. This increase in efficiency is usually obtained at the expense of added components, because Class A amplifiers are typically operated *single-ended* in that a single transistor is used, whereas Class B amplifiers typically use two transistors connected *push-pull*. The main types of Class A amplifiers are *direct-coupled load*, *transformer-coupled load*, and *RC-coupled load*. The Class B amplifier frequently uses transformer coupling at both the input and output terminals. The major features of each type of amplifier are discussed in the sections that follow.

11.2. Transistor considerations for power-amplifier use.   The discussions in Sec. 11.1 bring to light some of the basic operating aspects of large-signal amplifiers. It is necessary, however, to discuss completely the various transistor attributes that (a) limit the useful length of the a-c load line to something less than the ideal length just mentioned and (b) impose limitations on the actual positioning of the a-c load line on the transistor characteristic. In considering the actual useful length of the a-c load line, recall for the moment the shape of the common-emitter output characteristic presented in Fig. 5.10 for a real transistor. The phenomenon of collector saturation voltage makes it impossible to reduce the collector voltage to zero. The phenomenon of leakage current makes it impossible to reduce the collector current to zero. For a real transistor we would expect the situation shown in Fig. 11.2(a). Here we observe that the useful portion of the load line is confined to a length of $A'B'$ rather than the ideal length AB. The exact degree to which the real situation differs from the ideal situation is a function of the particular transistor being used.

The physical positioning of the a-c load line is limited to an area bounded in the horizontal direction by the breakdown rating of the transistor and in the vertical direction by the power-dissipation rating of the transistor. These regions are shown in conjunction with the load-line length limitations in Fig. 11.2(b). The matter of voltage breakdown has already been discussed.

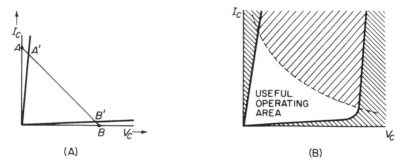

(A)   (B)

Fig. 11.2 (A) Limitations in ideal load line due to leakage and saturation voltage. (B) Composite restrictions including power dissipation limitation and voltage breakdown.

Notice that the voltage-limitation region is a "redirected" extension of the leakage limitation. This matter was discussed thoroughly in Chapter 4. The voltage-breakdown phenomenon is acknowledged in practical circuitry by assuring that a transistor is never operated so that the circuit a-c load line crosses the vertical or near-vertical portion of the voltage-breakdown line. As a matter of discretion it is generally considered a safe design practice to avoid even the carrier-multiplication region. This will assure that degradation effects, which are apt to occur during the lifetime of a transistor and which might lower the value of breakdown voltage, do not harm our circuit. At this point, however, we intend only to alert the reader to the undesirable effects of having the load line cross the vertical or near-vertical portion of the breakdown curve. The breakdown rating of a transistor is always stated by the manufacturer on the transistor's specification sheet. It is the obligation of the circuit designer to manipulate the circuit conditions within the capability of the transistor.

The power-dissipation rating also is set by the manufacturer. The basic matter here is the operating temperature of the transistor. The maximum allowed operating temperature of the transistor is a function of the melting points of its materials, the maximum temperatures used in its manufacture, and its constructional aspects which determine the flow of heat away from its high-temperature parts. The constructional features are very significant from a practical viewpoint. Some transistors, such as the alloy device in Fig. 11.3(a), have the base support annular ring connected to the header.

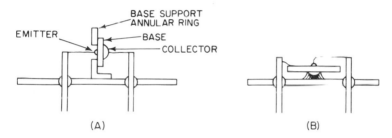

Fig. 11.3 (A) Cross section of typical alloy transistor (medium power type). (B) Power device—collector connected directly to case of device.

Certain types of higher-power transistors have the collector region connected to the case with some type of metallic bonding material. In each situation an effort is being made to take heat away from the active transistor regions to the transistor case itself, where it is radiated away at a rate that depends on the ambient temperature and the surface area of the transistor case. Often attachments called *heat sinks* are employed to increase the effective surface area of the transistor case. Heat sinks may take the form of spring clips that attach concentrically to the case, or they may be heavier pieces of sheet stock to which devices like power transistors are actually bolted. Still other sinks may be intricately varied. Regardless of physical form, their purpose is the same: to aid in the removal of heat.

During the manufacturing process the active transistor and its encapsulating parts are subjected to numerous heat treatments and stabilizing bakes. In the interests of maintaining the built-in stability and thus good reliability in the transistor application, the manufacturer places a junction-temperature limitation on the device. Operation of the device in excess of this temperature is potentially hazardous as internal parts may outgas, causing destabilizing or reactivation of the active surface of the transistor. This can lead to unreliable or erratic transistor performance and is to be avoided. The manufacturer, knowing the efficiency of heat transfer away from the active transistor, relates the junction-temperature limitation to a maximum-power-dissipation limitation. To the user, the power-dissipation rating represents the maximum power that can be dissipated for the specified ambient-temperature and heat-sink conditions, and still have the transistor within the allowed junction-temperature rating. The power-dissipation line shown in Fig. 11.2(b) is the locus of all current-voltage products that equal the maximum dissipation of the device in question. It is the obligation of the user to assure that the worst-case average power dissipation does not exceed the maximum allowed power rating. As a general rule in large-signal amplifiers this means that the load line should not pass through the maximum-power-dissipation region.

The user should be alert to the details of the specification sheet when searching for the maximum-power rating. Sometimes it is specified with no heat sink at room temperature, at other times with an infinitely large heat sink at room temperature, and sometimes even in terms of a particular value of transistor case temperature. In all circumstances it is the responsibility of those who use transistors to properly mount and to account for adequate air flow to cool the transistors in their applications' equipment. For other than room-temperature or 25°C ambients, the manufacturer provides a power-derating curve. This indicates for higher ambients the reduced amount of power allowed that still keeps the transistor within its maximum-junction-temperature rating. Such a curve is shown in Fig. 11.4. Note that zero power is allowed at an ambient equal to the maximum junction temperature.

Referring back to Fig. 11.2(b), we can sum up by indicating that in

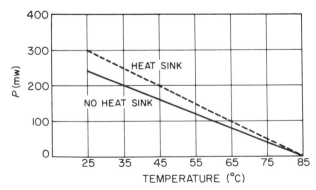

Fig. 11.4 Transistor power derating curve. Maximum junction $T = 85°C$.

general for most large-signal amplifiers the useful part of any a-c load line must fall in the area that is unshaded. This, of course, requires that the value of supply voltage and the value of the a-c and d-c loads be compatible in not only allowing the a-c load line to fall into the allowed area but also permitting the attainment of the desired circuit objectives.

11.3. Direct-coupled Class A. This circuit is the same as that drawn in Fig. 11.1(a); that is, the load is connected directly to the collector, and the same resistance serves as the a-c and d-c load on the transistor. For convenience this circuit is redrawn in Fig. 11.5. The equations for the d-c load line and for the a-c load line are repeated here:

$$V_c = V_{cc} - I_c R_L \qquad (11.1)$$

and

$$V = IR_L \qquad (11.2)$$

where V_c = d-c collector voltage
I_c = d-c collector current
V_{cc} = supply voltage

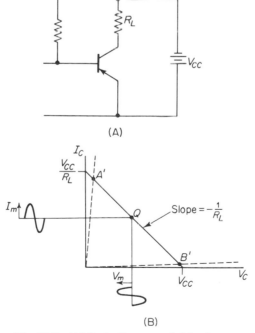

(A)

(B)

Fig. 11.5 (A) Basic direct-coupled-load power amplifier. (B) Load-line representation of circuit in (A).

V = a-c output voltage, rms
I = a-c output current, rms

The slope of both the a-c and d-c load lines is $-1/R_L$. The horizontal intercept is V_{CC} and the vertical intercept is V_{CC}/R_L. In the material that follows, we will consider the output power in an ideal transistor and will then consider the effects of saturation voltage and leakage current reducing the length of the load line. It is not necessary to consider the power and voltage limitations in the operational analysis of the amplifier. They do not directly affect the nature of the design equations. In a practical way we need only assure ourselves that these particular ratings are not exceeded. On the other hand, the load-line length can be realistically reflected in the circuit-design equations.

For the ideal case, the bias network would be adjusted to place the quiescent operating point midway on the a-c load line. The coordinates of such an operating point are

$$V_Q = \frac{V_{CC}}{2} \tag{11.3}$$

$$I_Q = \frac{V_{CC} - V_Q}{R_L} = \frac{V_{CC}}{2R_L} \tag{11.4}$$

The general expressions for the waveforms of the output voltage and output current are

$$v = V_m \sin \omega t \tag{11.5}$$

$$i = I_m \sin \omega t \tag{11.6}$$

where v = instantaneous voltage
i = instantaneous current
V_m = peak value of voltage
I_m = peak value of current

The rms output power can be expressed as

$$P_{\text{rms}} = VI \tag{11.7}$$

Applying the expected conversion from peak to rms values, that is

$$V = \frac{V_m}{\sqrt{2}} \tag{11.8}$$

$$I = \frac{I_m}{\sqrt{2}} \tag{11.9}$$

and incorporating the relationship of Eq. (11.2), we obtain

$$\text{ideal } P_{\text{rms}} = \frac{V_m^2}{2R_L} \tag{11.10}$$

From the output characteristic we can observe that the maximum ideal value of V_m is $V_{CC}/2$. Substituting this specific-case value into the general-case

Eq. (11.10), we would obtain as the maximum ideal rms output power

$$\text{ideal } P_{\text{max}} = \frac{V_{cc}^2}{8R_L} \qquad (11.11)$$

The *efficiency* of a large-signal amplifier is defined as the ratio of rms output power to d-c battery power. This ratio evaluates the conversion of battery power to useful output power. The battery power at any time is defined as the product of battery voltage and the average current flowing through the battery. That is for any circuit,

$$P_{\text{BATT}} = V_{cc}I_{\text{AVG}} \qquad (11.12)$$

Referring back to Fig. 11.5(b), we note that the average current is the same regardless of the amplitude of the a-c current waveform:

$$\text{ideal } I_{\text{AVG}} = \frac{V_{cc}}{2R_L} = I_Q \qquad (11.13a)$$

The battery power at all times for the ideal case is given by substituting 11.3a in 11.12

$$\text{ideal } P_{\text{BATT}} = \frac{V_{cc}^2}{2R_L} \qquad (11.13b)$$

A general case efficiency expression is

$$\text{eff} = \frac{P_{\text{rms}}}{P_{\text{BATT}}} \qquad (11.14)$$

For our ideal case direct-coupled circuit, the efficiency value can be determined by a ratio of Eqs. (11.10) and (11.13b), that is

$$\text{ideal. eff.} = \frac{V_m^2}{V_{cc}^2} \qquad (11.15)$$

The maximum ideal efficiency is obtained when the amplitude of V_m reaches its maximum ideal value. It can be shown that the direct-coupled Class A amplifier has a maximum ideal efficiency of 25 per cent.

The matters that reduce the length of the active load line can be treated by referring again to Fig. 11.5(b). Here the actual load-line length is labeled $A'B'$. To obtain the maximum power from this available load line we must select a new quiescent operating point $V_{Q'}I_{Q'}$ where

$$V_{Q'} = \frac{V_{B'} - V_{A'}}{2} + V_{A'} \qquad (11.16a)$$

$$I_{Q'} = \frac{V_{cc} - V_{Q'}}{R_L} \qquad (11.16b)$$

Notice that we are using information available only from the graphical analysis of where the load line is positioned on the transistor characteristic. Once the real quiescent point is known, appropriate action can be taken to design the necessary bias network. The general-case expression for rms output power as given in Eq. (11.7) applies. The maximum real rms output power will be something less than the ideal quantity. It can be calculated by

$$\text{real } P_{\max} = \frac{(V_B - V_A)^2}{8R_L} \tag{11.17a}$$

The maximum real efficiency will be affected accordingly.

The battery power at all times for the real case is given by

$$\text{real } P_{\text{BATT}} = V_{CC}I_{Q'} \tag{11.17b}$$

where $I_{Q'}$ is given by Eq. (11.16b).

11.4. Example: direct-coupled Class A circuit. Let us determine the maximum ideal power, the maximum real power, and the maximum real efficiency of a circuit with $V_{CC} = 12$ v, $R_L = 150$ ohms. The output charac-

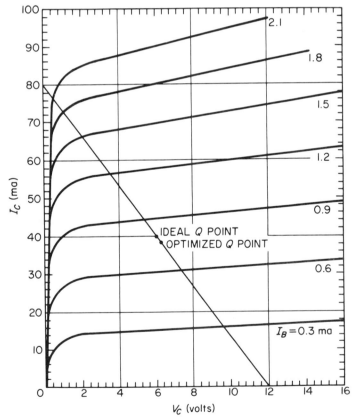

Fig. 11.6 Load-line situation when $R_L = 150\,\Omega$ is direct-connected. $V_{CC} = 12$ v.

teristic is shown in Fig. 11.6. The ideal load line is constructed by using Eq. (11.1). The intercepts are 12 v and 80 ma. The ideal quiescent point has the coordinates 6 v, 40 ma. The maximum ideal rms output power is, by Eq. (11.11),

$$\text{ideal } P_{\max} = \frac{V_{CC}^2}{8R_L} = \frac{12^2}{8(150)} = 120 \text{ mw}$$

In order to determine the real power, we must determine the actual useful length of the load line. The ideal load line and the saturation voltage intersect at $A' = .5$ v. A typical I_{CEO} value of 150 μa is not discernible on the ordinate and will be ignored for the present.

The useful load-line length is $B - A'$ or 11.5 v. The optimum quiescent point for the real load line is, by (11.16a) and (11.16b),

$$V_{Q'} = \frac{V_{B'} - V_{A'}}{2} + V_{A'} = \frac{11.5}{2} + .5 = 6.3 \text{ v}$$

$$I_{Q'} = \frac{V_{CC} - V_{Q'}}{R_L} = \frac{12.0 - 6.3}{150} = 38 \text{ ma}$$

The maximum real rms power is, by Eq. (11.17a),

$$\text{real } P_{\max} = \frac{(V_{B'} - V_{A'})^2}{8R_L} = \frac{(11.5)^2}{8(150)} = 110 \text{ mw}$$

The maximum real efficiency can be determined by

$$\text{eff.} = \frac{\text{real } P_{\max}}{\text{real } P_{\text{BATT}}} = \frac{110}{12(38)10^{-3}} = 24\%$$

11.5. Transformer-coupled Class A. The circuit for this connection is shown in Fig. 11.7. Here the actual load R_L is being transformer-coupled to the collector circuit of the transistor. As explained in Chapter 9,

$$R_L' = n^2 R_L \qquad (11.18)$$

where $n = n_p/n_s \qquad (11.19)$

n_p = primary turns

n_s = secondary turns

The d-c resistance of the primary winding can be symbolized as $R_{d\text{-}c}$. This circuit, like all others that we discuss in the future, has a major difference from the direct-coupled amplifier. The d-c and a-c load lines are not coincident, but intersect only at the operating point of the stage. Locating this operating point is the main problem in obtaining a

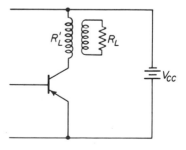

Fig. 11.7 Transformer-coupled load power amplifier.

properly operating amplifier. The equation for the d-c load line is

$$V_C = V_{CC} - I_C R_{\text{d-c}} \qquad (11.20)$$

The a-c current and voltage relation is

$$V = IR'_L \qquad (11.21)$$

The most straightforward approach is to draw the d-c load line first. The a-c load line will then be positioned to obtain the desired a-c performance requirement. In most audio-output transformers the d-c resistance of the primary is small. In developing the analysis for an ideal situation we will assume that this primary d-c resistance is negligible. The d-c load line would appear as shown in Fig. 11.8(a). The slope is infinity with a horizontal-intercept value of V_{CC}. The a-c load line as described by (11.21) can be positioned at will merely by adjusting the d-c collector current with d-c bias network. The ideal location of the a-c load line is at the singular collector-current level that results in an a-c and d-c load-line intersection that bisects the a-c load line. The largest, equal swings in voltage are thus available in either direction from the quiescent operating point. A little study of the graphical situation indicates that the ideal interception of the a-c load line with the horizontal occurs at a voltage value of $2V_{CC}$. The application of an a-c input signal will cause variations in the output voltage and the output current. The general-case amplitudes are labeled V_m and I_m, respectively, as in the direct-coupled case. The main factor to heed is that in the transformer case the V and I values are related by Eq. (11.21). The general-case expression for output power is given then by

$$\text{ideal } P_{\text{rms}} = \frac{V_m^2}{2R'_L} \qquad (11.22)$$

From the output characteristic of Fig. 11.8 we can observe that the maximum ideal value of V_m is V_{CC}. Substituting this specific case into (11.22), we obtain as the maximum ideal rms output power:

$$\text{ideal } P_{\text{max}} = \frac{V_{CC}^2}{2R'_L} \qquad (11.23)$$

In order to determine the efficiency of the transformer-coupled circuit, we must as before relate the useful rms power to the battery power. Referring to the situation depicted in Fig. 11.8(a), we note that the average current is always

$$\text{ideal } I_{\text{AVG}} = \frac{V_{CC}}{R'_L} = I_Q \qquad (11.24)$$

The battery power at all times in the ideal case is

$$\text{ideal } P_{\text{BATT}} = \frac{V_{CC}^2}{R'_L} \qquad (11.25)$$

The general-case efficiency expression is obtained by taking the ratio of Eqs. (11.22) and (11.25).

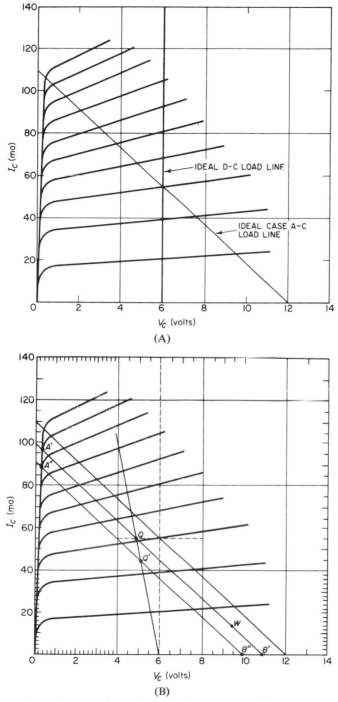

Fig. 11.8 (A) Ideal-case load-line situation for transformer coupling—$V_{CC} = 6$ v. (B) Real-case situation for load lines for transformer coupling. (1) Point Q is for a-c load line crossing real d-c load line at same current as when a-c load line crosses ideal d-c load line. (2) Q' is optimized to permit use of entire length of a-c load line, i.e., $Q'A'' = Q'B''$.

$$\text{ideal eff.} = \frac{V_m^2}{2V_{CC}^2} \tag{11.26}$$

The maximum ideal efficiency is obtained when the amplitude of V_m reaches its maximum ideal value. Since the maximum value of V_m is V_{CC}, it can be shown that a transformer-coupled Class A amplifier has a maximum ideal efficiency of 50 per cent.

The matters that must be acknowledged in the real case may be illustrated with the help of Fig. 11.8(b). When biased as though ideal conditions prevailed, the a-c load line is seen to cross the real case d-c load line at point Q. The interception of the a-c load line and the saturation-voltage region is labeled A', and the extremity of the a-c load line that crosses the leakage-current line is labeled B'. The B' value of voltage is not apt to be significantly different from twice the supply-voltage magnitude. This is especially true in a situation where the ordinate values of current involve big numbers. It is apparent from Fig. 11.8(b) that the voltage amplitude $Q - A'$ is considerably less than the voltage amplitude $B' - Q$. The maximum value of undistorted output power is determined by the voltage amplitude $(Q - A')$. Using Q as a quiescent operating point, the maximum realizable undistorted rms output power would be

$$\text{real } P_{\max} = \frac{(V_Q - V_{A'})^2}{2R_L'} \tag{11.27}$$

It is worthwhile to note that with point Q as an operating point there is a fair amount of unused load line $B'W$. To allow the operating point to remain at point Q means that an unnecessary amount of battery power will be wasted in providing the maximum amount of undistorted output power. Propriety would suggest that the operating point be lowered to point Q'. At this operating point the voltage amplitude $Q' - A''$ is essentially equal to the amplitude of $B'' - Q'$. The lower current level corresponding to Q' represents lower battery consumption for the same amount of maximum useful output power. The expression for power now becomes

$$\text{real } P_{\max} = \frac{(V_{Q'} - V_{A''})^2}{2R_L'} \tag{11.28}$$

The maximum real efficiency will be affected accordingly.

11.6. Example: transformer-coupled Class A circuit. To illustrate the preceding material, consider the situation where a transformer reflects a load of 120 ohms to a transistor with an output characteristic as shown in Fig. 11.9. The supply voltage is 6 v, and the d-c resistance of the primary winding is 20 ohms. The procedure for determining both ideal and real performance characteristics is as follows.

(a) The d-c load line for an ideal situation is a vertical line intersecting the horizontal axis at a value of 6 v.

(b) The horizontal intercept for the ideal a-c load line is a value twice

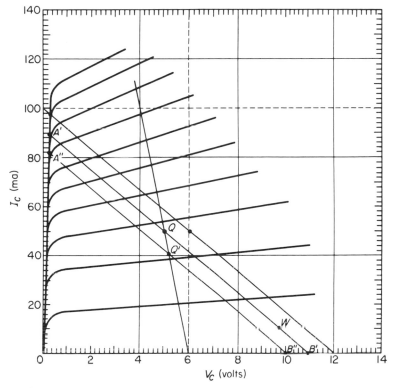

Fig. 11.9 Load-line situation for Class A transformer-coupled design example. $V_{CC} = 6$ v, $R_L = 120\ \Omega$. $R_{\text{d-c}} = 20\ \Omega$.

the magnitude of the supply voltage, or 12 v. The vertical intercept is actually twice the maximum amplitude of the a-c current. Thus

$$I_{\text{intercept}} = 2\,\frac{\max V_m}{R_L'} \tag{11.29}$$

$$= \frac{2V_{CC}}{R_L'} \tag{11.30}$$

For our problem $I_{\text{intercept}}$ equals 100 ma.

(c) The ideal quiescent operating point has coordinate values of 6 v and 50 ma.

(d) The maximum ideal rms output power by (11.23) is

$$\text{ideal } P_{\max} = \frac{V_{CC}^2}{2R_L'}$$

$$= \frac{6^2}{2(120)} = 150\ \text{mw}$$

(e) Knowing that the d-c load line intersects the horizontal axis at 6 volts, we need only determine another coordinate point in order to draw a real-case d-c load line. This may be done by assuming a current value and determining the corresponding voltage from Eq. (11.20). If $I_C = 100$ ma, we have

$$V_C = V_{CC} - I_C R_{\text{d-c}}$$
$$= 6 - (100)10^{-3}(20) = 4 \text{ v}$$

(f) When the transistor is biased to a quiescent collector current of 50 ma, the real-case quiescent voltage becomes 5 volts.

(g) The limiting voltage swing is

$$V_Q - V_{A'} = 5 - .3 = 4.7$$

The maximum real power at this 50-ma operating point is given by Eq. (11.27).

$$\text{real } P_{\max} = \frac{(V_Q - V_{A'})^2}{2R'_L}$$

$$= \frac{4.7^2}{2(120)} = 92 \text{ mw}$$

(h) The battery power is

$$P_{\text{BATT}} = V_{CC}I_Q = 6(50) = 300 \text{ mw}$$

The maximum efficiency becomes

$$\text{eff.} = \frac{P_{\text{rms}}}{P_{\text{BATT}}} = \frac{92}{300} = 30.6 \text{ per cent}$$

(i) The efficiency of performance can be improved by lowering the operating current to eliminate the unused load-line length $B'W$. A compromise adjustment of the load line gives Q' as the optimum operating point. The coordinates of this point are 5.2 v and 40 ma. The voltage amplitudes that are possible from this operating point are

$$V_{Q'} - V_{A''} = 5.2 - .3 = 4.9 \text{ v}$$
$$V_{B''} - V_{Q'} = 10 - 5.2 = 4.8 \text{ v}$$

Using the 4.8-v amplitude we find

$$\text{real } P_{\max} = \frac{(V_{B''} - V_{Q'})^2}{2R_{L'}} = \frac{4.8^2}{2(120)} = 96 \text{ mw}$$

$$P_{\text{BATT}} = V_{CC}I_{Q'} = 6(40) = 240 \text{ mw}$$

$$\text{eff.} = \frac{\text{real } P_{\max}}{P_{\text{BATT}}} = \frac{96}{240} = 40 \text{ per cent}$$

It is important to appreciate that an optimized design cannot be achieved without adequate information about saturation-voltage and leakage-current limits. The worst-case values of these parameters are always available from the transistor manufacturer.

11.7. Class A RC-coupled.   The RC-coupled amplifier was introduced in Chapter 9. The basic matters of load lines and load-line equations remain the same. Since, however, we are now talking about large-signal amplifiers, we will emphasize the attributes of power output, distortion, and efficiency. RC-coupled amplifiers find limited use in large-signal applications because their efficiency of operation is quite poor. We shall comment here on the highlights of their performance.

An amplifier configuration that is useful for the purpose at hand is the fixed-bias circuit shown in Fig. 11.10. In an ideal situation we showed in Chapter 9 that the following equations were pertinent. For the power in the load

$$P_{\text{rms}} = \frac{V_m^2}{2R_L} \tag{11.31}$$

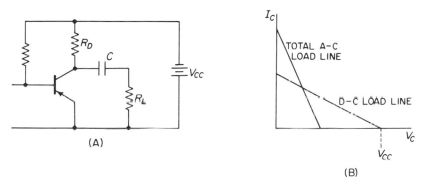

$$(A)$$

$$(B)$$

Fig. 11.10   (A) RC-coupling of load in a power amplifier. (B) A-C and d-c load line situation for (A).

The d-c load line was expressed by

$$V_C = V_{CC} - I_C R_D \tag{11.32}$$

The total a-c load-line equation was

$$V_m = I_m R_{\text{TOT}} \tag{11.33}$$

where

$$R_{\text{TOT}} = \frac{R_D R_L}{R_D + R_L} \tag{11.34}$$

When designing so that the d-c load line intercepted the a-c load line at a point midway on the a-c load line, we found that

$$V_m = \frac{V_{CC} R_L}{R_D + 2R_L} \tag{11.35}$$

$$R_D = R_L\left(\frac{V_{CC}}{V_m} - 2\right) \tag{11.36}$$

Equation (11.35) indicates the specific value of V_m that for a given R_L and R_D represents the voltage value for the midpoint of the total a-c load line. Equation (11.36) indicates the value of R_D that for a given required V_m results in an a-c d-c load-line intersection midway on the a-c load line. To complete the interpretation of Eqs. (11.35) and (11.36), one should be aware that the quiescent operating voltage is

$$V_Q = V_m \tag{11.37}$$

where V_m is given by Eq. (11.35) or is the value used in Eq. (11.36). The quiescent operating current can be obtained from the equation for the a-c load line as stated by Eq. (11.33). It is interesting to note that no general equation relating maximum ideal rms power and supply voltage exists for RC-coupled amplifiers. Instead we can only hope to maximize output power as a function of V_{CC}, R_L, and R_D with the use of Eq. (11.35).

The efficiency of an RC-coupled amplifier is determined as follows. Substituting Eq. (11.35) into (11.31), we obtain for *optimum* load power

$$P_{\text{rms}} = \frac{V_{CC}^2 R_L}{2(R_D + 2R_L)^2} \tag{11.38}$$

It can be shown that the battery power is

$$P_{\text{BATT}} = \frac{V_{CC}^2(R_L + R_D)}{R_D(R_D + 2R_L)} \tag{11.39}$$

By the definition of efficiency we have

$$\text{eff.} = \frac{P_{\text{rms}}}{P_{\text{BATT}}} = \frac{R_L R_D}{2(R_D + 2R_L)(R_L + R_D)} \tag{11.40}$$

Note that this is the efficiency for a general-case circuit giving optimum load power in that the operating point has been placed midway on the a-c load line resulting for the given R_L and R_D. This is the optimized power-output condition. The circuit efficiency varies as a function of the relative values of R_D and R_L. Equation (11.40) indicates that both very small and very large R_D caused the efficiency to equal zero. At some in-between condition, we can obtain optimum load power *and* maximum efficiency. By taking the derivative of Eq. (11.40) with respect to R_L and setting it equal to zero, we find that maximized efficiency occurs at

$$R_D = \sqrt{2}R_L$$

At this time the efficiency is 8.59 per cent. Efficiencies of such low magnitude discourage widespread use of RC-amplifiers for large-signal amplifiers.

If one were to include the effects of saturation voltage but exclude the effects of leakage, Eqs. (9.58) and (9.59) could apply, with the result that

$$V_m = \frac{R_L[V_{cc} - V_{\text{SAT}}]}{R_D + 2R_L}$$ (11.41a)

$$R_D = R_L\left[\frac{V_{cc} - V_{\text{SAT}}}{V_m} - 2\right]$$ (11.41b)

It can be shown that the maximized efficiency is the same as the ideal case.

11.8. Distortion in Class A Amplifiers. In the previous sections the emphasis was on the circuit operation and the analyses yielding maximum output power or maximum efficiency conditions. The matter of distortion was only touched upon lightly with reference to the clipping conditions that ensue when a stage is overdriven beyond the useful length of available load line. Distortion, however, in the broadest sense is any condition that results in a deformation of a signal waveform from other than the ideal objective of a true sinusoid. In any Class A amplifier there are three potential sources of distortion: (a) the clipping caused by overdriving of the stage, (b) the decrease in current gain h_{FE} that occurs at high currents, and (c) the non-linear input resistance of the transistor. The total amount of distortion that exists depends on the extent to which each cause of distortion is active. Distortion is usually measured by the use of harmonic distortion analyzers. Naturally, the less distortion in a circuit design the better. As a figure of merit, the power level at which perhaps 10 per cent distortion occurs is typically quoted by manufacturers of radios or phonographs as an indicator of the control of distortion in their circuit designs.

The matter of clipping has been discussed. This a readily controlled design factor. It requires only that the useful length of load line be known, with a vertification that the desired power level can in fact be obtained with that particular load line. If not, such matters as increased supply voltage, with either appropriate operating point adjustment or decreased load imped-ance have to be considered. Either step implies increased battery size, increased battery current, and therefore reduced battery life and perhaps a respecification of tran-sistor to prevent violation of cur-rent, voltage or power limitations.

The matter of current-gain degradation at high current levels is largely a matter of specification control to assure parameter be-havior commensurate with the circuit requirement. In Sec. 5.10 we discussed the variation of

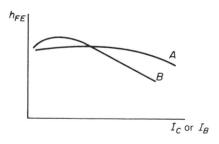

Fig. 11.11 Plot of current gain versus col-lector or base current.

current gain with collector current. Two possible situations are shown in Fig. 11.11. The common-emitter output characteristic involves various values of base current. Thus, as explained in Chapter 5, successive steps of base current and a decreasing current-gain function cause bunching of the collector characteristic at higher current levels. In considering the placement of a load line as shown in Fig. 11.12(a) we might anticipate the suppression of the high-current peak of the alternation in output current. This type of distortion is avoided by a transistor specification restricting the amount that the current gain can degrade as the collector current is increased from a mid to a high value.

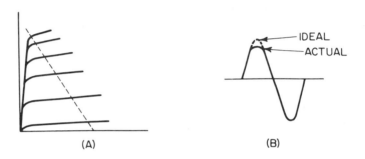

(A)   (B)

Fig. 11.12   (A) Collector characteristic showing h_{FE} falloff at high I_C. (B) Typical waveform distortion due to h_{FE} falloff.

The last factor that contributes to distortion is an input-circuit phenomenon. The d-c input impedance of both common-emitter and common-base connections decreases as the input current increases. This is shown with the help of the common-emitter input characteristic of Figure 11.13(a). Here we see three values of base current, I_1, I_2, and I_3 in an ascending order of magnitude. The d-c resistance at any of these operating points is determined by the slope of a straight line drawn from the origin to the operating point in question. It is easy to see that the d-c resistance at high values of current is *less than* the d-c resistance at low values of current. A plot of d-c input resistance vs base current is shown in Figure 11.13(b). The plot for the common-base connection is similar.

Consider now the situation that occurs when a *sinusoidal voltage source* causes the input current to vary from an arbitrarily chosen quiescent point, I_Q. The relation between source voltage e_g and input current i_{in} is given by

$$i_{in} = \frac{e_g}{R} \qquad (11.42)$$

where R is the instantaneous value of d-c input impedance. As the source

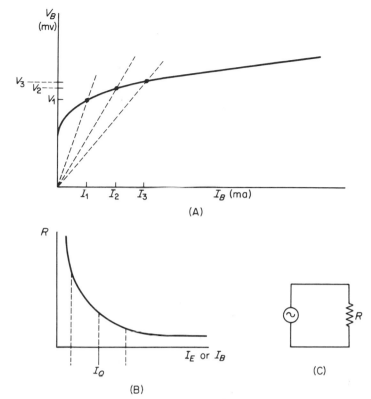

Fig. 11.13 (A) Graphical technique for determining d-c input resistance at various operating points on common-emitter input characteristic. Resistance is proportional to slope of line between origin and operating point. (B) Typical variation of R with input current. (C) Circuit for sinusoidal voltage source.

voltage increases, the input current increases. Since, however, for each successive increment of voltage, the input impedance *decreases*, the corresponding current value is greater in magnitude than the sinusoidal correspondence of current and voltage that would occur if R were constant. In like manner we notice that as e_g decreases, the incremental value of R increases. Thus the resultant current value is less in magnitude than the sinusoidal correspondence that would have occurred if R were constant. The input-current waveform would appear then as in Fig. 11.14, even though the stage is being driven by a sinusoidal voltage source. As seen, the input current contains a flattening of one peak and a lengthening of the second peak. This distortion would appear amplified in the output should no output distortion occur. The only remedy applicable in

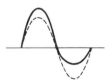

Fig. 11.14 Collector-current waveform resulting from a non-linear resistance R being driven by a sinusoidal voltage source. True sine wave shown dotted.

minimizing input distortion is the use of current sources as power sources. The purpose here is to swamp the input-impedance variations by means of the high impedance associated with the current source. This is not always desirable because of the attendant sacrifices in gain. In large-signal amplifiers where the quiescent current and the signal-current swings are large, the distortion associated with *decreasing* input impedance is practically non-existent.

11.9. Class B push-pull amplifier theory.   The various features of Class A amplifiers have been discussed. Probably the most important single aspect of a Class A amplifier is that efficiency is a maximum when the amplifier is delivering maximum output power, and that the efficiency diminishes to zero as the output power reduces. An alternate power-amplifier connection, *the push-pull amplifier*, uses two transistors operating close to a Class B mode, and offers improved efficiency and higher power output than that obtainable from either of the individual transistors operating separately in a single-ended Class A amplifier. An idealized version of a Class B push-pull amplifier is shown in Fig. 11.15. Here we observe that two transistors with their emitters connected directly are fed from a transformer with a center-tapped

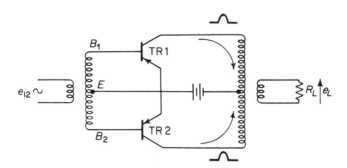

Fig. 11.15   Circuit connection for Class B push-pull power amplifier.

secondary. In the output circuitry we see that the collectors are tied together through an output transformer with a center-tapped primary connection to a common supply voltage. The operation of such an amplifier can be described qualitatively in the following manner.

Notice first that there is no bias network shown. The instantaneous-current level in either transistor is dependent strictly on the instantaneous magnitude and polarity of signal appearing at the input terminals. Since the

secondary of the driver transformer is center-tapped, a voltage e_{12} applied
at the primary appears at the secondary as shown in Fig. 11.16(a). During
the first 180° of the cycle, the base of TR1 is positive with respect to the
emitter and no collector current flows. During this same 180°, however, the
base of TR2 is negative with respect to its emitter. Collector current will
flow in TR2 in accordance with the magnitude of the applied forward bias.
During the second 180° of the cycle, the base of TR1 goes negative relative
to the emitter, forward-biasing TR1 so that it turns on and conducts. The
base of TR2 goes positive at this time, causing TR2 to become nonconducting.
The waveforms of collector current, Fig. 11.16(b), show that only one tran-

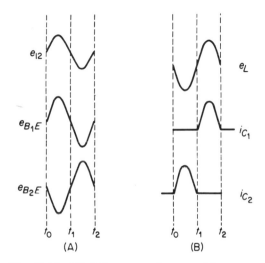

Fig. 11.16   (A) Voltage waveforms at driver transformer. (B) Collector circuit waveforms phased
relative to input waveforms.

sistor is conducting at any given time, and that the nature of conduction is
Class B—that is, that the off period of each transistor is equal to the on
period. The final feature to note is that each collector current is essentially
pulsating d-c, flowing from the ends of the output transformer primary, to
the center tap, to the battery. The fact that current is alternately changing
directions in the primary results in an induced voltage in the secondary
which is sinusoidal in nature. Thus the overall circuit performance involves
conversion of an a-c signal to pulsating d-c at the transistors, to a-c at the
output transformer secondary.

A quantitative study can begin with some specific statements about the load into which each transistor works. Let R'_L be defined as the impedance between an end and the tap on the output transformer. The quantity R'_L is the load seen by either transistor. If n is the ratio of primary turns to secondary turns, we can define

$$R_{C-C} = n^2 R_L \tag{11.43}$$

$$R'_L = \left(\frac{n}{2}\right)^2 R_L = \frac{n^2 R_L}{4} \tag{11.44}$$

The quantity R_{C-C} in Eq. (11.43) is the total impedance end-to-end at the primary. Assuming now that the primary has zero d-c resistance, we can construct the graphical depiction of a single transistor operating in the Class B push-pull mode. See Fig. 11.17. The d-c load line is drawn vertically with a voltage intercept of V_{CC}. The slope of the a-c load line is $-1/R'_L$. To comply with the operating description whereby the device is off until it is biased on by the a-c input signal, we draw the a-c load line so that it intercepts the d-c load line at a quiescent-current level of zero. The vertical intercept is V_{CC}/R'_L. For the half-sinusoids of current and voltage the relation between rms and peak values is

$$V = \frac{V_m}{2} \tag{11.45}$$

$$I = \frac{I_m}{2} \tag{11.46}$$

$$I_m = \frac{V_m}{R'_L} \tag{11.47}$$

We can now substitute these specific relations into the general rms relationship of Eq. (11.7) to obtain for one transistor

$$\text{ideal } P_{\text{rms}} = \frac{V_m^2}{4R'_L} \tag{11.48}$$

It is imperative to note that the power given by (11.48) is for a single one of the two transistors. The output of the pair of transistors requires only a summation of this equation two times; thus, for two transistors,

$$\text{ideal } P_{\text{rms}} = \frac{V_m^2}{2R'_L} \tag{11.49}$$

An alternate form for expressing rms power is to use the relation of R'_L and R_{C-C} as given by Eqs. (11.43) and (11.44). This, for two transistors,

$$\text{ideal } P_{\text{rms}} = \frac{2V_m^2}{R_{C-C}} \tag{11.50}$$

The rms power maximizes when V_m is a maximum. Referring to Fig. 11.17, we can note that the maximum ideal value of V_m is V_{CC}. For two transistors,

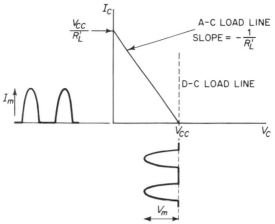

Fig. 11.17 Single characteristic analysis for Class B push-pull performance. (Ideal case.)

$$\text{ideal } P_{\max} = \frac{V_{CC}^2}{2R_L'} \tag{11.51}$$

$$= \frac{2V_{CC}^2}{R_{c\,c}} \tag{11.52}$$

In order to calculate battery power we must calculate the average current through the battery. At this point we recognize an important aspect of the Class B push-pull amplifier: the battery current is a function of the output power. For the half-sinusoidal waveform,

$$\text{ideal } I_{\text{AVG}} = \frac{I_m}{\pi} \tag{11.53}$$

Substituting the information of Eq. (11.47), we can write

$$\text{ideal } I_{\text{AVG}} = \frac{V_m}{\pi R_L'} \tag{11.54}$$

The battery power required for one transistor is

$$\text{ideal } P_{\text{BATT}} = V_{CC}\frac{V_m}{\pi R_L'} \tag{11.55}$$

For two transistors,

$$\text{ideal } P_{\text{BATT}} = \frac{2V_{CC}V_m}{\pi R_L'} \tag{11.56}$$

The maximum battery power is required when V_m is its maximum value of V_{CC}. Thus for one transistor

$$\text{max ideal } P_{\text{BATT}} = \frac{V_{CC}^2}{\pi R_L'} \tag{11.57}$$

For two transistors

$$\text{max ideal } P_{\text{BATT}} = \frac{2V_{CC}^2}{\pi R_L'} \qquad (11.58)$$

In the alternate form involving R_{C-C} for one transistor

$$\text{max ideal } P_{\text{BATT}} = \frac{4V_{CC}^2}{\pi R_{C-C}} \qquad (11.59a)$$

For two transistors

$$\text{max ideal } P_{\text{BATT}} = \frac{8V_{CC}^2}{\pi R_{C-C}} \qquad (11.59b)$$

The efficiency of circuit performance is determined by the ratio of rms power to battery power. Mathematically by (11.14)

$$\text{eff} = \frac{P_{\text{rms}}}{P_{\text{BATT}}} \qquad (11.14)$$

Substituting Eqs. (11.48) and (11.55) into (11.14) we obtain

$$\text{ideal eff} = \frac{\pi V_m}{4 V_{CC}} \qquad (11.60)$$

For our ideal mode of operation, the maximum value of V_m is V_{CC}. Thus the maximum ideal efficiency for a Class B circuit is seen to be 78.5 per cent.

The difference between battery power and rms output power is the actual power being dissipated in the transistors. Mathematically we say

$$P_{\text{DISS}} = P_{\text{BATT}} - P_{\text{rms}} \qquad (11.61)$$

Substituting Eqs. (11.48) and (11.55) into (11.61), we obtain as a general expression

$$\text{ideal } P_{\text{DISS}} = \frac{V_{CC} V_m}{\pi R_L'} - \frac{V_m^2}{4 R_L'} \qquad (11.62)$$

In order to determine the conditions at which the transistor dissipation maximizes, we take the derivative of (11.62) with respect to V_m. Setting the result equal to zero, we obtain the critical value of V_m causing maximum transistor dissipation. That value is

$$\text{critical } \quad V_m = \frac{2}{\pi} V_{CC} \qquad (11.63)$$

The discussion of actual dissipation magnitude is reserved for a later section.

11.10. Class AB push-pull theory.   The equations and discussions have thus far dealt with ideal transistors operating in a true Class B mode. We should now direct our attention to real transistors. It will soon be apparent that true Class B operation is undesirable for real transistors.

Consider the input characteristics of two transistors drawn in relation to each other as shown in Figure 11.18. This is a useful depiction as it suggests the switching of conduction from one transistor to the other as the base driving voltage changes polarity in the real circuit. Suppose that these transistors are now operated with no d-c forward bias between each emitter-base pair. This is, of course, the bias condition for Class B. Until the base driving voltage exceeds a value corresponding to B_1, the base current for $TR1$ is zero. It is only during the time period t_1 to t_2 that base current flows in $TR1$ in response to the base-driving voltage. Likewise $TR2$ responds to base-driving voltage only during the time period t_4 to t_5. Neither transistor then has base current flowing for a full 180° half cycle when the devices are biased Class B. The curved portion of the base current waveform at low

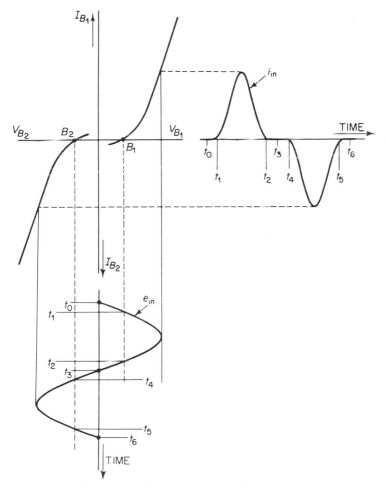

Fig. 11.18 Composite of input circuitry conditions for two real transistors operating Class B push-pull. Note that the waveform for i_{in} is not continuous and has distortion.

current levels is caused by the nonlinear knee region of the input characteristic.

The situation in the collectors of real transistors biased Class B is shown in Figure 11.19. We should first of all anticipate that the time duration of each collector current pulse is less than a complete 180° half cycle. Next we should remember that I_{CEO} current flows in the collector of a common emitter transistor when its base current is zero. Since the collector current pulses flow in response to base conduction, we would expect a curved transition from the I_{CEO} to the conduction state in each collector-current waveform. Figure 11.19(b) shows the waveform of current in each collector

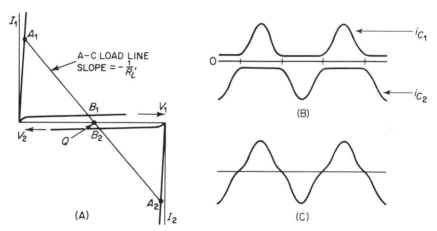

Fig. 11.19 (A) Collector observations—real transistors in Class B push-pull. (B) Actual-case waveforms for each collector current. (C) Composite load current showing "crossover" distortion.

for Class B biasing. The waveform of interest is, of course, the output of the transformer. The amplitude of the output waveform is less than the peak amplitude of each individual collector-current pulse by an amount equal to the magnitude of I_{CEO} current. The step or notch which occurs in the output waveform is called *crossover distortion*. It is caused as we now know by collector-current conduction for less than a full 180° and by the nonlinear parts of the input characteristic.

The only way to eliminate this crossover distortion is to provide some amount of d-c bias so that the quiescent base current is beyond the knee of the input characteristic. The approach can be visualized on the characteristic form of Fig. 11.18 by effectively sliding the characteristics over each other as shown in Fig. 11.20. Since the Q point is in the linear portion of the input characteristic, the base-current waveform is not discontinuous in the transition period when the transistors are switching their conduction mode. The distortion is eliminated because the individual transitors are conducting for a full half-cycle in response to the input driving signal. The presence of a quiescent component of collector current makes the operational mode slightly Class A; hence it is called *Class AB.*

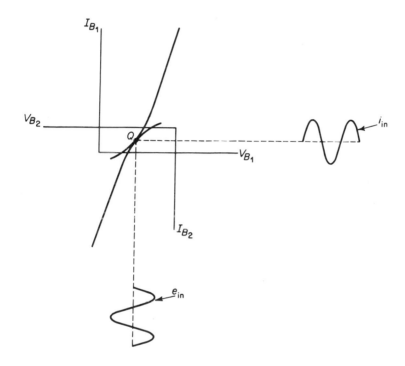

Fig. 11.20 Composite input characteristic for Class AB push-pull. Note the continuous i_{in} waveform.

Typically, the selection of the quiescent current is quite arbitrary, based on the individual transistors at hand. The general rule of thumb, however, is merely to provide sufficient forward bias so that the quiescent base current is beyond the knee of the input characteristic. The composite collector characteristics for Class AB are shown in Fig. 11.21. The actual circuitry for forward-biasing Class AB transistors will be discussed later.

The analysis of a real transistor operating in the Class AB mode can be studied with the help of the single transistor characteristic of Fig. 11.22. The d-c load line is drawn from the equation

$$V_c = V_{cc} - I_c R_{\text{d-c}} \qquad (11.64)$$

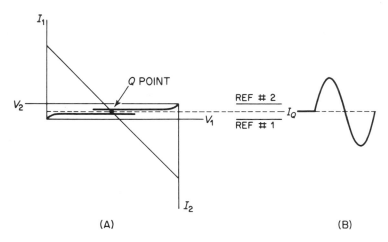

Fig. 11.21 (A) Composite collector characteristic for Class AB. (B) Waveform shows elimination of crossover distortion for Class AB operation.

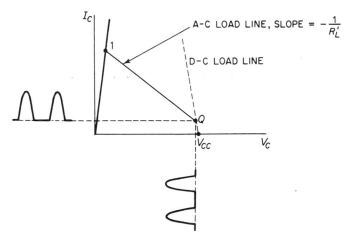

Fig. 11.22 Actual-case load-line situation for one transistor of Class AB pushpull.

Once the necessary quiescent-current level is established, the quiescent operating voltage is determined from Eq. (11.64). This value is, incidently, quite close in magnitude to V_{CC}. The a-c load line is a line with slope equaling $-1/R'_L$ drawn through the quiescent operating point Q. The coordinate point 1 represents the intersection of the a-c load line and the saturation curve. As a *general* case we can say

$$V_m = V_Q - V_x \qquad (11.65a)$$

$$I_m = I_x - I_Q \qquad (11.65b)$$

The maximum useful amplitudes for the real case are

$$\max V_m = V_Q - V_1 \qquad (11.66a)$$

$$\max I_m = I_1 - I_Q \qquad (11.66b)$$

The subscript x is used to designate a general-case coordinate point. Since the interrelation of I_m and V_m as given by (11.47) still applies, we can say

$$(I_x - I_Q) = \frac{V_Q - V_x}{R'_L} \qquad (11.67)$$

The rms values of current and voltage are determined in the normal manner.

$$V = \frac{V_Q - V_x}{2} \qquad (11.68a)$$

$$I = \frac{I_x - I_Q}{2} \qquad (11.68b)$$

$$I = \frac{V_Q - V_x}{2R'_L} \qquad (11.68c)$$

The expression for general-case rms power from one transistor is

$$\text{real } P_{\text{rms}} = \frac{(V_Q - V_x)^2}{4R'_L} \qquad (11.69a)$$

$$= \frac{(I_x - I_Q)^2 R'_L}{4} \qquad (11.69b)$$

The d-c value of collector current flowing in *one* transistor is

$$\text{real } I_{\text{d-c}} = \frac{I_x - I_Q}{\pi} + I_Q \qquad (11.70)$$

The battery power required in the operation of a *single* transistor is

$$\text{real } P_{\text{BATT}} = V_{CC}\left(\frac{I_x - I_Q}{\pi} + I_Q\right) \qquad (11.71)$$

$$= V_{CC}\left(\frac{V_Q - V_x}{\pi R'_L} + I_Q\right) \qquad (11.72)$$

The general-case expression for efficiency is obtained by taking a ratio of Eqs. (11.69a) and (11.72). The result is

$$\text{real eff.} = \frac{\pi V_m^2}{4V_{CC}(V_m + I_Q \pi R'_L)} \qquad (11.73)$$

The quantity V_m in Eq. (11.73) is given by Eq. (11.65a). The maximum real-case efficiency can be considerably less than the ideal maximum of 78.5 per cent depending on the saturation voltage and quiescent current levels.

The power dissipation for a real-case transistor is now found by substituting Eqs. (11.72) and (11.69a) into (11.61). The result is

$$\text{real } P_{\text{DISS}} = V_{CC}\left(\frac{V_Q - V_x}{\pi R'_L} + I_Q\right) - \frac{(V_Q - V_x)^2}{4R'_L} \tag{11.74}$$

In taking the derivative of Eq. 11.74 to determine the value of critical voltage amplitude giving maximum transistor dissipation, we find

$$\text{critical } (V_Q - V_x) = \frac{2V_{CC}}{\pi} \tag{11.75}$$

In comparing (11.75) with (11.63), we observe that the actual-case and real-case criteria for maximum transistor dissipation are the same. This is not to imply that the *magnitudes* of maximum transistor dissipation are the same in the real and ideal cases. They are *not* as we shall soon see.

Improved insight into Class B ideal case and Class AB performance is obtained from plots of battery power and rms output power normalized to maximum rms output power. The results of such plots are shown in Fig. 11.23. Let us first rewrite the expression for maximum ideal rms power as

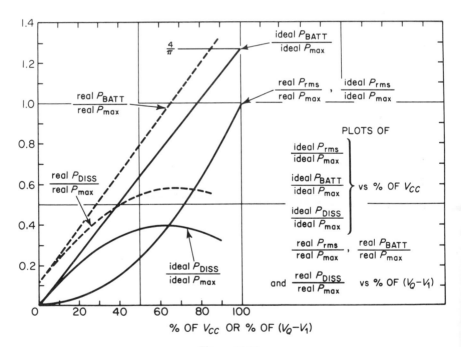

Figure 11.23

$$\text{ideal } P_{\max} = \frac{V_{CC}^2}{4R'_L} \tag{11.76}$$

The plot of ideal P_{rms} normalized to ideal $P_{\max}$ is determined by taking the ratio of Eqs. (11.48) and (11.76). The result is

$$\frac{\text{ideal } P_{\text{rms}}}{\text{ideal } P_{\text{max}}} = \left(\frac{V_m}{V_{CC}}\right)^2 \qquad (11.77)$$

The plot of ideal P_{rms} normalized to ideal P_{max} is obtained by substituting percentage values of V_{CC} for V_m. The result is the square of the percentage and is shown in Fig. 11.23.

By way of illustration let us consider a circuit operating at a V_m level of 4.5 v. If V_{CC} is equal to 9 v, then V_m is 50 per cent of V_{CC}. By substituting the quantity $.5\,V_{CC}$ into Eq. (11.77) for V_m we determine that

$$\frac{\text{ideal } P_{\text{rms}}}{\text{ideal } P_{\text{max}}} = \left(\frac{.5\,V_{CC}}{V_{CC}}\right)^2 = .25$$

This merely states that the ideal P_{rms} is 25 per cent of the ideal P_{max} when V_m is 50 per cent of V_{CC}. All other points on this particular curve have correspondent significance.

To construct the plot of ideal P_{BATT} normalized to ideal P_{max} we first recall the expression for ideal P_{BATT} as stated in Eq. (11.55). That is

$$\text{ideal } P_{\text{BATT}} = \frac{V_{CC}V_m}{\pi R'_L} \qquad (11.55)$$

Taking the ratio of (11.55) and (11.76) we obtain

$$\frac{\text{ideal } P_{\text{BATT}}}{\text{ideal } P_{\text{max}}} = \frac{4V_m}{\pi V_{CC}} \qquad (11.78)$$

Since the maximum V_m is V_{CC} for the ideal case, the normalized ratio is the product of $4/\pi$ and the per cent value of V_{CC} chosen for V_m.

For illustration let us again consider a circuit where $V_{CC} = 9$ v and the operating value of $V_m = 4.5$ v. The V_m value is 50 per cent of V_{CC}. Substituting this percentage into Eq. (11.78) we obtain

$$\frac{\text{ideal } P_{\text{BATT}}}{\text{ideal } P_{\text{max}}} = \frac{4}{\pi}\left(\frac{.5\,V_{CC}}{V_{CC}}\right) = .64$$

This merely states that the magnitude of ideal battery power is 64 per cent of the value of ideal P_{max} when V_m is 50 per cent of supply voltage V_{CC}. Other points on this curve have correspondent significance,

The difference between the normalized P_{BATT} and P_{rms} curves is a curve that represents the transistor dissipation normalized to the maximum ideal rms output power. Note that the peak of this curve occurs at an abscissa value of .64 or $2/\pi$. This was indicated by Eq. (11.63).

In treating now the real case we first realize that the maximum swing in voltage for the real case $(V_Q - V_1)$ is less than the maximum swing in voltage for the ideal case (V_{CC}). The expression for maximum real rms output power is

$$\text{real } P_{\text{max}} = \frac{(V_Q - V_1)^2}{4R'_L} \qquad (11.79a)$$

The plot of real P_{rms} is obtained by taking the ratio of Eqs. (11.69a) and (11.79a). The result is

$$\frac{\text{real } P_{rms}}{\text{real } P_{max}} = \left(\frac{V_Q - V_x}{V_Q - V_1}\right)^2 \tag{11.79b}$$

Substituting fractional values of $(V_Q - V_1)$ for $(V_Q - V_x)$, we find that the normalized plots for real P_{rms} and ideal P_{rms} are the same.

The plot of real P_{BATT} normalized to real P_{max} is obtained by taking the ratio of Eqs. (11.72) and (11.79a). The result is

$$\frac{\text{real } P_{BATT}}{\text{real } P_{max}} = \frac{4V_{cc}(V_Q - V_x)}{\pi(V_Q - V_1)^2} + \frac{4V_{cc}I_Q R_L'}{(V_Q - V_1)^2} \tag{11.80}$$

The second term is an additive constant appearing only because of the quiescent power of the Class AB biasing. Substituting fractional values of $(V_Q - V_1)$ for $(V_Q - V_x)$ into equation (11.80) we get a plot as shown in Fig. 11.23. The real power curve is displaced upwards from the ideal-case curve for normalized P_{BATT} because of the additive term. The real-case power curve has more slope than the ideal-case curve because the ratio of $V_{cc}/(V_Q - V_1)$ is a number greater than unity.

The difference between the normalized P_{BATT} and P_{rms} curves for the real case is shown. Not only does the transistor dissipation increase, it occurs at a higher value of abscissa parameter. This is because the critical value of voltage as given by (11.75) is a higher percentage of the real-case maximum voltage swing $(V_Q - V_1)$ than (11.63) is of the ideal-case maximum voltage swing (V_{cc}).

The behavior of each individual *real*-case transistor will differ from the ideal, depending on the quiescent operating point and the magnitude of the saturation voltage. Three specific traits will exist: (1) the critical voltage causing maximum dissipation is always the same absolute value as given by Eq. (11.63) or (11.75), (2) the max P_{rms} as given by (11.79a) is less than the ideal case, and (3) the battery power as given by (11.72) is greater than the ideal case because the presence of the I_Q term overcompensates the quantity $(V_Q - V_x)$.

The actual magnitude for maximum transistor dissipation is obtained by substituting the critical swing voltage into Eq. (11.74). The result is

$$\text{real max } P_{DISS} = \frac{V_{cc}^2}{\pi^2 R_L'} + V_{cc}I_Q \tag{11.81}$$

By substituting the critical value of voltage into Eq. (11.48) or (11.69a), we can see that for either a real or ideal device maximum dissipation occurs when the device is delivering

$$\text{critical } P_{rms} = \frac{V_{cc}^2}{\pi^2 R_L'} \tag{11.82}$$

Taking the ratio of (11.82) to the expression of real $P_{\max}$ [(11.79a)], we get

$$\frac{\text{critical } P_{\text{rms}}}{\text{real } P_{\max}} = \frac{4}{\pi^2} \frac{V_{CC}^2}{(V_Q - V_1)^2}$$

i.e.,

$$\text{critical } P_{\text{rms}} = \frac{4V_{CC}^2}{\pi^2(V_Q - V_1)^2} \text{ real } P_{\max} \qquad (11.83)$$

For an ideal device

$$\text{critical } P_{\text{rms}} \cong .4(\text{ideal } P_{\max}) \qquad (11.84)$$

$$\cong .2(\text{ideal } P_{\max} \text{ for two}) \qquad (11.85)$$

It can also be shown that for an ideal device

$$\text{ideal max } P_{\text{DISS}} \cong .4(\text{ideal } P_{\max}) \qquad (11.86)$$

$$\cong .2(\text{ideal } P_{\max} \text{ for two}) \qquad (11.87)$$

Equations (11.84) through (11.87) are useful as first-order approximations for the values of critical P_{rms} and max P_{DISS} for the real case. The correct magnitudes are determined in conjunction with (11.82) and (11.81). Reversing the context of Eq. (11.87), we observe that the rms power obtainable in a Class AB push-pull circuit is approximately five times the dissipation rating of the transistors being used. This is indeed a dramatic difference from a transformer-coupled Class A circuit, where the maximum ideal power obtainable is only one-half of the dissipation rating of the transistor being used. Better appreciation of Class AB performance will be obtained in a problem exercise. First, however, we will discuss the biasing of Class AB stages.

11.11. Biasing the Class AB stage. We found earlier that some amount of quiescent forward biasing was necessary to eliminate the crossover distortion due to the nonconduction region in, and the nonlinear aspect of, the input characteristic. A common way of establishing such a forward bias is shown in Fig. 11.24. Here a bleeder network R_1 and R_2 is connected around the supply voltage so that the voltage drop across R_1 appears directly in the emitter-base loop of each transistor. When conventional current flows through R_1, the resultant voltage drop serves to forward-bias the emitter-base

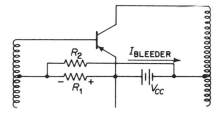

Fig. 11.24 Typical circuitry for biasing a push-pull pair slightly Class A.

junction of each transistor simultaneously. The quiescent value of base voltage should be beyond the knee of the input characteristic. This was shown in Fig. 11.21. Mathematically we can say

$$V_{bq} = \frac{R_1}{R_1 + R_2} V_{cc} \qquad (11.88)$$

The current that flows through R_1 and R_2 is called the *bleeder current*. It is not desirable that this be high in value as battery life would be considerably shortened. Thus R_1 and R_2 cannot be too low in value. On the other hand, R_1 and R_2 can not be made too high in value, because R_1 contributes in making the effective impedance seen by the transformer too high in value. Practice alone will serve to establish the compromise values of bleeder-network components.

Often an appreciable temperature variation is associated with the operating ambient of a push-pull amplifier. Nonlinear components such as diodes or thermistors are substituted then for R_1.

11.12. Input considerations—Class AB circuits.

The manner in which the Class AB stage is biased requires special consideration to assure that the stage is driven to obtain the desired peak power. The factors that must be considered are the decrease in current gain of a transistor at high collector currents, and the bias resistor R_1 and transformer secondary resistance R_{sec} which are in series with the transistor input. A correct design requires that the driving source provide adequate compensation for these factors.

At the peak value of collector current determine the value of current gain from a curve such as that shown in Fig. 11.11. The ratio of the peak collector current and current gain at this current is the peak base current, $I_{b(peak)}$. The desired output power will not be obtained unless this required $I_{b(peak)}$ flows in the input circuitry. A curve such as the input characteristic of Fig. 11.20 shows the value of $V_{b(peak)}$ corresponding to the peak base current, $I_{b(peak)}$. The required peak value of voltage at the secondary for each transistor is

$$V_{peak} = V_{b(peak)} + I_{b(peak)}(R_1 + R_{sec}) - V_{bq} \qquad (11.89)$$

When we know the peak value of voltage at the secondary, the next useful information is the available load line in the driver transistor collector. These facts gathered, we may proceed to determine straightforwardly the design of the driver transformer.

11.13. Design example for Class AB.

Let us consider a practical example showing the embodiments of Class AB design. A pair of transistors with $h_{FE} = 50$ at $I_C = 40$ ma are to be used. The supply voltage is 12 v. The output transformer has an efficiency assumed to be 100 per cent. Assume

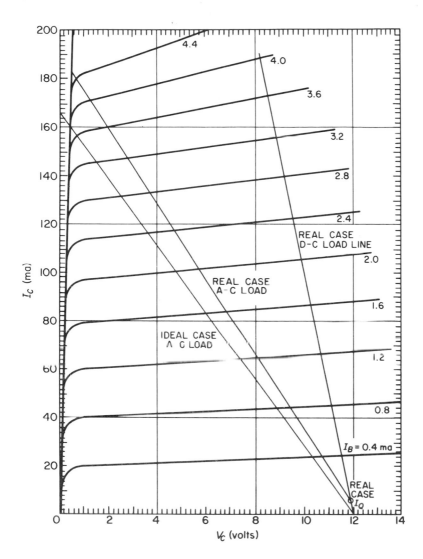

Fig. 11.25 $I_C - V_C$ plot for Class AB design example.

also that the d-c resistance of each half of the primary winding will be 20 ohms. It is desired to obtain a power output of 1 w. Applicable characteristics are shown in Figs. 11.25, 11.26, and 11.27. Determine:

(a) ideal-case R'_L.
(b) ideal-case I_C peak.
(c) critical V_m at which maximum dissipation occurs.

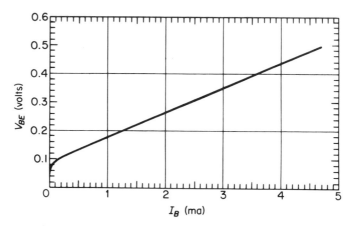

Fig. 11.26 $V_B - I_B$ plot for Class AB design example.

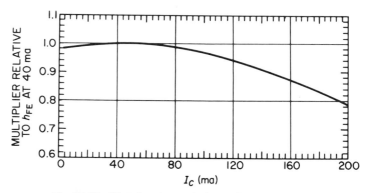

Fig. 11.27   Plot showing variation of h_{FE} versus I_C.

(d) ideal-case maximum dissipation.

(e) appropriate real-case quiescent current for minimum crossover.

(f) actual-case R'_L.

(g) actual-case maximum dissipation.

(h) maximum real-case efficiency.

(i) appropriate resistors for the bias network if the bleeder current is to be maintained at about 5 ma maximum.

(j) the peak voltage at the driver secondary.

The solutions to these questions are as follows.

(a) Knowing maximum ideal rms power for two transistors, we use (11.51) to obtain

$$R'_L = \frac{V_{CC}^2}{2(\text{ideal } P_{\text{max}})}$$

$$= \frac{12^2}{2(1)} = 72 \ \Omega$$

(b) The peak value of collector current is

$$\text{ideal peak } I_c = \frac{V_{CC}}{R'_L}$$

$$= \frac{12}{72} = 167 \text{ ma}$$

(c) The critical V_m at which maximum dissipation occurs in each transistor is given by Eq. (11.63). That is,

$$\text{critical } V_m = \frac{2}{\pi} V_{CC}$$

$$= \frac{2}{\pi}(12) = 7.65 \text{ v}$$

(d) Maximum dissipation in a transistor for the ideal case is given by (11.81), if we set I_Q equal to zero.

$$P_{\text{DISS}} = \frac{V_{CC}^2}{\pi^2 R'_L} + V_{CC} I_Q$$

$$= \frac{12^2}{\pi^2 72} \mid 0 - 203 \text{ mw}$$

This is the answer indicated by (11.87) also.

(e) A choice of quiescent operating point requires an analysis of the input characteristic of Fig. 11.26. A base voltage of .1 v appears adequate for minimized knee effects. The corresponding I_B is .1 ma. A check of Fig. 11.27 indicates that h_{FE} does not degrade significantly at I_C less than 40 ma. Taking 50 as an undegraded worst-case h_{FE} at low currents for the devices being used, we obtain as a quiescent collector current

$$I_Q \cong h_{FE} I_B$$

$$= 50(.1) = 5 \text{ ma}$$

The effects of leakage are small enough to be ignored. Since the d-c resistance is 20 ohms, Eq. (11.64) suggests that

$$V_Q = V_{CC} - I_Q R_{\text{d-c}}$$

$$= 12 - 5(10^{-3})20 = 11.9 \text{ v}$$

(f) The calculation of real-case R'_L to obtain the desired 1 w from the pair of output transistors requires an estimation of V_{SAT}. One method is to draw the ideal-case load line through the intercept points of 167 ma, 0 v and 0 ma, 12 v. This load line on Fig. 11.25 crosses the saturation curve at

.5 v. The real-case peak current will certainly be of this order. Let us select V_{SAT} as .6 v for safe measure. The maximum real-case voltage swing is

$$V_Q - V_1 = 11.9 - .6 = 11.3 \text{ v}$$

By appropriate substitution in (11.79a)

$$\text{real } P_{\max} = \frac{(V_Q - V_1)^2}{2R'_L}$$

$$\therefore \quad R'_L = \frac{(11.3)^2}{2(1)} = 64\Omega$$

(g) The maximum transistor dissipation is, by (11.81),

$$\text{real max } P_{\text{DISS}} = \frac{V_{cc}^2}{\pi^2 R'_L} + V_{cc} I_Q$$

$$= \frac{12^2}{\pi^2 64} + 12(5) 10^{-3} = 288 \text{ mw}$$

(h) The maximum real-case efficiency occurs when maximum rms power is being achieved. At such time the battery power for a single device is, by (11.72),

$$\text{real } P_{\text{BATT}} = V_{cc} \left(\frac{V_Q - V_x}{\pi R'_L} + I_Q \right) = 12 \left[\frac{11.3}{\pi 64} + 5(10^{-3}) \right] = 735 \text{ mw}$$

$$\therefore \quad \text{eff.} = \frac{P_{\text{rms}}}{P_{\text{BATT}}} = \frac{500}{735} = 68 \text{ per cent}$$

(i) The quiescent bias voltage was determined in step (e) to be .1 volt. Since the bleeder current is to be of the order of 5 ma, we say

$$I_{\text{BLEEDER}} = \frac{V_{cc}}{R_1 + R_2}$$

$$\therefore \quad R_1 + R_2 = \frac{V_{cc}}{I_{\text{BLEEDER}}} = \frac{12}{.005} = 2200 \ \Omega$$

Now by (11.88)

$$R_1 = \frac{V_{bQ}(R_1 + R_2)}{V_{cc}}$$

$$= \frac{.1(2200)}{12} \cong 18 \ \Omega$$

$$\therefore \quad R_2 \cong 2.2 \text{ K}$$

The bias network chosen gives a quiescent current of about 5 ma.

(j) The peak value of collector current is 184 ma. This is the intersection of the real-case a-c load line and the saturation line on Fig. 11.25. Figure 11.27 indicates that at 184 ma, the actual current gain is .825 times the reference value of 50. Thus at 184 ma

$$h_{FE} = .825(50) = 41$$

Thus

$$I_{b(\text{peak})} = \frac{\text{peak } I_c}{h_{FE}}$$

$$= \frac{184}{41} = 4.5 \text{ ma}$$

From Fig. 11.26 $V_{b(\text{peak})} = .48$ v at the peak I_b of 4.5 ma. Assuming now that the d-c resistance of half of the secondary can be held to 20 ohms, we use (11.89) to obtain

$$V_{\text{peak}} = V_{b(\text{peak})} + I_{b(\text{peak})}(R_1 + R_{\text{sec}}) - V_{bQ}$$
$$= .48 + 4.5(10^{-3})(20 + 20) - .1$$
$$= .56 \text{ v}$$

11.14. Distortion in Class AB amplifiers. The most significant distortion in a Class AB amplifier is the crossover distortion that occurs if the operating current is too low in value. The importance of slight forward bias in curing this problem has already been discussed. It should be noted that a high effective source impedance at the driver secondary is also helpful. Since this implies a small turns ratio and severe limitations on driver transistor performance, each practical case should be considered on an individual basis.

The next most important distortion is the clipping that occurs at the high-current ends of the a-c load line. There is no phenomenon of cutoff clipping in a Class AB amplifier. One transistor is always picking up from the other as the quiescent-current level is approached. The saturation clipping that does occur requires some special attention, as two transistors are involved. The optimum condition occurs when transistors with *matched* current gains are used. This implies that the current gain of one transistor does not degrade

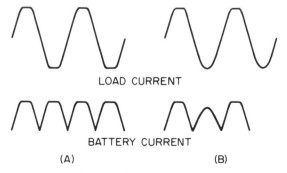

LOAD CURRENT

BATTERY CURRENT

(A)   (B)

Fig. 11.28 Relation of battery and load currents for (A) matched current gain devices (B) unmatched current gain devices.

appreciably more than the second transistor at high collector-current levels. The result is symmetrical clipping of the output waveform. If devices with significantly different current gains were used together, the distortion at high currents would not be symmetrical. Rather, the high-gain unit would go into distortion first. The effects of matching characteristics are shown in Fig. 11.28. Figure 11.28(a) shows symmetry in both output current and battery current when matched units are used. Figure 11.28(b) shows the unsymmetrical condition that results when unmatched units are used. The effects of the low-gain unit are especially noticeable in the battery-current waveforms. The current-gain matching must be a specified parameter on the transistor specification sheet to assure minimized distortion resulting from current-gain mismatch.

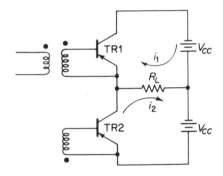

Fig. 11.29 Circuit for direct load connected push-pull.

11.15. Special audio circuits. Two other power-amplifier configurations deserve comment: direct load-connected push-pull, and complementary symmetry. Each configuration exploits the omission of an output transformer. A basic circuit for connecting the load directly in push-pull is shown in Fig. 11.29. The significant items are a split secondary for the driver transformer and a split supply voltage. As the a-c input signal biases TR1 on, it biases TR2 off, and vice versa. Pulses of current flow through R_L as shown, creating a-c power in R_L. The analysis of this circuit is essentially the same as for conventional push-pull.

The basic complementary symmetry circuit is shown in Fig. 11.30. Here an NPN device is used in conjunction with a PNP device. We again have a situation where one device is biased on while the second is biased off, and vice versa. The major drawback in this circuit is the general dissimilarity in

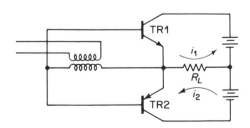

Fig. 11.30 Complementary symmetry circuit.

characteristics of NPN and PNP devices. The variation of current gain with collector current is not the same for both constructions. It is difficult, then, to obtain symmetrical clipping. Thus, although both of these circuits have the economical aspect of fewer transformers, the direct load-connected push-pull yields more desirable operating results.

11.16. Summary. The common-emitter connection is used most frequently in power-amplifier applications. The common-base connection has the desirable trait of a very linear output characteristic, providing minimized distortion. The undesirable aspect of this connection, which more than compensates any desirable traits, is the very high current drive required (since current gain is less than unity). The common-collector connection also tends towards low distortion because of the inherent large amounts of a-c feedback, but the high voltage drive required (voltage gain of the order of unity) imposes operational limitations on this connection. The common-emitter connection with its high power gain becomes the most desirable. Feedback can be applied as required to improve the distortion levels. The resultant gain is still likely to exceed the common-base or common-collector gain.

The salient aspects of power-amplifier design are maximized power output with minimized distortion. The power-dissipating capabilities of the transistor type being used establish the power obtainable from the circuit. The transistor also is the major factor in the matter of distortion: examples are current-gain degradation at high collector current, and nonlinear input characteristics. Although the design of power amplifiers has been reduced to a number of straightforward mathematical expressions, the compatibility of the transistor and its circuit parameters to the requirements can never be overlooked.

SUGGESTED READING

1. R. F. Shea, *Transistor Audio Amplifiers*. New York: John Wiley & Sons, Inc., 1955.
2. Jones and Hilbourne, *Transistor A. F. Amplifiers*. New York: Philosophical Library, 1957.

PROBLEMS

1. Discuss the basic design objectives of power amplifiers.
2. Explain the situation in a Class A amplifier when clipping is occurring in the output waveform.
3. The transistor type that has the derating curve of Fig. 11.4 is to be operated

in a fixed ambient of 45°C. What is the maximum ideal power available from such a device in a transformer-coupled class A amplifier?

4. Define and discuss the meaning of the term *efficiency* as it applies to power amplifiers.

5. Explain why the ideal peak value of voltage for transformer Class A is $2V_{CC}$.

6. Three transistor types are available. The power dissipation and BV_{CEO} ratings are as follows: Type A, 200 mw and 30 v; Type B, 150 mw and 35 v; and Type C, 250 mw and 20 v. Which type or types are usable in a transformer Class A that is to deliver 85 mw with a 12-v supply? Explain.

7. A transformer reflects a load of 100 ohms to a transistor with an output characteristic similar to Fig. 11.9. The primary winding has a d-c resistance of 25 ohms. Determine the real-case operating point, power output, and efficiency for the situation yielding optimized maximum efficiency if the supply voltage is 6 v.

8. For a power amplifier delivering 50 mw or more, draw the typical waveform one might expect in a Class A amplifier when considering the effects of non-linear input impedance. Explain how the output waveform might differ in a low-power Class A amplifier.

9. A pair of transistors with $h_{FE} = 50$ at $I_C = 40$ ma are available. A supply voltage of 9 v is available. Assume that the d-c resistance of each half of the output transformer is 20 ohms. Design a Class AB push-pull circuit to deliver 750 mw. Determine:
   (a) ideal-case R'_L.
   (b) ideal-case I_C peak.
   (c) critical V_m at which maximum dissipation occurs.
   (d) ideal-case maximum transistor dissipation.
   (e) appropriate real-case quiescent current.
   (f) actual-case R'_L.
   (g) actual-case maximum transistor dissipation.
   (h) maximum real-case efficiency.
   (i) bleeder-network resistors.
   (j) peak voltage at the driver secondary (assume driver secondary half has 20 ohms d-c resistance).
   Use Figs. 11.25, 11.26, and 11.27 in determining your solutions.

10. A transistor type has a dissipation capability of 200 mw. What is the maximum ideal circuit power when such devices are used single-ended transformer-coupled Class A, and push-pull Class AB?

12

HIGH-FREQUENCY

AMPLIFIER

APPLICATIONS

In our work thus far, we have covered the operational aspects of low-frequency amplifiers: biasing, a-c parameters, cascade stages, frequency response, and power amplifiers. In this chapter we begin discussing the high-frequency realm of transistor applications. This includes categorically: high-frequency amplifiers, oscillators, and logic circuits. The present chapter deals specifically with the high-frequency equivalent circuit for a transistor, a discussion of high-frequency transistor types, and the design and analysis of high-frequency amplifiers.

12.1. Transistor behavior at high frequencies. In Sec. 10.5 we learned that several attributes of transistors affected their performance in the high audio range. A review of this material is suggested at this time. The first matter mentioned was *barrier capacitance* C_{ob}, due to the back bias on the collector base junction. The corresponding common-emitter output capacitance C_{oe} is related to C_{ob} by Eq. (10.74), repeated here:

$$C_{oe} = (1 + h_{21e})C_{ob} \qquad (12.1)$$

The next matter was *transit time*, which is explained by the *diffusion capacitance*, $C_{b'e}$, due to the forward bias across the emitter-base regions of a transistor. This phenomenon causes a deterioration of forward-current gain as frequency increases. A definitive parameter is the *small-signal forward-current-gain cutoff frequency*, f_{hfb}. This is the frequency at which the common-base forward-current gain has decreased 3 db or is equal to .707 of the low-frequency value. Some relevent expressions are

$$h_{21b\text{(high)}} = \frac{h_{21b}}{1 + j\dfrac{f}{f_{hfb}}} \tag{12.2}$$

$$h_{21e\text{(high)}} = \frac{h_{21e}}{1 + j\dfrac{f}{f_{hfb}}} \tag{12.3}$$

$$f_{hfe} = \frac{f_{hfb}}{1 + h_{21e}} \tag{12.4}$$

where h_{21b} = common-base forward-current gain at low frequency
$\quad\quad h_{21e}$ = common-emitter forward-current gain at low frequency
$h_{21b\text{(high)}}$ = value at high frequency
$h_{21e\text{(high)}}$ = value at high frequency
$\quad\quad\quad f$ = high frequency of interest
$\quad\quad f_{hfb}$ = common-base forward-current-gain cutoff frequency
$\quad\quad f_{hfe}$ = common-emitter forward-current-gain cutoff frequency

The most useful equivalent-circuit depiction of a transistor at high frequency is shown in Fig. 12.1. It is called the *hybrid π equivalent circuit.*

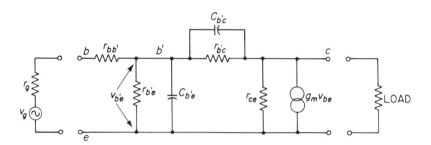

Fig. 12.1 Hybrid π common-emitter equivalent circuit.

The common-emitter circuit is shown since the common emitter is the most prevalent connection for high-frequency applications. This equivalent circuit is popular because it suggests the physical aspect of the transistor, has no parameter dependent on frequency, and is applicable at any frequency of interest, even low frequencies. The quantities that compromise the hybrid π circuit are:

$r_{bb'}$, the extrinsic base resistance,
$r_{b'e}$, the forward-biased emitter-base diode impedance,

$C_{b'e}$, the diffusion capacitance,

$r_{b'c}$, the reverse-biased collector-base feedback resistance,

$C_{b'c}$, the reverse-biased collector-base barrier capacitance,

r_{ce}, the shunt-collector resistance,

g_m, the intrinsic transconductance.

Point b' denotes the real-case base where transistor action in the base occurs.

The significance of $r_{bb'}$ and the "real-case" base can be explained with the help of Fig. 12.2. Recall that most carriers injected into the base of a

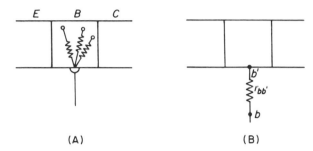

Fig. 12.2 (A) Real-case situation showing resistance through which a replenishing charge must flow from the external base lead to a recombination center in the base. (B) Equivalent situation—series resistor $r_{bb'}$ accounts for mean real path.

transistor diffuse on to the collector. For those majority carriers of the base which are involved in recombinations with carriers injected from the emitter, there is a replenishing flow of charges from the external base circuitry. As Fig. 12.2(a) suggests, there is a specific resistance for the path each replenishing charge sees in traveling to the specific recombination center. This resistance is a function of the amount of doping or impurity concentration in the base and the path length. A single value of resistance can be calculated as an average of all paths in this base. This is called the *extrinsic base resistance* $r_{bb'}$. This resistance can be considered in series with the ohmic contact to the base "b" and the actual center of transistor action in the base "b'." See Fig. 12.2(b).

In discussing the diode equivalent circuit in Sec. 2.7, we stated the dynamic impedance of the forward-biased junction to be

$$r_p = \frac{26}{I} \tag{12.5}$$

Looking into the emitter of a forward-biased emitter-base junction, we could say

$$r_e = \frac{26}{I_E} \tag{12.6}$$

$$= \frac{v_{b'e}}{i_e} \tag{12.7}$$

where r_e = dynamic impedance referred to the emitter
I_E = d-c emitter current in ma
$v_{b'e}$ = incremental emitter-base voltage
i_e = incremental emitter current

In changing our reference from the emitter to the base, we can define

$$r_{b'e} = \frac{v_{b'e}}{i_b} \tag{12.8}$$

Similar to the evolution of relations between h_{FB} and h_{FE} in Secs. 4.1 and 4.3, it can be shown that

$$i_e = \frac{i_b}{1 - h_{fb}} = (1 + h_{fe})i_b \tag{12.9}$$

Thus by substituting Eq. (12.9) into Eq. (12.8), we obtain

$$r_{b'e} = (1 + h_{fe}) \frac{v_{b'e}}{i_e} \tag{12.10}$$

$$= (1 + h_{fe})r_e \tag{12.11}$$

$$= (1 + h_{fe}) \frac{26}{I_E} \cong h_{fe} \frac{26}{I_E} \tag{12.12}$$

The current generator, $g_m v_{b'e}$, in the collector circuit introduces a new parameter, g_m. This intrinsic transconductance relates response of collector current to variations in the base-emitter driving voltage. Mathematically,

$$g_m = \frac{i_c}{v_{b'e}} \tag{12.13}$$

Since the collector current i_c in a transistor is approximately equal to the emitter current i_e, we can note the similarity of content in Eqs. (12.13), (12.7), and thus (12.6). We may say then that

$$g_m \cong \frac{1}{r_e} \tag{12.14}$$

$$\cong \frac{I_E}{26} \tag{12.15}$$

Note that I_E in Eq. (12.15) has units of ma. Note also that g_m is a function of the true base-emitter voltage $v_{b'e}$ rather than the applied-voltage source v_{in}. This fact acknowledges the loss contribution of the series base resistance $r_{bb'}$.

The lump-sum effects of transit time in the base region have already been explained. The related parameters, diffusion capacitance and current-gain cutoff frequency, have new significance when the hybrid π circuit is studied closely. By definition, the current-gain cutoff frequency is that frequency at which current gain is down 3 db from the low-frequency value. From the hybrid-π-circuit parameters, we infer that $g_m v_{b'e}$ has reduced 3 db from its low-frequency value at this particular frequency. This directs attention to the variation in reactance of $C_{b'e}$ and hence the value of $v_{b'e}$ as frequency varies. The value of $v_{b'e}$ is 3 db less than its low-frequency value at the precise time that the reactance due to $C_{b'e}$ equals the impedance of $r_{b'e}$. Since this is the forward-current-gain cutoff frequency, we say

$$\frac{1}{2\pi f_{hfe} C_{b'e}} = r_{b'e}$$

$$C_{b'e} = \frac{1}{2\pi f_{hfe} r_{b'e}} \text{ farads} \tag{12.16}$$

Using other relations already developed in this section, we can show that

$$C_{b'e} = \frac{1}{2\pi f_{hfb} r_e} \tag{12.17}$$

$$= \frac{I_E}{2\pi f_{hfb} 26} \tag{12.18}$$

$$= \frac{g_m}{2\pi f_{hfb}} \tag{12.19}$$

The remaining equivalent-circuit parameters, $r_{b'c}$, $C_{b'c}$, and r_{ce}, are relatively straightforward in concept. The barrier capacitance is the most important of these in determining transistor performance at high frequency. The values of these as well as all of the hybrid π parameters are found on the specification sheets of high-frequency transistors.

12.2. General considerations—high-frequency amplifiers. The major factors in the discussion of high-frequency amplifiers are gain, bandwidth, stability, and noise. As was the case for low-frequency small-signal amplifiers, gain is the most predominant single factor. Bandwidth and stability are of interest because the magnitude of bandwidth and the degree of stability or instability contribute directly to the amount of gain possible. Noise factor has importance because it represents a practical limitation on how small a "wanted" signal can be amplified.

The transit-time effects have been shown to be the main factor in the high-frequency behavior of transistors. The power-gain variation with frequency should be expected to resemble the variation of current gain with frequency as shown in Fig. 10.17. A plot of power gain versus frequency for the common-emitter connection is shown in Fig. 12.3. There are three

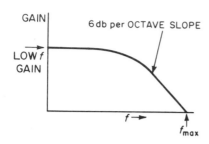

Fig. 12.3 General-case gain versus frequency plot.

points of interest on this curve. The first is the low-frequency level of gain. The second is the general behavior trend of gain versus frequency in the falloff range. The last is the value of frequency at which the power gain has decreased to unity or zero db. This frequency is called the *maximum frequency of oscillation* or $f_{\max}$. It has been shown [1] that

$$f_{\max} = \frac{1}{4\pi}\left(\frac{g_m}{r_{bb'}C_{b'e}C_{b'c}}\right)^{1/2} \qquad (12.20)*$$

Substituting Eq. (12.18) into (12.20), we have as an alternate expression

$$f_{\max} = \left(\frac{f_{hfb}}{8\pi r_{bb'}C_{b'c}}\right)^{1/2} \qquad (12.21)$$

In the frequency range where gain is decreasing to unity, the performance at any frequency may be described as

$$G = \left(\frac{f_{\max}}{f}\right)^2 \qquad (12.22)$$

$$= 20 \log\left(\frac{f_{\max}}{f}\right) \qquad (12.23)$$

where G = gain
         f = frequency of interest

Substituting Eq. (12.21) into (12.22) we obtain

$$G = \frac{f_{hfb}}{8\pi f^2 r_{bb'}C_{b'c}} \qquad (12.24)$$

In order to predict the maximum-available-gain figure associated with the low-frequency plateau, one can consider the modified circuit of Fig. 12.4. This is the basic hybrid π circuit with the permissible omission of the high values of shunt reactances due to $C_{b'e}$ and $C_{b'c}$ at low frequencies. The input impedance of the circuit is

$$R_{\text{in}} = r_{bb'} + r_{b'e} \qquad (12.25)$$

$$\cong r_{b'e} \qquad (12.26)$$

Under the ideal condition where the source is matched to the input, the maximum power that can be delivered to the input is

---

*In the reference text *Handbook of Semiconductor Electronics* by L. P. Hunter, the symbol C_c is used instead of $C_{b'c}$ for the reverse-biased collector-base barrier capacitance.

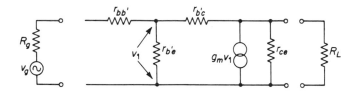

Fig. 12.4 Modified hybrid π for low-frequency use.

$$P_{\text{in}} = \frac{v_g^2}{4r_{b'e}} \tag{12.27}$$

The power available from the output terminals is

$$\text{avail } P_{\text{out}} = (g_m v_1)^2 r_{ce} \tag{12.28}$$

Under the ideal condition of a load that is matched to the output of the transistor, the maximum power that could be transferred to the load is

$$P_{\text{out}} = = \frac{1}{4} (g_m v_1)^2 r_{ce} \tag{12.29}$$

The maximum available power gain is determined then by taking a ratio of Eqs. (12.29) to (12.27).

$$G_{\text{avail}} = \frac{(g_m v_1)^2 r_{ce} r_{b'e}}{v_g^2} \tag{12.30}$$

Since the source was matched to the input impedance as given by Eq. (12.26), we note for this condition that

$$v_1 = \frac{v_g}{2} \tag{12.31}$$

Substituting (12.31) into (12.30) we get

$$G_{\text{avail}} = \frac{g_m^2 r_{ce} r_{b'e}}{4} \tag{12.32}$$

Knowing now the value of f_{max}, gain at any frequency, and the maximum available gain at low frequency, we have complete mathematical expressions for Fig. 12.3. To actually draw Fig. 12.3 from known transistor parameters, one should first calculate the maximum gain figure for low frequencies. After calculating f_{max}, one can proceed backwards from f_{max} by calculating gain at another frequency value and drawing a straight line through the two points, extending it to the horizontal line that denotes the low-frequency gain value. Only at the knee of the resulting curve is our picture an approximation to reality. One should also note that the slope of the falloff portion of the curve is 6 db per octave. That is, gain decreases 6 db every time frequency value doubles.

Most high-frequency amplifiers tend to be unstable over some frequency range. This occurs when the time constant of the $r_{b'c}C_{b'c}$ feedback path is such that some component of the output generator $g_m v_{b'e}$ gets fed back in phase with the input. If such a situation is permitted, the amplifier tends to operate regeneratively and the gain cannot be controlled. The cure for such a condition is to provide negative feedback from the output in order to cancel the positive feedback internal to the transistor. The process of providing negative feedback is called *neutralization* and is discussed more completely in a later section.

The phraseology *bandwidth* merely denotes the frequency range between the half-power or 3-db points in the gain-versus-frequency characteristic. This attribute is of interest in most amplifier applications.

In succeeding sections we will talk about the two major application classifications for high-frequency amplifiers: the *narrow-band amplifier* and the *wide-band amplifier*.

12.3. Example: high-frequency performance calculations. An example illustrating this material follows. A transistor type has the following parameters at $I_E = 1$ ma.

$$r_{bb'} = 85\ \Omega \qquad\qquad C_{b'e} = 650\ \text{pf}$$
$$r_{b'e} = 2.1\ \text{K}\Omega \qquad\qquad C_{b'c} = 10\ \text{pf}$$
$$r_{ce} = 185\ \text{K}\Omega \qquad\qquad g_m = 22{,}600\ \text{mhos}$$
$$r_{b'c} = 4.3\ \text{M}\Omega$$

Calculate: (a) maximum available low-frequency gain, (b) $f_{\max}$, and (c) gain at .4 Mc. Draw the gain-versus-frequency curve. The solution is as follows.

(a) By (12.32)

$$G_{\text{avail}} = \frac{g_m^2 r_{ce} r_{b'e}}{4}$$
$$= \frac{(22.6)^2 (10^{-3})^2 (185\ \text{K})(2.1\ \text{K})}{4}$$
$$= 49{,}600$$
$$= 47\ \text{db}$$

(b) By (12.20)

$$f_{\max} = \frac{1}{4\pi} \left(\frac{g_m}{r_{bb'} C_{b'e} C_{b'c}} \right)^{1/2}$$
$$= \frac{1}{4\pi} \left[\frac{22.6(10^{-3})}{85(650)10^{-12}(10)10^{-12}} \right]^{1/2}$$
$$= 16\ \text{Mc}$$

(c) By (12.23)

$$G = 20 \log \left(\frac{f_{max}}{f} \right)$$
$$= 20 \log \left(\frac{16}{.4} \right)$$
$$= 32 \, db$$

The appropriate gain-versus-frequency curve is shown in Fig. 12.5.

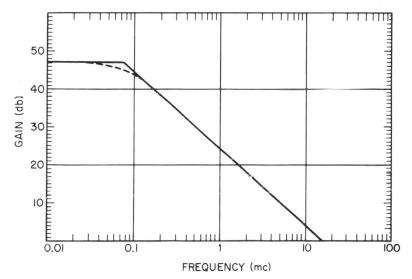

Fig. 12.5   Gain versus frequency for illustrative example.

12.4. Narrow-band amplifiers.   Generally speaking, a narrow-band amplifier is one where the operational objectives are high-gain performance over a relatively narrow range of frequency, and a very low gain for frequencies outside of the desired spectrum. The ideal gain-frequency characteristic can be imagined as a square wave. In actuality, the typical response appears as shown in Fig. 12.6. The frequency f_o is the center frequency of the band where maximum gain is desired. The half-power points are designated by frequencies f_2 and f_1. The bandwidth is expressed as

$$BW = \Delta f = f_2 - f_1 \tag{12.33}$$

Generally in narrow-band amplifiers the bandwidth is numerically small in comparison to the magnitude of the center frequency f_o. Since maximum gain is desired, transformer coupling is used between stages to provide

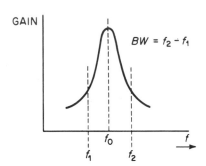

GAIN

$BW = f_2 - f_1$

f_0

f_1 f_2

f

Fig. 12.6 Typical gain-frequency response characteristic for narrow-band amplifier.

impedance matching and minimized coupling losses. The requirements of the frequency characteristic can be satisfied readily with the use of a resonant circuit. Since the attainment of the response characteristic is largely a matter of design of the resonant interstage coupling circuit, narrow-band amplifiers are frequently called *tuned amplifiers*. A practical tuned-amplifier stage is shown in Fig. 12.7. Major points of interest are the presence of components R_n and C_n to provide neutralization and thus stable opera-

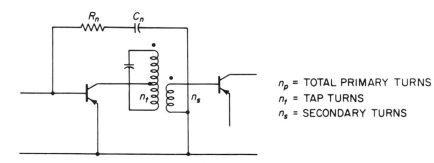

n_p = TOTAL PRIMARY TURNS
n_t = TAP TURNS
n_s = SECONDARY TURNS

Fig. 12.7 Typical coupling stage for a tuned or narrow-band amplifier.

tion, and the use of a coupling transformer with a tapped primary winding. The values of the neutralizing components will be mentioned later. The tapped primary is necessary to establish an acceptable compromise between gain and bandwidth for a real-case transformer.

An analysis of a tuned amplifier begins with the equivalent circuit for Fig. 12.7. This is drawn in Fig. 12.8. It is common practice to convert the hybrid π circuit to a normal π circuit as shown in Fig. 12.9. Many of the references cited at the conclusion of this chapter treat this subject. A detailed analysis of this conversion is provided by Wolfendale [2]. The results are

$$R_1 = r_{bb'} + \frac{r_{b'e}(r_{b'e} + r_{bb'})}{r_{b'e} + r_{bb'} + \omega^2(C_{b'e} + C_{b'c})^2 r_{b'e}^2 r_{bb'}} \tag{12.34}$$

$$C_1 = \frac{C_{b'e} + C_{b'c}}{\left(1 + \frac{r_{bb'}}{r_{b'e}}\right)^2 + \omega^2(C_{b'e} + C_{b'c})^2 r_{bb'}^2} \tag{12.35}$$

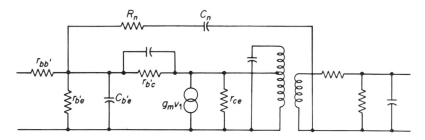

Fig. 12.8 Equivalent circuit for Fig. 12.7.

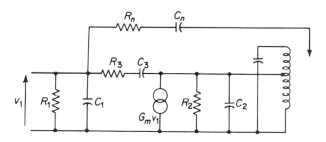

Fig. 12.9 Normal π-circuit equivalent of Fig. 12.8.

$$\frac{1}{R_2} = g_{ce} + g_{b'c} + g_m \left[\frac{g_{b'c}(g_{bb'} + g_{b'e}) + \omega^2 C_{b'e}C_{b'c}}{(g_{bb'} + g_{b'e})^2 + \omega^2 C_{b'e}^2} \right] \qquad (12.36)$$

$$C_2 = C_{b'c} \left[1 + \frac{g_m(g_{bb'} + g_{b'e})}{(g_{bb'} + g_{b'e})^2 + \omega^2 C_{b'e}^2} \right] \qquad (12.37)$$

$$G_m = \frac{g_m}{\left[\left(1 + \frac{r_{bb'}}{r_{b'e}} \right)^2 + [r_{bb'}\omega(C_{b'e} + C_{b'c})]^2 \right]^{1/2}} \qquad (12.38)$$

$$R_3 = r_{bb'} \left(1 + \frac{C_{b'e}}{C_{b'c}} \right) + \frac{1 + \frac{r_{bb'}}{r_{b'e}}}{r_{b'c}\omega^2 C_{b'c}^2} \qquad (12.39)$$

$$C_3 = \frac{C_{b'c}}{1 + \frac{r_{bb'}}{r_{b'e}} - \frac{r_{bb'}}{r_{b'c}} \left(\frac{C_{b'e}}{C_{b'c}} \right)} \qquad (12.40)$$

In order to determine now the proper magnitudes of neutralizing components we need only remember that the real and reactive components of neutralizing current must equal the real and reactive components of current through R_3 and C_3, respectively. If

$$\frac{n_t}{n_s} = n = \sqrt{\frac{R_2}{R_1}} \qquad (12.41)$$

therefore

$$R_n = \frac{R_3}{n} \tag{12.42}$$

$$C_n = nC_3 \tag{12.43}$$

The neutralizing components R_n and C_n are directly in parallel with the input of our stage. The parallel equivalents of R_n and C_n in series are

$$R_4 = \frac{R_n^2 + X_n^2}{R_n} \tag{12.44}$$

$$X_4 = \frac{R_n^2 + X_n^2}{X_n} \tag{12.45}$$

$$C_4 = \frac{1}{2\pi f_0 X_4} \tag{12.46}$$

The effects of R_4 and C_4 at the output terminals must be factored by the presence of the coupling transformer. A composite equivalent circuit for the neutralized device is shown in Fig. 12.10. In this diagram the values of R_5 and C_5 are given by

$$R_5 = n^2 R_4 \tag{12.47}$$

$$C_5 = \frac{C_4}{n^2} \tag{12.48}$$

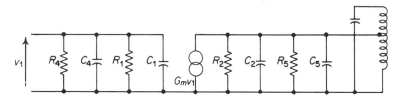

Fig. 12.10 Adjustment of normal π circuit to denote presence of neutralization.

If we now let R_{in} be the parallel equivalent of R_4 and R_1, C_{in} be the parallel equivalent of C_4 and C_1, R_{out} be the parallel equivalent of R_5 and R_2, and C_{out} be the parallel equivalent of C_5 and C_2, we obtain the equivalent circuit of Fig. 12.11. The major point of analysis is the optimized narrow-band transfer of power from the isolated output circuitry of one stage to the isolated input circuitry of a following stage. The terminology and symbolism just generated are used repetitiously, assuming identical devices are used, for the stages involved. Our attention is directed to the portion of the circuit set off in Fig. 12.11. Herein is the major consideration in a tuned amplifier: the design of a coupling transformer to yield the gain and narrow-band

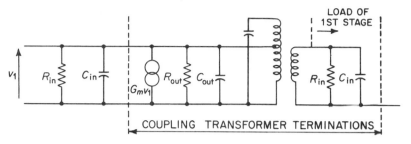

Fig. 12.11 Form of equivalent circuit when appropriate R's and C's are paralleled.

properties desired. If we transform the tuning capacitor, C_T, to an equivalent value, C', at the tap, we obtain

$$C' = \left(\frac{n_p}{n_t}\right)^2 C_T \tag{12.49}$$

Transforming R_{in} and C_{in} to the tap, we obtain

$$R'_{\text{in}} = n^2 R_{\text{in}} \tag{12.50}$$

$$C'_{\text{in}} = \frac{C_{\text{in}}}{n^2} \tag{12.51}$$

The total capacitance that exists at the tap is the summation of the individual capacitances, C_{out}, C', and C'_{in}; that is,

$$C = C_{\text{out}} + C' + C'_{\text{in}} \tag{12.52}$$

The final equivalent circuit for consideration is shown in Fig. 12.12. The effective inductance at the tap is depicted by L, the loss of the real-case inductance is represented by the resistor R. The quality factor or figure of merit for any coil is the *Q-factor* or, commonly, Q. For the coil alone

$$Q_c = \frac{R}{X} \tag{12.53}$$

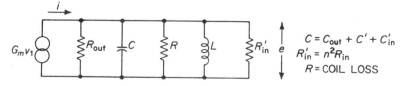

Fig. 12.12 Final equivalent circuit involving elements to be coupled. All impedances are at the tap.

where X = reactance at resonance
       = $X_C = X_L$

For a loaded coil, that is, a coil with terminating impedances,

$$Q_L = \frac{Z}{X} \qquad (12.54)$$

where Z is the total impedance, including the loss resistance R which shunts L. It has also been shown that an alternate expression for Q_L is

$$Q_L = \frac{f_0}{BW} \qquad (12.55)$$

The basic factors in the tuned amplifier can now be considered quantitatively: the value of reactance to obtain resonance, the relative values of impedances to maximize gain, and the relation of Q_L and gain.

Usually the bandwidth is a variable that is preselected. Thus, by Eq. (12.55), one knows the level of loaded Q_L. Rearranging Eq. (12.54), we say

$$Q_L X = Z$$

$$= \frac{\dfrac{R_{\text{out}} R'_{\text{in}}}{R_{\text{out}} + R'_{\text{in}}} (R)}{\dfrac{R_{\text{out}} R'_{\text{in}}}{R_{\text{out}} + R'_{\text{in}}} + R}$$

From Eq. (12.53)

$$R = Q_c X$$

Substituting, we obtain

$$Q_L X = \frac{\dfrac{R_{\text{out}} R'_{\text{in}}}{R_{\text{out}} + R'_{\text{in}}} (Q_c X)}{\dfrac{R_{\text{out}} R'_{\text{in}}}{R_{\text{out}} + R'_{\text{in}}} + Q_c X}$$

Solving for X, we obtain

$$X = \frac{R_{\text{out}} R'_{\text{in}}}{R_{\text{out}} + R'_{\text{in}}} \left(\frac{Q_c - Q_L}{Q_c Q_L} \right) \qquad (12.56)$$

The quantity X in Eq. (12.56) is the reactance of the coil or of the tuning capacitor for given values of R_{out}, R'_{in}, Q_c, and Q_L. The situation to resolve now is the magnitude of R'_{in} to transfer maximum power from R_{out} to R_{in} in the presence of the loss resistor R. As a general case the power in R_{in} can be called P_{load} and expressed as

$$P_{\text{load}} = \frac{e^2}{R'_{\text{in}}} = \frac{i^2 Z^2}{R'_{\text{in}}}$$

$$= \frac{i^2 Q_L^2 X^2}{R'_{\text{in}}} \qquad (12.57)$$

Substituting the value of X as given by (12.56), we get

$$P_{\text{load}} = \frac{i^2 Q_L^2}{R'_{\text{in}}} \left[\frac{R_{\text{out}} R'_{\text{in}} (Q_C - Q_L)}{(R_{\text{out}} + R'_{\text{in}}) Q_C Q_L} \right]^2 \tag{12.58}$$

This equation is of the form

$$P_{\text{load}} = K R'_{\text{in}} \left(\frac{R_{\text{out}}}{R_{\text{out}} + R'_{\text{in}}} \right)^2 \tag{12.59}$$

where K is a factored constant.

Taking the derivative of this expression with respect to R'_{in} and setting the result equal to zero, we find that the power in the load is a maximum when

$$R'_{\text{in}} = R_{\text{out}} \tag{12.60}$$

Thus no matter what the coil loss, the reflected impedance of the succeeding input should equal the output resistance of the driving stage to transfer maximum power from the source to the load. Substituting (12.60) back into (12.56), we get

$$X = \frac{R_{\text{out}}}{2} \left[\frac{Q_C - Q_L}{Q_C Q_L} \right] \tag{12.61}$$

This is the reactance at maximum power-transfer matching conditions. The amount of power loss due to the lossiness of the coil is determined by an attribute known as *insertion loss*. By definition

$$\text{insertion loss} = \frac{P_{\text{avail}}}{P_{\text{actual}}} \tag{12.62}$$

where P_{avail} = power available to the load for an ideal transformer

P_{actual} = power delivered to the load for a real-case transformer

The powers in the load can be related to the values of voltage developed in the given reflected impedance R'_{in}. This is permissible since R'_{in} is equal to R_{out} for both the real and ideal coil. As a general case

$$v_{\text{load}} = iZ \tag{12.63}$$

For the ideal transformer

$$\text{ideal } v_{\text{load}} = i \frac{R_{\text{out}}}{2} \tag{12.64}$$

For the real transformer terminated for maximum power in the load.

$$\text{real } v_{\text{load}} = i Q_L X$$
$$= i Q_L \frac{R_{\text{out}}}{2} \left[\frac{Q_C - Q_L}{Q_C Q_L} \right] \tag{12.65}$$

$$\therefore \quad \frac{\text{ideal } v_{\text{load}}}{\text{real } v_{\text{load}}} = \frac{Q_C}{Q_C - Q_L} \tag{12.66}$$

As mentioned, the value of R'_{in} is the same for ideal and real transformers. The power ratio can be expressed as the voltage ratio squared, or

$$\frac{P_{ideal}}{P_{real}} = \left(\frac{v_{ideal}}{v_{real}}\right)^2 \qquad (12.67)$$

$$= \left(\frac{Q_C}{Q_C - Q_L}\right)^2 \qquad (12.68)$$

$$\therefore \quad \text{insertion loss, db} = 20 \log\left(\frac{Q_C}{Q_C - Q_L}\right) \qquad (12.69)$$

The total gain of a single complete stage can now be determined as the ratio of actual power in the load to input power. That is,

$$\text{actual gain} = \frac{\text{actual } P_{load}}{P_{in}} \qquad (12.70)$$

The actual-load-power expression is obtained by substituting Eq. (12.60) into (12.58) for R'_{in}. The result is

$$\begin{aligned}\text{actual } P_{load} &= \frac{i^2 R_{out}(Q_C - Q_L)^2}{4Q_C^2} \\ &= \frac{G_m^2 v_1^2 R_{out}(Q_C - Q_L)^2}{4Q_C^2}\end{aligned} \qquad (12.71)$$

The power input to the stage is

$$P_{in} = \frac{v_1^2}{R_{in}} \qquad (12.72)$$

The power gain is

$$\text{actual gain} = \left(\frac{G_m^2 R_{out} R_{in}}{4}\right)\left[\frac{(Q_C - Q_L)^2}{Q_C^2}\right] \qquad (12.73)$$

If the amplifier stage had a lossless transformer in the collector, the load power could be expressed by

$$\text{ideal } P_{out} = \frac{(\text{ideal } v_{load})^2}{R'_{in}} \qquad (12.74)$$

Recalling Eqs. (12.60) and (12.64) as conditions prevailing for maximum load power in the ideal case, we can substitute into (12.74) to get

$$\text{ideal } P_{out} = \frac{G_m^2 v_1^2 R_{out}}{4} \qquad (12.75)$$

The ideal-case power gain is

$$\text{ideal gain} = \frac{G_m^2 R_{out} R_{in}}{4} \qquad (12.76)$$

If, now, in the definition of insertion loss in Eq. (12.62) we divided numerator and denominator by the quantity P_{in}, we could also express insertion loss as a ratio of ideal power gain to actual power gain. Recalling the expression for insertion loss, Eq. (12.69), and ideal power gain, Eq. (12.76), we can consider the form of Eq. (12.73) to note that actual power gain is the ratio of ideal power gain and insertion of loss in accordance with the suggested definition of insertion loss; thus we can say that

actual gain = ideal gain in db

— insertion loss in db   (12.77)

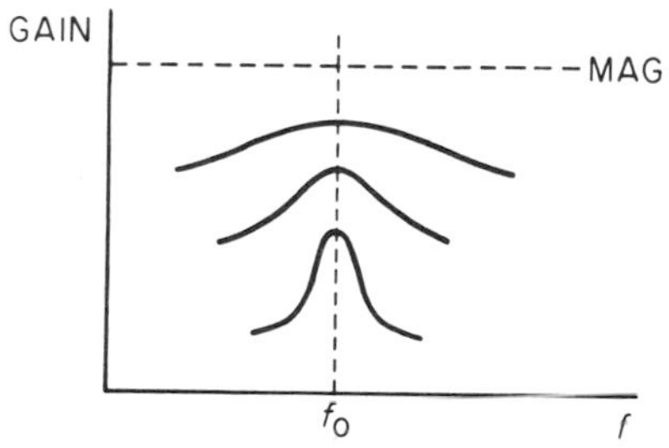

In reviewing the material on tuned-amplifier design, we can extract as important mathematical statements the following equations.

GAIN

MAG

f_0

f

Fig. 12.13 General concept of increased selectivity (narrow band) reducing gain.

$$Q_L = \frac{f_0}{BW} \tag{12.55}$$

$$\text{actual gain} = \frac{G_m^2 R_{out} R_{in}}{4}\left(\frac{Q_c - Q_L}{Q_c}\right)^2 \tag{12.73}$$

$$X = \frac{R_{out}}{2}\left(\frac{Q_c - Q_L}{Q_c Q_L}\right) \tag{12.61}$$

$$\text{insertion loss} = 20 \log \frac{Q_c}{Q_c - Q_L} \tag{12.69}$$

$$\frac{n_t}{n_s} = \left(\frac{R_2}{R_1}\right)^{1/2} \tag{12.41}$$

The major observation is that as BW increases, insertion loss decreases, and the actual stage gain increases. This is shown qualitatively in Fig. 12.13.

12.5. Narrow-band design problem. In order to demonstrate the applicability of the material in the preceding section, let us design a narrow-band amplifier such that with a coil with a $Q_c = 200$ the following is achieved:

maximum gain, $f_0 = 455$ Kc, $BW = 8$ Kc

The transistor to be used has the following parameters at 1 ma:

$r_{bb'} = 70\ \Omega$	$g_m = 38.4(10^{-3})$ mho
$r_{b'e} = 1800\ \Omega$	$C_{b'e} = 750$ pf
$r_{ce} = 80$ KΩ	$C_{b'c} = 10$ pf
$r_{b'c} = 4$ MΩ	

Calculate: (a) neutralizing components, (b) gain, (c) insertion loss, (d) total primary tuning capacitance. (e) Complete the design of transformer to allow use of a 200-pf tuning capacitor.

We proceed as follows.

(a) Useful preliminary calculations are:

$$g_{bb'} = 14.3(10^{-3}) \text{ mho} \qquad g_{b'c} = .25(10^{-6}) \text{ mho}$$
$$g_{b'e} = .555(10^{-3}) \text{ mho} \qquad 2\pi f_o = 2\pi(455)(10^3) = 2.86(10^6)$$
$$g_{ce} = 12.5(10^{-6}) \text{ mho} \qquad (2\pi f_o)^2 = [2.86(10^6)]^2 = 8.16(10)^{12}$$

By (12.34)

$$R_1 = r_{bb'} + \frac{r_{b'e}(r_{b'e} + r_{bb'})}{r_{b'e} + r_{bb'} + \omega^2(C_{b'e} + C_{b'c})^2 r_{b'e}^2 r_{bb'}}$$

$$= 70 + \frac{1800(1870)}{1800 + 70 + 8.16(10^{12})[760(10^{12})]^2(1800^2)70} = 1215 \ \Omega$$

By (12.35)

$$C_1 = \frac{C_{b'e} + C_{b'c}}{\left(1 + \dfrac{r_{bb'}}{r_{b'e}}\right)^2 + \omega^2(C_{b'e} + C_{b'c})^2 r_{bb'}^2}$$

$$= \frac{760(10^{-12})}{\left(1 + \dfrac{70}{1800}\right)^2 + 8.16(10^{12})[760(10)^{12}]^2 70^2} = 690 \text{ pf}$$

By (12.36)

$$\frac{1}{R_2} = g_{ce} + g_{b'c} + g_m \left[\frac{g_{b'c}(g_{bb'} + g_{b'e}) + \omega^2 C_{b'e} C_{b'c}}{(g_{bb'} + g_{b'e})^2 + \omega^2 C_{b'e}^2} \right]$$

$$= 12.5(10^{-6}) + .25(10^{-6}) + 38.4(10^{-3})$$

$$\times \left\{ \frac{.25(10^{-6})14.85(10^{-3}) + 8.16(10^{12})750(10)10^{-24}}{[14.85(10^{-3})]^2 + 8.16(10^{12})[750(10^{-12})]^2} \right\}$$

$$= 23.85(10^{-6})$$

$$\therefore \quad R_2 = 41.8 \text{ K}$$

By (12.37)

$$C_2 = C_{b'c}\left[1 + \frac{g_m(g_{bb'} + g_{b'e})}{(g_{bb'} + g_{b'e})^2 + \omega^2 C_{b'e}^2}\right]$$

$$= 10(10^{-12})\left[1 + \frac{38.4(10^{-3})[14.85(10^{-3})]}{[14.85(10^{-3})]^2 + 8.16(10^{12})[750(10^{-12})]^2}\right] = 35.4 \text{ pf}$$

By (12.38)

$$G_m = \frac{g_m}{\left[\left(1 + \dfrac{r_{bb'}}{r_{b'e}}\right)^2 + [r_{bb'}\omega(C_{b'e} + C_{b'c})]^2\right]^{1/2}}$$

$$= \frac{38.4(10^{-3})}{\left(1 + \dfrac{70}{1800}\right)^2 + [70(2.86)(10^6)760(10^{-12})]^2}{}^{1/2}$$

$$= 36.6(10^{-3}) \text{ mho}$$

By (12.39)

$$R_3 = r_{bb'}\left(1 + \frac{C_{b'e}}{C_{b'c}}\right) + \frac{1 + \dfrac{r_{bb'}}{r_{b'e}}}{r_{b'c}\omega^2 C_{b'c}^2}$$

$$= 70\left(1 + \frac{750}{10}\right) + \frac{1 + \dfrac{70}{1800}}{4(10^6)8.16(10^{12})[10(10^{-12})]^2}$$

$$= 5620 \ \Omega$$

By (12.40)

$$C_3 = \frac{C_{b'c}}{1 + \dfrac{r_{bb'}}{r_{b'e}} - \dfrac{r_{bb'}}{r_{b'c}}\left(\dfrac{C_{b'e}}{C_{b'c}}\right)}$$

$$= \frac{10(10^{-12})}{1 + \dfrac{70}{1800} - \dfrac{70}{4(10^6)}\dfrac{750}{10}} = 9.6 \text{ pf}$$

Since we have determined R_2 and R_1, we can substitute into Eq. (12.41) to obtain

$$n = \frac{n_t}{n_s} = \left(\frac{R_2}{R_1}\right)^{1/2}$$

$$= \left(\frac{41.8 \text{ K}}{1.215 \text{ K}}\right)^{1/2} = 5.86$$

By (12.42)

$$R_n = \frac{R_3}{n} = \frac{5620}{5.86} = 962 \ \Omega$$

By (12.43)

$$C_n = nC_3 = 5.86(9.6) = 56.1 \text{ pf}$$

(b) In order to determine gain, we must determine the shunt equivalents of R_n and C_n at both the input and output portions of our stage. This in turn enables us to calculate R_{in}, C_{in}, R_{out}, and C_{out}.

$$X_n = \frac{1}{2\pi f_o C_n}$$

$$= \frac{1}{2.86(10^6)56.1(10^{-12})}$$

$$= 6.22 \text{ K}$$

By (12.44)

$$R_4 = \frac{R_n^2 + X_n^2}{R_n}$$

$$= \frac{962^2 + (6.22 \text{ K})^2}{962}$$

$$= 39.6 \text{ K}$$

By (12.45)

$$X_4 = \frac{R_n^2 + X_n^2}{X_n}$$

$$= \frac{962^2 + (6.22 \text{ K})^2}{6.22 \text{ K}} = 6.12 \text{ K}$$

By (12.46)

$$C_4 = \frac{1}{2\pi f_o X_4}$$

$$= \frac{1}{2.86(10^6)6.12 \text{ K}} = 57 \text{ pf}$$

By (12.47)

$$R_5 = n^2 R_4 = 34.4(39.6 \text{ K}) = 1.36 \text{ M}\Omega$$

By (12.48)

$$C_5 = \frac{C_4}{n^2} = \frac{57}{34.4} = 1.66 \text{ pf}$$

Now we can calculate R_{in}, R_{out}, C_{in}, and C_{out} as follows

$$R_{in} = \frac{R_4 R_1}{R_4 + R_1}$$

$$= \frac{39.6 \text{ K}(1.215 \text{ K})}{40.8 \text{ K}} = 1.18 \text{ K}$$

$$C_{in} = C_1 + C_4$$

$$= 690 + 57 = 747 \text{ pf}$$

$$R_{out} = \frac{R_5 R_2}{R_5 + R_2}$$

$$= \frac{1.36(10^6)(41.8 \text{ K})}{1.42(10^6)} = 40 \text{ K}$$

$$C_{out} = C_5 + C_2$$

$$= 1.66 + 35.4 = 37 \text{ pf}$$

The final quantity needed before calculating gain is the loaded Q or Q_L.
By (12.55)

$$Q_L = \frac{f_o}{BW} = \frac{455(10^3)}{8(10^3)} = 57$$

By (12.73)

$$\text{circuit gain} = \left(\frac{G_m^2 R_{out} R_{in}}{4}\right)\left(\frac{Q_C - Q_L}{Q_C}\right)^2$$

$$= \frac{[36.6(10^{-3})]^2(40 \text{ K})(1.18 \text{ K})}{4}\left(\frac{100 - 57}{100}\right)^2$$

$$= 2920 = 34.64 \text{ db}$$

(c) The insertion loss is calculated by Eq. (12.69):

$$\text{insertion loss} = 20 \log \frac{Q_C}{Q_C - Q_L}$$

$$= 20 \log \frac{100}{100 - 57}$$

$$= 7.3 \text{ db}$$

(d) The total reactance at the tap of the transformer is given by Eq. (12.61):

$$X = \frac{R_{\text{out}}}{2}\left(\frac{Q_C - Q_L}{Q_C Q_L}\right) = \frac{40 \text{ K}}{2}\left[\frac{100 - 57}{100(57)}\right] = 151 \ \Omega$$

The capacitance is

$$C = \frac{1}{2\pi f_o X} = \frac{1}{2.86(10^6)151} = 2220 \text{ pf}$$

(e) The ratio of tap turns to secondary turns has already been established as 5.86. A knowledge of the ratio of total primary turns to tap turns will complete the turns-ratio information about the transformer. This ratio can be determined if we calculate the quantity C', which represents the step of the 200-pf tuning capacitor to the tap. By (12.51)

$$C'_{\text{in}} = \frac{C_{\text{in}}}{n^2}$$

$$= \frac{747 \text{ pf}}{34.4} = 21.7 \text{ pf}$$

By (12.52)

$$C = C_{\text{out}} + C' + C'_{\text{in}}$$

$$\therefore \quad C' = C - C_{\text{out}} - C'_{\text{in}}$$

$$= 2220 - 37 - 22 = 2141 \text{ pf}$$

$$\therefore \quad \frac{n_p}{n_t} = \left(\frac{2141}{200}\right)^{1/2} = 3.28$$

12.6. Tuned-amplifier applications.　The typical circuit configuration for the I-F section of a radio is shown in Fig. 12.14. This figure shows some interesting aspects of the practical application of tuned amplifiers. The first observation is the way in which the d-c operating point is established. The network consisting of the 47-K, 2.7-K, and 470-ohm resistors biases the first stage, while the 39-K, 2.2-K and 330-ohm network biases the second stage. The .05-μf and .01-μf capacitors shunting the base-to-ground and emitter-to-ground resistors are very low reactances at 455 Kc. It is possible, then, to obtain very good d-c operating-point stability without having the bias network degrade the a-c performance of the transistor. Neutralizing net-

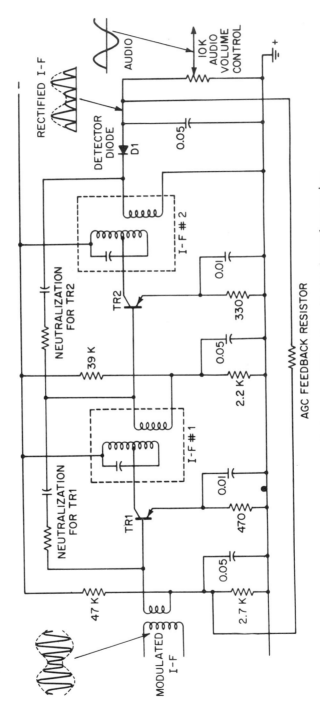

Fig. 12.14 Typical two-stage I-F section of a superheterodyne receiver.

works are shown for each stage. It is worth mentioning that neutralizing is not always necessary. Some transistor types have low values of feedback capacitance—for example, 2–4 $\mu\mu$f. Such types are not apt to require neutralizing, as they would normally tend to be stable at 455 Kc.

The input to the first I-F stage is a 455-Kc center frequency, which has been modulated with audio information in the preceding converter stage. The second I-F stage is terminated by a *diode detector circuit*. The diode D1 serves to rectify the modulated I-F. The waveform at the output side of the diode is shown in the inset in Fig. 12.14. At this point, the .05-μf capacitor serves to shunt 455-Kc component to ground. At audio frequencies the reactance of the .05 μf capacitor is large compared to 10 K. Thus the audio information flows into the 10-K potentiometer which is serving as a volume control for the audio stages following.

Coupled from the detector to the base of the first stage is negative feedback called *automatic gain control* or *AGC*. This feedback serves to keep the audio signal at a constant level even though the signal strength at the input of the radio may fluctuate. This is accomplished if the first I-F is biased to be operating at a current level less than that at which peak gain in the stage occurs (see Fig. 12.15).

If the input to the I-F strip decreases, the d-c value of the signal at the diode decreases. The AGC line makes the base of the first stage less

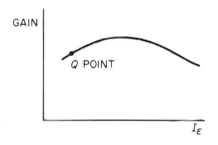

Fig. 12.15 Behavior of gain versus current for a typical transistor. Operating point is optimum if device is to respond properly to AGC signals.

positive, which makes the emitter-base junction more forward-biased. The emitter current increases in value, causing stage gain to increase in an attempt to compensate for the audio-level loss of the diode. The converse action also occurs if input-signal level increases.

12.7. Wide-band amplifiers.   When an amplifier has its lower half-power frequency of the order of cycles and its upper half-power frequency of the order of megacycles, it is classified as a *wide-band amplifier*. The attainment of such performance depends largely on the incorporation of appropriate response-shaping circuits. These were covered adequately in Chapter 10, so they need not be discussed again at this point.

12.8. Review of high-frequency transistors.   The early sections of this chapter made plain the importance of various transistor parameters in determining the usefulness of the transistor at high frequencies. The parameters most frequently used to evaluate high-frequency performance are current-gain cutoff frequency f_{hfb}, extrinsic base resistance $r_{bb'}$, and collector barrier capacitance $C_{b'c}$. The single composite of these parameters is the maximum frequency of oscillation, $f_{\max}$, which is stated in Eq. (12.21):

$$f_{\max} = \left(\frac{f_{hfb}}{8\pi r_{bb'} C_{b'c}}\right)^{1/2}$$

It is quite apparent from this expression that the magnitude of f_{hfb} should be large and the product $r_{bb'} C_{b'c}$ small in order to have high-frequency performance. In this section we will review the types of transistors available for high-frequency applications. In the broadest of classifications, the types of interest are: alloy junction transistors, grown junction devices, and diffused-base mesa and planar devices.

The cross section of a conventional alloy junction transistor is shown in Fig. 12.16. If it is a PNP device, pellets of indium, for example, are

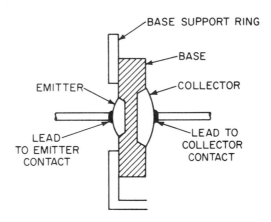

Fig. 12.16   Cross section of an alloy-junction transistor.

positioned with the help of a jig on opposite sides of an N wafer. At high temperature the P materials interact with the N wafer and when the composite is cooled, recrystallization creates the emitter-base and collector-base PN junctions, respectively. These correspond generally to the regions of deepest penetration of P materials into the N wafer. Although $r_{bb'}$ can be made low, 30–60 ohms, the value of $C_{b'c}$ is usually high, 9–20 pf.

Conventional alloy devices have current-gain cutoff frequencies of the order of 10–20 Mc. The frequency of operation may be extended if the base wafer is etched chemically in a localized area to a thickness and tolerance finer than that which is typical for the conventional alloy. This technique extends the cutoff frequency to the order of 50–100 Mc. A device processed this way is called a *micro alloy device*. Another variation on the conventional alloy device is the so-called *drift transistor*. This device has a gradation in the impurity concentration in the base. For a PNP device, the portion of the base closest to the emitter has a higher concentration of N impurities than does the region of the base closest to the collector. The collector-base voltage curve is no longer a straight line. In addition, the curve extends closer to the emitter-base junction than is usual for a conventional alloy construction. Thus the effective transit time is reduced, and higher frequencies of operation are possible. The cross sections of a micro alloy and a drift field device are shown in Fig. 12.17.

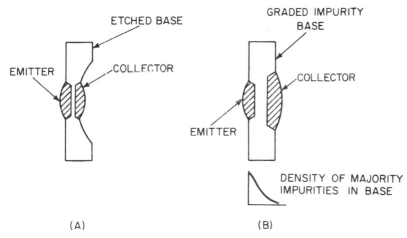

Fig. 12.17   (A) Cross section of microalloy transistor. (B) Cross section of drift or graded base transistor. Inset shows density of majority base carriers.

A *grown junction device* is typically a small bar containing either two P regions separated by a narrow N region or vice versa. The base region is created by cyclically varying the impurity concentration while attempting to prepare a single crystal bar of material. After such a crystal is cut appropriately, the single piece of bar material comprising the transistor appears as shown in Fig. 12.18. The major disadvantage of this device is the single contact to the base region. This causes $r_{bb'}$ to be high (40–150 Ω) and offsets the otherwise desirable low value of collector capacitance (1–4 pf) which is typical.

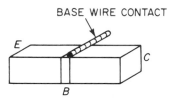

Fig. 12.18 Grown junction bar transistor.

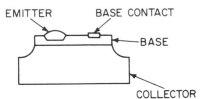

Fig. 12.19 Diffused mesa transistor.

The most desirable properties are obtained from *mesa* and *planar* devices. In a typical mesa (Fig. 12.19) a P-type material is diffused into a piece of N material which serves as the collector. An N-type emitter is obtained by alloying or diffusing a small piece of a N material into the base. Contact to the base is by an alloy contact also. Mesa devices have $f_{\max}$ frequencies ranging up to 1000 Mc. The extrinsic base resistance is low, about 30–50 ohms, and the collector capacitance is also desirably low, about 1–3 pf. This type of construction is very useful for high-frequency applications.

The planar device is shown in Fig. 12.20. Its name is derived from the fact that the edges of both the emitter-base and collector-base junctions lie in the same geometrical plane. This is accomplished by diffusing first the base into the collector and then the emitter into the base. Very high frequencies of performance are possible with this device (1000 Mc and up).

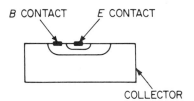

Fig. 12.20 Planar transistor.

The epitaxial transistor uses a technology that provides very high-frequency performance without the loss of desirable electrical properties, such as high voltage of operation. This type of device is made by deposition of a fairly resistive layer of silicon onto the surface of a highly conductive piece of silicon. The base diffusion is made into the epitaxial layer such that a controlled thickness of the high-resistance material still remains between the base and the low-resistance bulk. The fine layer of epitaxial material controls the value of collector breakdown at a high level. The emitter is diffused into the base in the conventional way.

REFERENCES

1. L. P. Hunter, *Handbook of Semiconductor Electronics*, 2nd ed. New York: McGraw-Hill Book Co., 1962, pp. 12-13–12-16.

2. E. Wolfendale, *The Junction Transistor and Its Applications*. New York: The Macmillan Co., copyright © by Heywood and Co. Ltd., 1958. Equations 16, 18, 21, 25, 27, 30, 33 p. 199–204 are reprinted with permission of the Macmillan Co.

SUGGESTED READING

1. F. Fitchen, *Transistor Circuit Analysis and Design*. Princeton, N.J.: D. Van Nostrand Co., 1960.

2. M. V. Joyce and K. K. Clarke, *Transistor Circuit Analysis*. Reading. Mass.: Addison-Wesley Publishing Co., 1961.

3. L. Giacolletto, "Study of PNP Junction Transistors from D.C. through Medium Frequencies," *RCA Review*, December 1954.

4. D. Holmes and T. Stanley, "Stability Considerations in Transistor IF Amplifiers," *Transistors I*, RCA Labs, Princeton, N.J., 1956.

5. C. Wilhelmsen, "Some Notes on the Hybrid II Transistor Equivalent Circuit," *IRE Transactions on Broadcast and Television Receivers*, March 1958.

PROBLEMS

1. A transistor has an $f_{\max}$ of 20 Mc. What is the gain this device will have at 5 Mc?

2. A transistor is operating at an emitter current of .6 ma. This device has $h_{21b} = -.985$, $r_{bb'} = 100$, $C_{b'c} = 10\ \mu\mu f$, and f_{hfe} measured to be 110 Kc. Calculate (a) g_m, (b) $r_{b'e}$, (c) $C_{b'e}$, (d) $f_{\max}$, (e) gain at 4.25 Mc.

3. A transistor is operating at 1 ma and has an $r_{b'e}$ of 1350 and a $C_{b'e}$ of 750 $\mu\mu f$. What is the value of h_{21e} at 40 Kc?

4. A transistor has the following parameters:

$r_{bb'} = 100\ \Omega$	$C_{b'c} = 8$ pf
$r_{b'e} = 2000\ \Omega$	$C_{b'e} = 800$ pf
$r_{ce} = 150$ KΩ	$g_m = 35$ milli mhos
$r_{b'c} = 3$ MΩ	

Calculate (a) d-c emitter current, (b) available gain, (c) f_{max}. (d) Draw the gain-frequency response curve.

5. Describe the salient features of a narrow-band amplifier.

6. Explain the need for neutralization in a tuned amplifier. How does neutralization affect stage gain?

7. For a transistor needing no neutralization, write the expression equivalent to Eq. (12.73) that would indicate the gain of the stage.

8. For the example in Sec. 12.5, recalculate the gain, insertion loss, and total capacitance if the bandwidth were increased to 9 Kc.

13

OSCILLATOR

PRINCIPLES AND

CIRCUITS

In this chapter we discuss circuits of a new class called *oscillators*. The basic purpose of any oscillator is the generation of a current or voltage of a given frequency. If the waveform is a sine wave, the oscillator is called a *sinusoidal oscillator* or a *harmonic generator*. Often the waveform is not sinusoidal; the oscillator is then classified as a *relaxation oscillator*. Practical insight into the operation of free-running oscillator circuits is provided in the sections that follow. Oscillators using negative-resistance devices are emphasized.

13.1. Basic oscillator principles. An idealized circuit illustrating the principles of oscillators is shown in Fig. 13.1. Here a precharged capacitor is connected through an open switch to an ideal, lossless transformer. When the switch is closed, the capacitor discharges into the inductor, the current flowing in the direction shown. The inductor prevents the current from building up instantaneously but tolerates rather a gradual build-up in the current amplitude. When the capacitor has

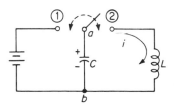

Fig. 13.1 Basic circuit illustrating oscillator operation. C is charged initially with switch in position 1. Oscillator action occurs with switch in position 2.

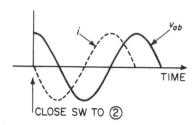

Fig. 13.2 Current and voltage wave-forms for Fig. 13.1.

discharged itself, the inductor does not permit the current to decrease instantaneously to zero. As the current is sustained it charges the capacitor so that point *a* is negative in relation to point *b*. When the capacitor discharges, the current flow reverses and flows through the capacitor from point *a* to point *b*. The waveforms of current and voltage for the exchanges of energy are shown in Fig. 13.2. The relative magnitudes of *L* and *C* determine the frequency at which energy is exchanged between the two components. The frequency of operation is

$$f = \frac{1}{2\pi\sqrt{LC}} \tag{13.1}$$

As long as *L* is ideal the amplitudes of the current and voltage waveforms remain constant.

A real coil has some amount of loss resistance. Thus, each time energy is transferred from the capacitor to the inductor, or from the inductor to the capacitor, some finite amount of energy is dissipated in the loss resistance. In this situation the amplitudes of current and voltage diminish each successive cycle until, finally, the energy exchange is damped out completely. See Fig. 13.3.

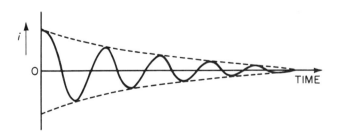

Fig. 13.3 Damped oscillation due to energy loss in resistance of a real inductor.

In order to sustain oscillations with a real coil, two courses of action are available. The first is to provide a small amount of energy each cycle to compensate for the energy lost in the loss resistor. Thus, if the frequency-controlling circuitry of *L* and *C* is used in conjunction with an active power amplifier such as a transistor, feedback techniques can be incorporated to sustain the circuit performance. Such a composite is called a *feedback oscillator*. The second approach is to incorporate devices, such as tunnel diodes or unijunction transistors, that display negative resistance at two terminals over some portion of their operating characteristic. When the frequency-controlling components are connected to the negative resistance, the loss resistance is canceled. Such a circuit is called a *negative-resistance oscillator*. Feedback oscillators, tunnel diodes, unijunction transistors, and negative-resistance oscillators are discussed in the sections that follow.

13.2. Feedback oscillators. A variety of basic feedback-oscillator circuits are shown in Fig. 13.4. These circuits are known as *tickler-coil oscillators*

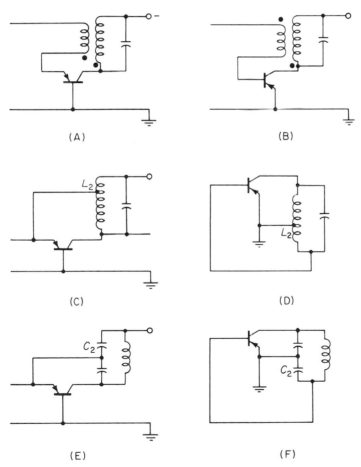

Fig. 13.4 Samples of feedback oscillators. (A) and (B) Tickler coil. (C) and (D) Hartley type. (E) and (F) Colpitts type.

[Figs. 13.4(a) and (b)], *Hartley-type oscillators* [Figs. 13.4(c) and (d)], and *Colpitts-type oscillators* [Figs. 13.4(e) and (f)]. Note that in all of the circuits shown, the frequency-controlling tank circuit is connected in the collector circuit of the transistor. The basic predominant attribute common to all of the circuits of Fig. 13.4 is that positive feedback of the right amount will cause the circuit operation to be regenerative. A second factor of operation is that the transistor circuit has a power gain greater than unity. Regenerative performance is attained when the feedback power is amplified to a degree sufficient to permit a successive increment of feedback to have a magnitude large enough to sustain continuing circuit operation.

Figure 13.4(a) shows a common-base stage with a tickler coil to provide positive feedback to the input. Since the input and output signals of a common-base stage are in phase, the tickler coil merely retains the phasing of the input and output signals. For the common-emitter circuit of Fig. 13.4(b) the tickler coil reverses the phase of the output signal in providing a feedback signal to the input. This, of course, is necessary if we want the feedback to be positive.

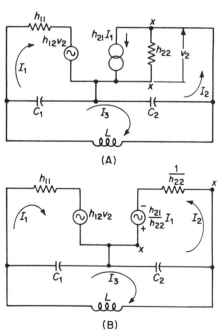

(A)

(B)

Fig. 13.5 (A) Equivalent circuit of common-emitter Colpitts oscillator. (B) Alternate form of equivalent circuit using series voltage source in output.

Figures 13.4(c) and (d) show the common-base and common-emitter configurations of Hartley-type oscillators with tuned collectors. This is really quite similar to the tickler-coil concept. We achieve the feedback by splitting the inductance portion of the collector tank circuit. In the Colpitts oscillators of Figs. 13.4(e) and (f) the capacitance portion of the tuned circuit is used to provide feedback. In both the Hartley and Colpitts connections L_2 and C_2, respectively, are providing the feedback signal.

In general the strength of oscillation—that is, the magnitude of oscillating-circuit waveform—is determined by the magnitude of the impedance of the tank circuit at resonance. The selection of d-c operating point determines, then, a useful dynamic load line which is in effect controlled by the tank impedance. This is similar to amplifier considerations in the past.

The magnitude of oscillation is limited by the device's being fully on or fully cut off. The frequency of oscillation is always controlled primarily by the tank circuit. The reactive nature of the transistor may sometimes affect the frequency of oscillation; this, of course, can be compensated if required.

We must analyze oscillator circuits mathematically to gain insight into the interaction necessary between transistor and tank for oscillations to occur, and to gain information on the actual frequency of oscillation. Consider first the common-emitter Colpitts-oscillator equivalent circuit of Fig. 13.5(a). Since loop equations must be written, it is convenient to convert the current generator in the output to a series voltage generator. We do this by looking into terminals X-X to observe

$$I_2 = h_{21}I_1 + h_{22}v_2 \tag{13.2}$$

Solving for v_2, we obtain

$$v_2 = \frac{I_2}{h_{22}} - \frac{h_{21}}{h_{22}}I_1 \tag{13.3}$$

Voltage v_2 and current i_2 are, of course, the voltage across and the current into the terminals of interest, X-X. An interpretation of Eq. (13.3) is implemented in Fig. 13.5(b). Here we note the quantity $1/h_{22}$ as an impedance and the quantity $(h_{21}/h_{22})I_1$ as a voltage generator. The current-voltage relationship at terminals X-X is the same in either equivalent circuit of Fig. 13.5. The loop equations can now be written with straight forward ease. For loop 1,

$$0 = I_1 h_{11} + h_{12}v_2 - jI_1 X_{C_1} + jI_3 X_{C_1} \tag{13.4}$$

Substituting Eq. (13.3) for v_2 and grouping terms, we obtain

$$0 = I_1 \left(h_{11} - \frac{h_{21}h_{12}}{h_{22}} - jX_{C_1} \right) + I_2 \frac{h_{12}}{h_{22}} + I_3 jX_{C_1} \tag{13.5}$$

For loop 2,

$$0 = \frac{I_2}{h_{22}} - \frac{h_{21}I_1}{h_{22}} - jX_{C_2}I_2 - jX_{C_2}I_3 \tag{13.6}$$

$$0 = -I_1 \frac{h_{21}}{h_{22}} + I_2 \left(\frac{1}{h_{22}} - jX_{C_2} \right) - I_3 jX_{C_2} \tag{13.7}$$

For loop 3,

$$0 = I_1 jX_{C_1} - I_2 jX_{C_2} + I_3 j(X_L - X_{C_1} - X_{C_2}) \tag{13.8}$$

Equations (13.5), (13.7), and (13.8) must be solved simultaneously. Let us generalize their form as follows

$$0 = a_1 I_1 + b_1 I_2 + c_1 I_3 \tag{13.9}$$

$$0 = a_2 I_1 + b_2 I_2 + c_2 I_3 \tag{13.10}$$

$$0 = a_3 I_1 + b_3 I_2 + c_3 I_3 \tag{13.11}$$

The determinant for this array is

$$\Delta = a_1 b_2 c_3 + b_1 c_2 a_3 + c_1 b_3 a_2 - a_3 b_2 c_1 - b_3 c_2 a_1 - c_3 b_1 a_2 \qquad (13.12)$$

For our circuit equations

$$a_1 = \left(h_{11} - \frac{h_{21} h_{12}}{h_{22}} - j X_{C_1} \right) \qquad (13.13)$$

$$b_1 = \frac{h_{12}}{h_{22}} \qquad (13.14)$$

$$c_1 = -j X_{C_1} \qquad (13.15)$$

$$a_2 = -\frac{h_{21}}{h_{22}} \qquad (13.16)$$

$$b_2 = \left(\frac{1}{h_{22}} - j X_{C_2} \right) \qquad (13.17)$$

$$c_2 = -j X_{C_2} \qquad (13.18)$$

$$a_3 = j X_{C_1} \qquad (13.19)$$

$$b_3 = -j X_{C_2} \qquad (13.20)$$

$$c_3 = j(X_L - X_{C_1} - X_{C_2}) \qquad (13.21)$$

Equations (13.13) through (13.21) are now substituted into Eq. (13.12). The *real* terms of the resulting expression can be manipulated to a preliminary form as follows:

$$X_{C_2}(X_L - X_{C_1})\Delta^h - X_{C_1} X_{C_2} h_{21} + X_{C_1}(X_L - X_{C_2}) \qquad (13.22)$$

The *imaginary* terms of the substitution can be manipulated to a preliminary form as follows:

$$X_L X_{C_1} X_{C_2} - (X_L - X_{C_1} - X_{C_2})\frac{h_{11}}{h_{22}} \qquad (13.23)$$

The frequency of oscillation is determined by setting the imaginary term equal to zero. Setting expression (13.23) equal to zero, we find

$$\omega^2 = \frac{h_{22}}{h_{11} C_1 C_2} + \frac{1}{L C_1} + \frac{1}{L C_2} \qquad (13.24)$$

Since the h_{22} parameter of a transistor is small, the first term of Eq. 13.24 can be considered negligible. We find then that

$$\omega^2 = \frac{1}{L C_1} + \frac{1}{L C_2} \qquad (13.25)$$

$$\omega^2 = \frac{1}{L}\left(\frac{C_1 + C_2}{C_1 C_2} \right) \qquad (13.26)$$

i.e.

$$X_L = X_{C_1} + X_{C_2} \qquad (13.27)$$

In order now to determine the circuit conditions that are necessary for oscillations to occur, we set the real term of our determinant, expression (13.22), equal to zero. If, as we do this, we substitute Eq. (13.27) for X_L in (13.22), we obtain

$$h_{21} = \frac{X_{C_2} \Delta^h}{X_{C_1}} + \frac{X_{C_1}}{X_{C_2}} \qquad (13.28)$$

To solve (13.28) we clear fractions to obtain a quadratic of the form

$$\Delta^h X_{C_2}^2 - h_{21} X_{C_1} X_{C_2} + X_{C_1}^2 = 0 \qquad (13.29)$$

The solution is

$$X_{C_2} = \frac{X_{C_1} h_{21} \pm \sqrt{h_{21}^2 X_{C_1}^2 - 4\Delta^h X_{C_1}^2}}{2\Delta^h} \qquad (13.30)$$

since

$$h_{21}^2 \gg 4\Delta^h \qquad (13.31)$$

$$X_{C_2} = X_{C_1} \frac{h_{21}}{\Delta^h} \qquad (13.32)$$

i.e.

$$C_1 = C_2 \frac{h_{21}}{\Delta^h} \qquad (13.33)$$

Equations (13.32), (13.27), and (13.26) are the key expressions telling the conditions for oscillation, the appropriate values of L, C_1, and C_2, and the frequency of oscillation.

The mathematics of the Hartley circuit can be written with the assistance of the equivalent circuit of Fig. 13.6. The loop equations must again be written. For loop 1,

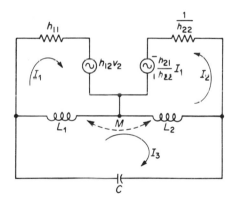

Fig. 13.6 Equivalent circuit of common emitter Hartley oscillator.

$$0 = I_1 h_{11} + h_{12} v_2 + I_1 j X_{L_1} - I_2 j X_m - I_3 (j X_{L_1} + j X_m) \qquad (13.34)$$

Substituting Eq. (13.3) for v_2 we get

$$0 = I_1 \left(h_{11} - \frac{h_{12} h_{21}}{h_{22}} + j X_{L_1} \right) + I_2 \left(\frac{1}{h_{22}} - j X_m \right) - I_3 j(X_{L_1} + X_m) \qquad (13.35)$$

For loop 2,

$$0 = \frac{I_2}{h_{22}} - \frac{h_{21}}{h_{22}} I_1 + I_2 j X_{L_2} - I_1 j X_m + I_3 (j X_{L_2} + j X_m) \qquad (13.36)$$

$$= I_1 \left(-\frac{h_{21}}{h_{22}} - j X_m \right) + I_2 \left(\frac{1}{h_{22}} + j X_{L_2} \right) + I_3 j(X_{L_2} + X_m) \qquad (13.37)$$

For loop 3,

$$0 = I_3 j(X_{L_1} + X_{L_2} - X_C - 2X_m) - I_1 j(X_{L_1} + X_m) + I_2 j(X_{L_2} + X_m) \tag{13.38}$$

$$= I_1 j(-X_{L_1} + X_m) + I_2 j(X_{L_2} + X_m) + I_3 j(X_{L_1} + X_{L_2} - X_C - 2X_m) \tag{13.39}$$

Equations (13.35), (13.37), and (13.39) must be solved simultaneously in a fashion similar to that used for the Colpitts oscillator. Setting the imaginary terms equal to zero, one obtains

$$\omega^2 = \frac{1}{C(L_1 + L_2 + 2M) - \dfrac{h_{22}}{h_{11}}(L_1 L_2 - M^2)} \tag{13.40}$$

Setting the real terms of the determinant equal to zero, one finds that the circuit conditions for oscillation are

$$L_2 + M = \frac{h_{21}}{\Delta^h}(L_1 + M) \tag{13.41}$$

As an example illustrating the major points for a Colpitts oscillator let us determine the component values for 1-Kc oscillation for a transistor with $h_{21} = 20$, $h_{11} = 2000$, $h_{12} = 2(10^{-4})$, and $h_{22} = 20(10^{-6})$. Let $C_1 = 4\,\mu\text{f}$. We start by computing Δ^h. By (7.93a)

$$\Delta^h = h_{11}h_{22} - h_{12}h_{21}$$
$$= 2000(20)10^{-6} - 2(10^{-4})20 = 360(10^{-4})$$

By (13.33)

$$C_2 = C_1 \frac{\Delta^h}{h_{21}}$$
$$= 4\left(\frac{.036}{20}\right) = .0072\,\mu\text{f}$$

By (13.26)

$$L = \frac{1}{\omega^2}\left(\frac{C_1 + C_2}{C_1 C_2}\right)$$
$$= \frac{1}{[2\pi(10^3)]^2}\left[\frac{4 + .0072}{4(.0072)}\right] = 3.5h$$

13.3. Tunnel-diode theory. The *tunnel diode*, or *Esaki diode* as it is sometimes called, is a two-terminal device which displays negative resistance over a finite portion of its current-voltage characteristic. This is the region 1–2 of the tunnel-diode characteristic shown in Fig. 13.7. The dynamic slope of the forward characteristic anywhere between points 1 and 2 has units of negative resistance, since the current decreases as voltage increases. This negative-resistance behavior results from a phenomenon called *quantum-*

mechanical tunneling—a behavioral pattern unique to the materials from which tunnel diodes are fabricated. The N-type and P-type materials used in tunnel diodes are very heavily doped, so much so that an unusual situation results relative to the location of the Fermi levels in each of the N+ and P+ materials.

Consider the situation in Fig. 13.8. The N+ material is doped very heavily, and the Fermi level exists up in the conduction band. The presence of many acceptors in the P+ material causes the Fermi level to be submerged into the valence band. At equilibrium conditions the Fermi levels of each material are aligned. For convenience we show

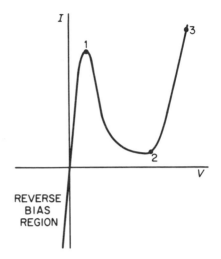

Fig. 13.7   General-case tunnel-diode characteristic.

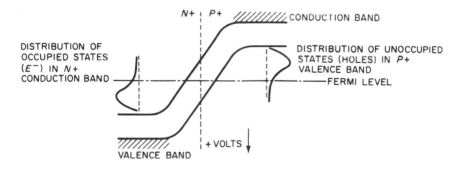

Fig. 13.8 Barrier voltage and carrier distributions for tunnel-diode junction at equilibrium.

positive voltage down and negative voltage up. This reverses the presentations of Chapter 2, but is a useful aid in understanding tunnel-diode behavior. The distributions of occupied and unoccupied states are shown for the N+ and P+ materials, respectively. In a normal junction, as discussed in Chapter 2, majority-carrier interaction resulted when majority carriers had sufficient energy to surmount the potential hill at the junction. For the tunnel diode, we have the unique situation whereby majority carriers of the two materials interact freely if they are at the same energy level and if they appear as available states to each other. Since the carriers do not pass over a potential barrier or hill, but rather pass *through it*, the phenomenon is called *tunneling*. At equilibrium, the high density of available electrons in the N+ material sees only a limited number of unoccupied holes in the P+ state, and thus only a small amount of tunneling occurs from the N+ to the P+ material. The tunnel current is counterbalanced by an equal amount of minority-carrier interaction. Thus at zero bias the equilibrium current is a net of zero.

As the tunnel-diode junction is forward-biased, the height of the potential hill is decreased and the Fermi levels of the materials are displaced relative to each other as shown in Fig. 13.9. This causes more of the occupied

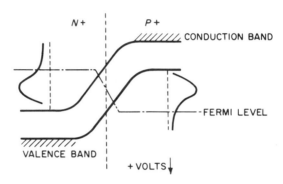

Fig. 13.9   Forward bias of N+P+ junction. Note how the alignment of the N+ and P+ distributions, and the degree of alignment, depends on the amount of forward bias.

states in the N+ material to see unoccupied states of the P+ material. Thus tunneling current increases. As forward biasing is increased further, tunneling current will maximize and then decrease to zero as the occupied and unoccupied distributions become completely misaligned. As forward bias increases further, normal forward-bias interaction occurs and the characteristic becomes similar to a conventional characteristic. The current value at which peak tunnel current occurs is called *peak current*. The voltage coordinate is called *peak voltage*. The current value corresponding to the transition from tunneling to conventional diode behavior is called *valley current*. The voltage coordinate is called *valley voltage*.

When the tunnel-diode junction is reverse-biased, the height of the potential hill increases. The peak points of the occupied and unoccupied distributions move apart. The effects of this situation can be shown with the help of Fig. 13.10. Note for the P+ material the distribution of occupied

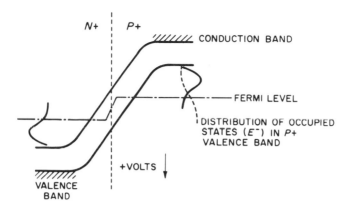

Fig. 13.10 Reverse bias of N+P+ junction. Occupied states in the P+ material now align with unoccupied states in the conduction band of the N+ material.

states (electrons) in the valence state. This is shown dotted. As the tunnel diode is reverse-biased, an increasing number of electrons in the P+ material see unoccupied states in the N+ material at the same energy level. Thus tunneling occurs from the P+ material to the N+ material. This is a current flow opposite to that which exists during forward biasing. Each successive increment of reverse bias causes more tunneling. The current-voltage characteristic that results is shown in Fig. 13.7.

The negative-resistance portion of the characteristic is not a straight line. The resistance at points 1 and 2 is infinity. Between these two points the resistance decreases to a minimum and then increases again as we pass through the inflection point of the characteristic. The use of a conductance whose value is equal to the reciprocal of the negative resistance is common in the industry. This value of conductance maximizes as the negative resistance minimizes in passing from the peak to the valley point.

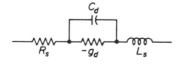

R_s = BULK RESISTANCE
L_s = LEAD INDUCTANCE
C_d = JUNCTION CAPACITANCE
$-g_d$ = JUNCTION CONDUCTANCE

Fig. 13.11 Equivalent circuit of tunnel diode.

Fig. 13.12 Symbol for tunnel diode.

The equivalent circuit for a tunnel diode is shown in Fig. 13.11. The quantity L_s denotes series lead inductance. R_s is the total bulk resistance. The quantity C_d is the junction capacitance, and the quantity $-g_d$ is the conductance at the chosen operating point. The symbol for a tunnel diode is shown in Fig. 13.12.

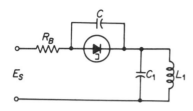

Fig. 13.13 Basic circuit for tunnel-diode sinusoidal oscillator.

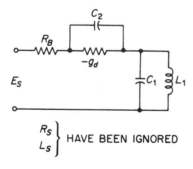

$\left.\begin{array}{l} R_S \\ L_S \end{array}\right\}$ HAVE BEEN IGNORED

Fig. 13.14 Equivalent circuit for tunnel-diode oscillator of Fig. 13.11.

13.4. Tunnel-diode sinusoidal oscillators. A circuit useful in obtaining sinusoidal oscillations is shown in Fig. 13.13. The tank circuit with the capacitor C_1 and inductor L_1 is the primary control of frequency. The equivalent circuit for the circuit of Fig. 13.13 is shown in Fig. 13.14.

The bulk resistance and series lead inductance can be ignored for most applications. The resistance R_B serves to control the operating point. For the situation of free-running sinusoidal oscillator, the d-c load line must intersect the negative-resistance portion of the diode characteristic, as shown in Fig. 13.15. The greatest ideal peak-to-peak value of useful current is determined by the largest increment of current that is possible from the "linear" portion of negative resistance. This quantity is approximately $(I_P - I_V)$. In order to obtain this maximum ideal-oscillator waveform, the diode must be biased so that the d-c operating point is the mid-current point of the negative-resistance portion of the characteristic. Using conventional load-line procedures, we can say

$$V_Q = E_S - \left(\frac{I_P - I_V}{2} + I_V\right) R_B \tag{13.42}$$

We should note that certain restrictions govern the magnitudes of E_S and R_B. They are

$$V_P < E_S < V_V \tag{13.43}$$

$$R_B < \left|\frac{1}{g_d}\right| \tag{13.44}$$

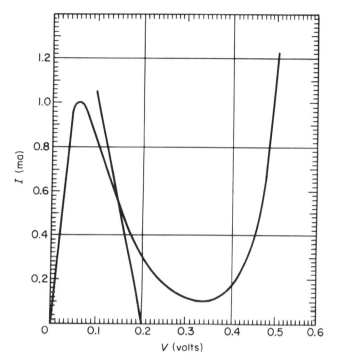

Fig. 13.15 Tunnel-diode characteristic and load-line condition for sinusoidal oscillator.

It has been shown in the *General Electric Tunnel Diode Manual* [1] that

$$\omega_o = \left[\frac{1}{L(C_1 + C_2)} - \frac{g_d^2}{C_2(C_1 + C_2)} \right]^{1/2} \tag{13.45}$$

$$C_2 = \left[\frac{g_d(1 - R_B g_d)}{R_B \omega_o^2} \right]^{1/2} \tag{13.46}$$

$$C_1 + \frac{C_2}{1 - R_B g_d} = \frac{1}{L \omega_o^2} \tag{13.47}$$

13.5. Example: tunnel-diode sinusoidal oscillator. Consider as an example the design of a 100-Kc oscillator using the tunnel diode whose characteristic is shown in Fig. 13.15. The design would proceed as follows.

(a) The peak current is 1 ma and the valley current is .1 ma. The conductance is $5(10^{-3})$ mhos; i.e., the negative resistance is 200 ohms. The ordinate value for the midpoint between the peak and valley currents is

$$\frac{I_P - I_V}{2} + I_V = \frac{1 - .1}{2} + .1 = .55\,\text{ma}$$

The coordinate value of voltage for the .55-ma current level is .150 v. Picking R_B as 100 ohms, we use Eq. (13.42) to obtain

$$E_S = V_Q + \left(\frac{I_P - I_V}{2} + I_V\right) R_B$$
$$= .15 + .55(10^{-3})\,100 = .205\,\text{v}$$

(b) The reactive elements in the circuit are calculated now. By (13.46)

$$C_2 = \left[\frac{g_d(1 - R_B g_d)}{R_B \omega_o^2}\right]^{1/2}$$
$$= \left\{\frac{5(10^{-3})[1 - 100(5)\,10^{-3}]}{100(39.6)\,10^{10}}\right\}^{1/2}$$
$$= 8(10^{-9})\,\text{f}$$

(c) Assuming L_1 equals .1 mh with a negligible amount of loss resistance, we can substitute into (13.47) to obtain

$$C_1 = \frac{1}{L\omega_o^2} - \frac{C_2}{1 - R_B g_d}$$
$$= \frac{1}{.1(10^{-3})39.6(10^{10})} - \frac{8(10^{-9})}{.5} = 9(10^{-9})\,\text{f}$$

If large values of inductance are used, the coil resistance becomes appreciable and must be included as part of the d-c load-line determination.

13.6. Unijunction-transistor theory. Another very important negative-resistance device is the *unijunction transistor* or, as it is sometimes called, the *double-base diode*. Its operation is best understood by reviewing its constructional aspects, as shown in Fig. 13.16. The two basic parts are a bar of N-type material which has ohmic contacts B_1 and B_2 at its extremities, and a P region E which is alloyed to the N bar. A voltage V_{BB} is applied to the N bar so that the B_2 end is positive in relation to the B_1 region. Since the N bar is doped uniformly, the potential level at any point within the bar is proportional to the length of bar involved. If the emitter is placed a distance D_1 from B_1, the voltage V_P at this point in the bar is given by

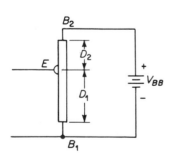

Fig. 13.16 Unijunction transistor diagram. Emitter is P type; bar is N type.

$$V_P \cong \eta V_{BB} \qquad (13.48)$$

where

$$\eta = \frac{D_1}{D_1 + D_2} \qquad (13.49)$$

The quantity η is called the *intrinsic stand-off ratio* and is usually given numerically by the manufacturer on the device specification sheet. For any emitter-to-base-one voltage, V_{EB_1}, less in magnitude than V_P, the emitter is reverse-biased relative to the bar and no current flows in the emitter. When the emitter voltage exceeds the magnitude of V_P, holes are injected from the emitter into the bar. These injected holes are attracted to the negative end of the bar. While holes are flowing towards B_1, charge-compensating electrons are supplied into B_1 by the base bias voltage. The presence of these excess electrons causes a decrease in resistance in the D_1 portion of the bar. This in turn causes a reduction in the effective value of standoff voltage. For such a situation, the emitter current can increase even though the applied emitter voltage decreases. The resultant negative-resistance characteristic is shown in Fig. 13.17.

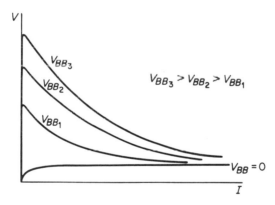

Fig. 13.17 Unijunction transistor: emitter characteristics.

The family of curves shown in Fig. 13.17 are easily understood. As the base-to-base supply voltage increases, the peak voltage increases. For each curve there is a valley point beyond which the device no longer displays the negative-resistance characteristic. The valley point occurs when the D_1 portion of the bar no longer displays reductions in resistance for increases in emitter-current level. The emitter junction reverts at this time to the display of a normal current-voltage characteristic. As might be expected, the valley point shifts towards

Fig. 13.18 Unijunction transistor symbol.

increasing levels of emitter current as the value of base-to-base voltage increases.

The complete specification of a typical unijunction transistor is shown in the appendix to this book. The symbol for a unijunction transistor is shown in Fig. 13.18.

13.7. Unijunction-transistor relaxation oscillators. It is possible to cause nonsinusoidal waveforms to be recurrent. The circuits that generate such nonsinusoidal waveforms are called *relaxation oscillators*. In this section we will discuss unijunction-transistor relaxation oscillators. Tunnel-diode relaxation oscillators are discussed in Sec. 13.9.

The basic form for the unijunction relaxation oscillator is shown in Fig. 13.19. When the base supply is applied, current flows in the $R_1 C_1$ circuit causing C_1 to charge. When the voltage in C_1 exceeds the critical or peak voltage for the transistor, the transistor conducts. During conduction, the charged capacitor serves as the driving potential, current being limited by the impedance R_{B_1} and the dynamic impedance of the emitter diode. After the voltage of the charged capacitor is dissipated, the charging and conduc-

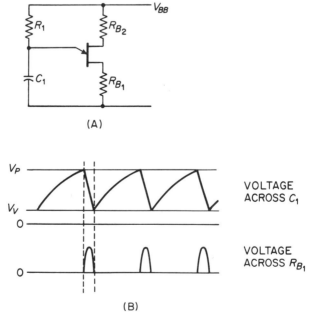

Fig. 13.19 Unijunction relaxation oscillator. (A) Circuit. (B) Pertinent voltage waveforms.

tion cycles begin again. The waveforms for the circuit are shown in Fig. 13.19(b). The charging of the capacitor is controlled by R_1 and C_1 with the time constant $1/R_1C_1$. The discharge of the capacitor occurs at a rapid rate because the discharge circuit consists of C_1 in series with R_{B_1} and the resistance of the emitter diode R_E. The sum of R_{B_1} and R_E is usually quite small in comparison with R_1. The voltage pulses that appear across R_{B_1} are caused by the pulsation in emitter current as it maximizes and then becomes zero at the completion of the capacitor discharge.

In order for the device to operate recurrently as just described, the d-c load line for the charging circuit must cross the negative-resistance portion of the device characteristic. The requirements on R_1 to satisfy this condition

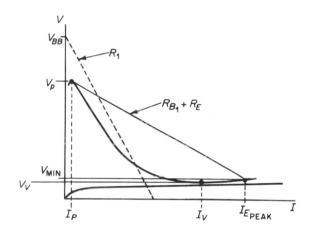

Fig. 13.20 Load lines for unijunction relaxation oscillator.

may be shown with the help of Fig. 13.20. The d-c load line crosses the negative resistance region if the following conditions occur simultaneously:

$$\frac{V_{BB} - V_P}{R_1} > I_P \tag{13.50}$$

$$\frac{V_{BB} - V_V}{R_1} < I_V \tag{13.51}$$

It has been shown [2, 3] that when these conditions are satisfied the frequency of operation is

$$f = \frac{1}{R_1 C_1 \ln\left(\dfrac{1}{1 - \eta}\right)} \tag{13.52}$$

The resistor R_{B_2} is present to offset the temperature-induced effects on diode voltage drop and bar resistivity. The value is given by [3]

$$R_{B_2} \cong \frac{.40 \, R_{BB}}{\eta \, V_{BB}} + \frac{(1 - \eta) \, R_{B_1}}{\eta} \qquad (13.53)$$

where R_{BB} is the total bar or interbase resistance as given on the device specification sheet.

During the time that the device conducts, the peak current is determined by the expression

$$I_{E(\text{peak})} = \frac{V_P - V_{\min}}{R_{B_1} + R_E} \qquad (13.54)$$

The voltage $V_{\min}$ mentioned in Eq. (13.54) is the voltage value where the a-c load line, $R_E + R_{B_1}$, crosses the characteristic curve in question. The minimum emitter-voltage value is typically about 2 volts. The magnitude of R_E diminishes as emitter current increases. Insight as to the magnitude of R_E at a particular current level is often available on the device specification sheet when the vendor indicates the *base-one peak pulse voltage*, V_{OB_1}. This parameter is specified for a circuit with a known V_{BB} and R_{B_1} and a device with a known η and V_v. Thus

$$I_{E(\text{peak})} = \frac{V_{OB_1}}{R_{B_1}} \qquad (13.55)$$

The quantity $I_{E(\text{peak})}$ can be substituted back into Eq. (13.54) to determine the value of emitter resistance R_E that corresponds to the current magnitude in question. The value of diode impedance can be determined at other values of current by varying the base voltage and experimentally observing the peak voltage that develops across a known R_{B_1}.

13.8. Example: unijunction relaxation oscillator performance. The device of Fig. 13.21 with R_{BB} of 6 K and η of .55 is used in the circuit of Fig. 13.19. The circuit components are $R_1 = 10$ K, $C_1 = .2 \, \mu\text{f}$, and $R_{B_1} = 20 \, \Omega$. If a base voltage of 20 v is used, calculate (a) the peak-point voltage V_P, (b) the current and voltage coordinates of the peak and valley points (graphically), (c) the value of R_{B_2}, and (d) the frequency of operation. If a V_{OB_1} of 3 v is developed, calculate (e) $I_{E(\text{peak})}$ and (f) the diode resistance assuming $V_{\min} = 2.7$ v. The solution is as follows.

(a) By (13.48)

$$V_P = \eta \, V_{BB} = .55(20) = 11 \text{ v}$$

(b) From Fig. 13.21 we confirm the V_P value of 11 v when $V_{BB} = 20$ v. We note also the coordinates of the peak and valley points, which are

$$V_P = 11 \text{ v}, \qquad V_V = 2.7 \text{ v}$$
$$I_P \cong .02 \text{ ma}, \qquad I_V = 20 \text{ ma}$$

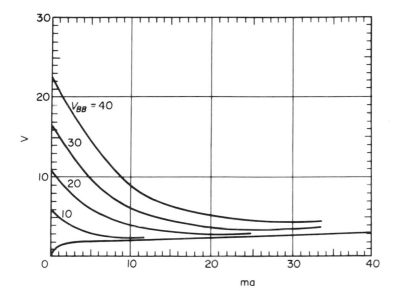

Fig. 13.21 Unijunction characteristic; $\eta = .55$, $R_{BB} = 6$ K.

(c) By (13.53)

$$R_{B_1} = \frac{.40\,R_{BB}}{\eta\,V_{BB}} + \frac{(1-\eta)\,R_{B_1}}{\eta}$$

$$= \frac{.4\,(6\mathrm{K})}{.55\,(20)} + \frac{.45\,(20)}{.55} = 234\,\Omega$$

(d) By (13.52)

$$f = \frac{1}{R_1\,C_1\,\ln\dfrac{1}{1-\eta}}$$

$$= \frac{1}{10\mathrm{K}\,(.2)\,10^{-6}\,\ln\,(1/.45)} = 626\,\mathrm{cps}$$

The oscillatory condition is confirmed by noting the satisfaction of Eqs. (13.50) and (13.51).

By (13.50)

$$\frac{V_{BB} - V_P}{R_1} = \frac{20 - 11}{10\mathrm{K}} = .9\,\mathrm{ma}$$

which *is* greater than $I_P = .1$ ma.

By (13.51)

$$\frac{V_{BB} - V_V}{R_1} = \frac{20 - 2.7}{10\mathrm{K}} = 17.3\,\mathrm{ma}$$

which *is* less than $I_V = 20$ ma.

(e) By (13.55)

$$I_{E(\text{peak})} = \frac{V_{OB_1}}{R_{B_1}} = \frac{3}{20} = 150 \text{ ma}$$

(f) By (13.54)

$$R_E = \frac{V_P - V_{\min} - I_{E(\text{peak})} R_{B_1}}{I_{E(\text{peak})}} = \frac{11 - 2.7 - 3}{.15}$$
$$= 35\,\Omega$$

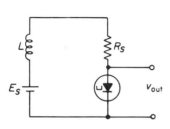

Fig. 13.22   Basic tunnel-diode relaxation oscillator.

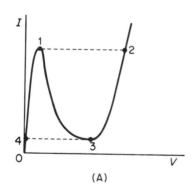

(A)

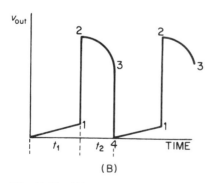

(B)

Fig. 13.23   (A) Key points noted on tunnel-diode characteristic. (B) Resultant output waveform for circuit in Fig. 13.22. Relative magnitudes of t_1 and t_2 are determined by circuit values.

13.9. Tunnel-diode relaxation oscillator. The basic form of a tunnel-diode relaxation oscillator is shown in Fig. 13.22. The basic requirement is that the d-c load line cross the negative-resistance portion of the characteristic. This condition and the key points in the operational analysis are shown in Fig. 13.23 (a). When the supply voltage is applied to the circuit, the current rises from zero to the peak value identified as point 1 on the characteristic. At this point 1 the dynamic impedance of the diode is infinity and the current value would like to decrease in magnitude. The inductor will not permit this to happen, and by virtue of its stored energy it prevents current from decreasing instantaneously to zero. In this situation the induced emf of the inductor adds to the supply voltage and the device switches to a higher voltage state, point 2. At this point the tunnel diode has higher voltage than the supply voltage, and finite resistance. Thus current decreases in the circuit, following the diode characteristic from point 2 to point 3. At point 3 the diode again presents infinite resistance. The action of the inductor in wanting to sustain current reductions causes an induced emf which switches the operating point to point 4. From this point the cycle for circuit operation begins again. The resulting waveform across the diode is shown in Fig.

13.23(b). In the *General Electric Tunnel Diode Manual* it has been shown [4] that certain portions of the tunnel-diode characteristic must be *linearized* in order to determine the frequency of operation of a tunnel-diode relaxation oscillator. These portions, shown in Fig. 13.24, are; the region where current grows from point 4 to the peak value, and the region where current decays from point 2 to the valley value. The key mathematical expressions [4] referenced to coordinate values indicated on Fig. 13.24 are

$$V'_P = .75 V_P \tag{13.56}$$

$$R_{D_1} = \frac{V'_P}{I_P} = \frac{.75 V_P}{I_P} \tag{13.57}$$

$$R_{T_1} = R_S + R_{D_1} \tag{13.58}$$

$$V'_V = \frac{V_{FP} + V_V}{2} \tag{13.59}$$

$$R_{D_2} = \frac{V_{FP} - V'_V}{I_P - I_V} \tag{13.60}$$

$$R_{T_2} = R_S + R_{D_2} \tag{13.61}$$

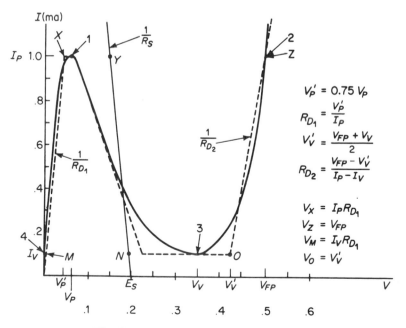

Fig. 13.24 Linearized tunnel-diode characteristic.

In order to approximate the time duration for current to grow from point 4 to point 1 we must be aware of the voltage *increments XY* and *MN*. These increments indicate the perturbation from the steady state that yield the inductive-controlled current growth. The expression for the time duration of current growth is

$$t_1 = \frac{L}{R_{T_1}} \ln \left(\frac{V_N - V_M}{V_Y - V_X} \right) \tag{13.62}$$

In order to determine the values of the pertinent voltages we consider first the generalized expression for the d-c load line. That is

$$V = E_S - I R_S \tag{13.63}$$

Thus the pertinent voltages are

$$V_N = E_S - I_V R_S \tag{13.64}$$

$$V_M = I_V R_{D_1} \tag{13.65}$$

$$V_Y = E_S - I_P R_S \tag{13.66}$$

$$V_X = I_P R_{D_1} \tag{13.67}$$

Substituting each into (13.62), we obtain

$$t_1 = \frac{L}{R_{T_1}} \ln \left(\frac{E_S - I_V R_{T_1}}{E_S - I_P R_{T_1}} \right) \tag{13.68}$$

In order now to approximate the time for current to decay from point 2 to point 3, we must be aware of the voltage increments *YZ* and *NO*. The expression for time duration of current decay is

$$t_2 = \frac{L}{R_{T_2}} \ln \left(\frac{V_Z - V_Y}{V_O - V_N} \right) \tag{13.69}$$

The pertinent voltages are

$$V_Z = V_{FP} \tag{13.70}$$

$$V_O = V_V' \tag{13.71}$$

Substituting these plus the expressions for V_Y and V_N into (13.69), we obtain

$$t_2 = \frac{L}{R_{T_2}} \ln \left(\frac{V_{FP} - E_S + I_P R_S}{V_V' - E_S + I_V R_S} \right) \tag{13.72}$$

The frequency of the pulsation is given by

$$f = \frac{1}{t_1 + t_2} \tag{13.73}$$

13.10. Example of tunnel-diode relaxation oscillator. Consider the oscillation that develops when the diode of Fig. 13.24 is used in circuit such as Fig. 13.22, where $E_S = .2$ v, $R_S = 100$ ohms, and $L = 300\ \mu$h. The d-c load line for this situation is already sketched in Fig. 13.24. Determine (a) the time for current decay, (b) the time for current growth, and (c) the frequency of the oscillation.

We begin by observing from Fig. 13.24 that

$$V_{FP} = .5 \text{ v} \qquad\qquad V_P = .06 \text{ v}$$
$$V_V = .35 \text{ v} \qquad\qquad I_P = 1 \text{ ma}$$
$$I_V = .1 \text{ ma}$$

We can now proceed as follows.

(a) By (13.59)

$$V_V' = \frac{V_{FP} + V_V}{2} = \frac{.5 + .35}{2} = .425 \text{ v}$$

By (13.60)

$$R_{D_2} = \frac{V_{FP} - V_V'}{I_P - I_V} = \frac{.5 - .425}{(1 - .1)10^{-3}} = 83\,\Omega$$

By (13.61)

$$R_{T_2} = R_S + R_{D_2} = 100 + 83 = 183\ \Omega$$

By (13.72)

$$t_2 = \frac{L}{R_{T_2}} \ln\left(\frac{V_{FP} - E_S + I_P R_S}{V_V' - E_S + I_V R_S}\right)$$
$$= \frac{300(10^{-6})}{183} \ln\left[\frac{.5 - .2 + 10^{-3}(100)}{.425 - .2 + .1(10^{-3})100}\right] = .87\,\mu\ \text{sec}$$

(b) By (13.57)

$$R_{D_1} = \frac{V_P'}{I_P} = \frac{.75\,V_P}{I_P} = \frac{.75(.06)}{10^{-3}} = 45\,\Omega$$

By (13.58)

$$R_{T_1} = R_S + R_{D_1} = 100 + 45 = 145\ \Omega$$

By (13.68)

$$t_1 = \frac{L}{R_{T_1}} \ln\left(\frac{E_S - I_V R_{T_1}}{E_S - I_P R_{T_1}}\right)$$
$$= \frac{300(10^{-6})}{145} \ln\left[\frac{.2 - .1(10^{-3})145}{.2 - 1(10^{-3})145}\right] = 1.98\,\mu\ \text{sec}$$

(c) By (13.73)

$$f = \frac{1}{t_1 + t_2}$$
$$= \frac{1}{(1.98 + .87)10^{-6}} = .35 \text{ Mc}$$

13.11. Astable multivibrators. The astable multivibrator consists of two *RC*-coupled stages connected so that the output of the second feeds back to the input of the first. This composite is basically a relaxation oscillator. The circuit operation and the control of the frequency of performance are the reasons for our treating this subject in a separate section.

The basic astable or free-running multivibrator is shown in Fig. 13.25.

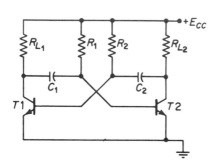

Fig. 13.25 Circuit for astable or free-running multivibrator.

In this circuit, transistor one is conducting while transistor two is nonconducting, and vice versa. The intervals of conduction and nonconduction of a transistor are controlled independently, which is a major difference between this circuit and the relaxation oscillators mentioned earlier. These aspects of the circuit are best understood by analyzing its operation. Let us begin assuming that transistor one (T1) is conducting and transistor two (T2) is nonconducting. If T2 is not conducting, there is no voltage drop in R_{L_2}.

Thus the collector of T2 is at supply voltage potential relative to ground. On the other hand, if T1 is fully conducting, its collector can be considered as being essentially at ground potential. In having passed from a nonconducting or OFF state to the conducting or ON state, the collector of T1 passed from a voltage level of $+E_{cc}$ to ground. That is, the collector of T1 has become $(-E_{cc})$ relative to its previous potential. The right side of C_1 experiences the same voltage excursion, and is also at a $-E_{cc}$ potential, since the capacitor cannot charge instantaneously. Since C_1 controls the voltage appearing at the base of T2, we have a confirmation that T2 is OFF when T1 is ON. As capacitor C_1 discharges through R_1, the base of $T2$ becomes more and more positive until T2 starts to conduct. When T2 conducts, the voltage on C_2 goes to $-E_{cc}$, cutting T1 off. Charge will leak from C_2 through R_2 until T1 triggers and the whole cycle repeats.

The waveforms for this circuit are shown in Fig. 13.26. As each collector switches to the OFF state, the leading edge of the voltage pulse is seen to be curved. The growth of the collector of T1 towards $+E_{cc}$ volts, for example, is controlled by the time constant $R_{L_1}C_1$. This is the time constant associated with the *charging* of C_1 such that its left terminal is approaching $+E_{cc}$ volts while its right terminal is at the quiescent level of base voltage causing conduction in $T2$. There is, of course, an equivalent situation to account for the curved leading edge in the OFF pulse associated with T2. We already

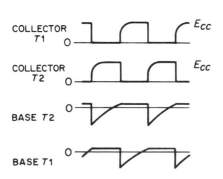

Fig. 13.26 Waveforms for astable multivibrator of Fig. 13.25.

know that C_1 pulses to a voltage level of $-E_{cc}$ when T1 triggers ON. From this state, C_1 will tend to charge towards a voltage level of $+E_{cc}$; that is, C_1 will want to change through a total increment of $+2E_{cc}$. C_1 will never reach the asymptote value of $+E_{cc}$ because as it gets slightly positive, T2 triggers ON. The time constant $R_1 C_1$ controls the ON time of T1 and the OFF time of T2. Likewise the time constant $R_2 C_2$ controls the OFF time of T1 and the ON time of T2. The separate control of conduction times is unique only to this multivibrator-type relaxation oscillator. For the circuit shown, the period of oscillation is

$$T = .69(R_1 C_1 + R_2 C_2) \qquad (13.74)$$

when $$R_1 C_1 = R_2 C_2 \qquad (13.75)$$

$$T = 1.38 \, R_1 C_1 \qquad (13.76)$$

13.12. Summary. The negative-resistance approach to oscillator circuits has been emphasized in this chapter. We have discussed the tunnel diode and unijunction transistor, which are playing an ever-increasing part in electronic-circuit applications, especially in oscillator applications. The free-running oscillator works continuously as long as battery power is supplied. The tunnel diode can be exploited to obtain either near-sinusoidal or distinctly nonsinusoidal waveforms. A sinusoidal waveform cannot be obtained with the unijunction transistor. Notice specifically for the unijunction that the requirements on the positioning of the d-c load line (magnitude of R_1, Fig. 13.19) contribute directly to determining the frequency of operation [Eq. (13.52)]. The maximum frequency of oscillation for a unijunction device is limited by the impedances, which set the d-c load line in the negative-resistance region of the characteristic. A similar restriction does not occur in tunnel-diode oscillators.

The astable or free-running multivibrator is included as a unique form of relaxation oscillator. This circuit is a compound connection of two RC circuits, with the output of the second connected as the input of the first. This circuit is unique in that the on and off times of either transistor are independently controlled.

Specific circuit modifications can be made to prevent free-running oscillation. These provide, instead, operation one cycle at a time as required or desired. This *triggered* mode of operation is useful in switching, pulse and counter applications, which are discussed in the next chapter.

REFERENCES

1. *General Electric Tunnel Diode Manual*, 1st ed., 1961, pp. 33–37.
2. *General Electric Transistor Manual*, 6th ed., 1962, pp. 191–201.

3. *General Electric Silicon Controlled Rectifier Manual,* 2nd ed., 1961, pp. 44–46.

4. *General Electric Tunnel Diode Manual,* 1st ed., 1961, pp. 50–52.

SUGGESTED READING

1. M. V. Joyce and K. K. Clarke, *Transistor Circuit Analysis.* Reading, Mass.: Addison-Wesley Publishing Co., 1961.

2. F. Fitchen, *Transistor Circuit Analysis and Design.* Princeton, N.J.: D. Van Nostrand Co., 1960.

3. E. Wolfendale, *The Junction Transistor and Its Applications.* New York: The Macmillan Co., 1958.

4. K. Pullen, *Handbook of Transistor Circuit Design.* Englewood Cliffs, N.J.: Prentice-Hall, Inc., 1961.

5. S. S. Hakim, *Junction Transistor Circuit Analysis.* New York: John Wiley & Sons, 1962.

6. L. P. Hunter, *Handbook of Semiconductor Electronics.* New York: McGraw-Hill Book Co., 1962.

7. J. D. Ryder, *Electronic Fundamentals and Applications.* Englewood Cliffs, N.J.: Prentice-Hall, Inc., 1964.

PROBLEMS

1. Explain the operational aspects of a feedback oscillator.

2. Explain the creation of the negative-resistance region in an Esaki or tunnel diode.

3. What is the theoretical maximum peak-to-peak value of current or voltage in a tunnel-diode sinusoidal oscillator?

4. What portion of the negative-resistance region provides the most distortion in a tunnel diode?

5. Explain why the mid-current point rather than the mid-voltage point in the peak-to-valley region is a more meaningful operating point for tunnel-diode sinusoidal oscillators.

6. For the problem in Sec. 13.5, if $R_B = 50$ ohms and $f = 500$ Kc, calculate the capacitors required for circuit operation.

7. A unijunction transistor has a peak current of .2 ma and a valley current of 20 ma. It is operated from a base supply of 20 volts. The stand off ratio is .6, and $C_1 = .2 \,\mu f$. What are the maximum and minimum frequencies of operation?

8. A unijunction is operating in a circuit similar to Fig. 13.19 with $R_{BB} = 6$ K,

$\eta = .6$, $I_V = 20$ ma, $V_V = 2.5$ v, and $I_P = .2$ ma, when $V_{BB} = 20$ v. A V_{OB_1} of 4 volts is obtained when $R_E = 40$ Ω. Calculate $I_{E_{peak}}$ and R_E at this current.

9. Suppose that in Problem 8 R_E were reduced to 20 Ω and a V_{OB_1} of 2 volts were desired. To what value could V_{BB} be reduced? Assume η remains the same as in Problem 8.

10. Explain the justification in expressing the unijunction relaxation-time period in terms of R_1 and C_1 alone, when there is in truth a finite time period for capacitor discharge.

11. Compare the magnitude of the output amplitude in a tunnel-diode relaxation oscillator with the amplitude possible in a tunnel-diode sinusoidal oscillator. Explain the reasons for differences.

12. Draw the collector waveforms and the base waveforms for two PNP transistors connected as an astable multivibrator.

13. An astable multivibrator similar to that shown in Fig. 13.25 has the following component values: $R_{L_1} = R_{L_2} = 1$ K, $R_1 = R_2 = 47$ K, $C_1 = C_2 = 200$ $\mu\mu$f. Calculate the frequency of operation.

14. Sketch the resultant waveforms if, for Problem 13, C_2 were made equal to 4000 $\mu\mu$f.

15. Consider the tunnel-diode characteristic of Fig. 13.24 and the diagram of 13.22. If $E_S = .22$ v, $R = 50$ Ω, and $L = 200$ μh, calculate the frequency of oscillation.

14

PULSE

CIRCUITS

In the latter sections of Chapter 13 we described the behavior of a variety of relaxation oscillator circuits: tunnel diode, unijunction transistor, and multivibrator. In the broadest of senses these circuits might also be defined as free-running pulse circuits. Such a definition is appropriate because a *pulse circuit* is one where the active device is nearly cut off if it is not operating. In addition, the wavefronts between the OFF and the ON states are very steep. In the ideal case, switching between the OFF and ON and ON and OFF states occurs instantaneously. We can see now the justification in the alternate classification of relaxation oscillators.

In this chapter we will study the methods of controlling more precisely the operation of pulse circuits, including the time control of circuit pulses, the holding of a device in either an ON or an OFF state, and the methods of *triggering* or inciting the device to assume either the ON or OFF mode as desired. In exploring controllable pulse-circuit fundamentals, we obtain knowledge basic to the entire field of timing, counter, and logic or computer applications. The circuits we discuss are monostable multivibrator and tunnel-diode circuits, and bistable multivibrator and tunnel diode circuits. We shall also gain some insight into logic applications.

14.1. Monostable multivibrators. The typical monostable multivibrator circuit is shown in Fig. 14.1. As the name implies, this circuit has one stable state, and switching then does not occur automatically back and forth between the two transistors. In Fig. 14.1 we can observe that there is no bias resistor from the base of T1 to the supply voltage. Since there is no path

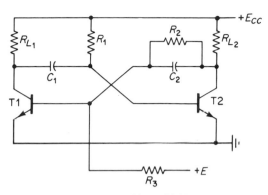

Fig. 14.1 Monostable multivibrator.

through which C_2 can at any time discharge to trigger T1 ON, we can assume properly that the stable situation for this circuit is T2 conducting and T1 OFF. In order to make T1 revert to the conducting state we must pulse its base positively. This can be done by a trigger pulse E applied through resistor R_3. When T1 turns ON, C_1 switches through $-E_{cc}$ volts and causes T2 to stop conducting. Gradually C_1 will discharge through R_1 until T2 turns ON. Capacitor C_2 switches through $-E_{cc}$ volts to turn T1 OFF. Since C_2 cannot discharge, the operation is maintained in a stable position with T2 conducting (ON) and T1 nonconducting (OFF). The entire cycle can be made to repeat itself when another pulse is applied to the base of T1. The waveforms of interest are shown in Fig. 14.2.

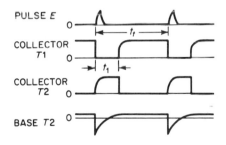

Fig. 14.2 Waveforms for monostable multivibrator of Fig. 14.1.

The time period of conduction for T1 is controlled by the time constant of $R_1 C_1$. It has been shown that the actual time is approximately

$$t_1 = .69 R_1 C_1 \tag{14.1}$$

The recurrence of the conduction pulse for T1 is determined strictly by the rate of trigger pulses. This is indicated in Fig. 14.2 as the time t_t. We have at our disposal the ability to generate at will a pulse of desired time duration. In addition, we are converting an arbitrary trigger-pulse shape to what is basically a known square-wave shape.

14.2. Monostable tunnel-diode circuits. In Fig. 14.3 we observe two separate load-line conditions, each of which intersects the tunnel-diode characteristic in a positive-resistance region. A circuit diagram which can be made to correspond to either load-line situation is shown in Fig. 14.4. In order to achieve the stable operating point A shown in Fig. 14.3, the magnitudes

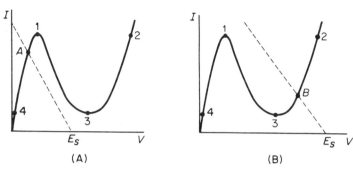

(A)   (B)

Fig. 14.3   Load-line possibilities which yield monostable operation of a tunnel diode. (A) Low-voltage quiescence. (B) High-voltage quiescence.

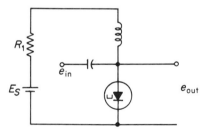

Fig. 14.4   Circuit diagram for mono-stable tunnel-diode relaxation oscillator. Relative magnitudes of R_1 and E_s determine quiescent point.

of R_1 and E_{S_1} should be such that the d-c load line crosses the diode characteristic only at point A. Likewise point B is obtained for a higher value of E_S such that the relative magnitudes of R_1 and E_{S_2} cause the d-c load line to intersect the diode characteristic only at point B. Since point A is a low-voltage state, the diode is said to be OFF for this level of operating point. Likewise, since point B is a high-voltage state, the diode is considered ON for this level of operating point. The tunnel diode can be pulsed or triggered out of either stable operating point.

Consider first the situation in Fig. 14.5(a). The diode is in stable state A. If we apply a positive pulse of sufficient magnitude to raise the current to the peak current magnitude, the diode will trigger to the ON state. The transient condition is exactly the same as the tunnel-diode relaxation oscillator described in Sec. 13.6. The inductor prevents the current from reducing instantaneously from the peak value. The induced emf shifts the operating point to point 2, from which the current and voltage decrease gradually. From point 3, the operating point shifts to point 4. The current increases

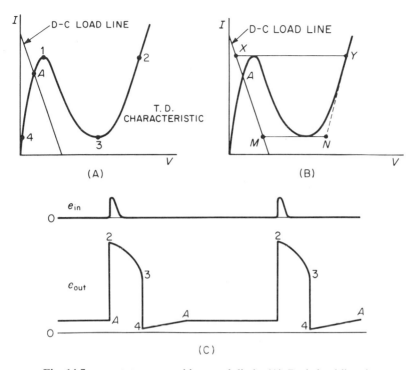

Fig. 14.5 OFF state monostable tunnel diode. (A) Basic load-line situation. (B) Voltage values of interest in approximating the ON pulse time. (C) Resultant triggered pulse shape; e_{in} is the trigger pulse, e_{out} is output waveform. Numbered points on output waveform correspond to numbers for abscissa voltage values in (A).

from point 4 until the stable state A is reached. The resultant waveform is shown in Fig. 14.5(c). Note that the transition from point A to point 2 is essentially instantaneous. The applied pulse carries us from point A to point 1 with no time delay. The diode will remain in the OFF state until another positive pulse triggers it to the ON transient.

In looking closely at the waveform of Fig. 14.5(c), we observe that the time associated with the growth of current from point 4 to point A is not truly associated with the ON-time pulse width, points 2 to 3. The actual ON pulse width can be approximated using the techniques of Sec. 13.9, where the tunnel-diode characteristic was linearized over certain portions to yield the results of Fig. 13.24. Consider Fig. 14.5(b). The voltage *increments* XY and MN are of interest, as they reflect the voltages that control the decay of current from point 2 to 3 on the true characteristic. From Sec. 13.9 we can restate the pertinent mathematical expressions.

$$V'_P = .75V_P \qquad (14.2)$$

$$R_{D_1} = \frac{V_P'}{I_P} = \frac{.75V_P}{I_P} \tag{14.3}$$

$$R_{T_1} = R_S + R_{D_1} \tag{14.4}$$

$$V_V' = \frac{V_{FP} + V_V}{2} \tag{14.5}$$

$$R_{D_2} = \frac{V_{FP} - V_V'}{I_P - I_V} \tag{14.6}$$

$$R_{T_2} = R_S + R_{D_2} \tag{14.7}$$

The general case d-c load line is

$$V = E_S - IR_S \tag{14.8}$$

The current-axis intercept is given by

$$I_{\text{int}} = \frac{E_S}{R_S} \tag{14.9}$$

The time for the diode to change from points 2 to 3, the ON-time pulse width, is given by

$$t_{\text{on}} = \frac{L}{R_{T_2}} \ln \left(\frac{V_Y - V_X}{V_N - V_M} \right) \tag{14.10}$$

The pertinent voltage values are

$$V_Y = V_{FP} \tag{14.11}$$

$$V_X = E_S - I_P R_S \tag{14.12}$$

$$V_N = V_V' \tag{14.13}$$

$$V_M = E_S - I_V R_S \tag{14.14}$$

We can now substitute in (14.10) to obtain

$$t_{\text{on}} = \frac{L}{R_{T_2}} \ln \left(\frac{V_{FP} - E_S + I_P R_S}{V_V' - E_S + I_V R_S} \right) \tag{14.15}$$

EXAMPLE. Consider now the tunnel-diode characteristic of Fig. 14.6. Assume that the diode is to be operated in a circuit similar to Fig. 14.4 where $R_S = 100$ ohms, $E_S = .1$ v, and $L = 300$ μh. Determine (a) the quiescent current of the device, (b) the current increment necessary to trigger the device to the ON state, (c) the time duration of the ON pulse.

(a) The current-axis intercept is determined by Eq. (14.9). Thus

$$I_{\text{int}} = \frac{E_S}{R_S} = \frac{.1}{100} = 1 \text{ ma}$$

The line connecting this vertical-intercept point of 1 ma and the horizontal-intercept point of .1 v is the d-c load line. This line crosses the diode characteristic at a current level of .67 ma. This is, of course, an OFF-state condition.

(b) The current increment to trigger the diode to the ON state is the peak current minus the quiescent current. That increment is $1 - .67$, or .33 ma.

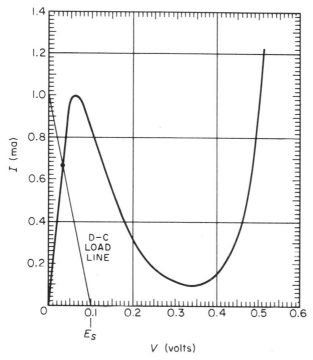

Fig. 14.6 Monostable example, OFF quiescence; $E_S = 0.1$ v, $R_S = 100\ \Omega$, $I_Q = 0.67$ ma.

(c) In order to determine the ON time, we must determine the quantities associated with the appropriate linearized regions. By (14.5)

$$V'_V = \frac{V_{FP} + V_V}{2} = \frac{.5 + .35}{2} = .425 \text{ v}$$

By (14.6)

$$R_{D_2} = \frac{V_{FP} - V'_V}{I_P - I_V} = \frac{.5 - .425}{(1 - .1)10^{-3}} = 83\ \Omega$$

By (14.7)

$$R_{T_2} = R_S + R_{D_2} = 100 + 83 = 183\ \Omega$$

By (14.15)

$$t_{\text{on}} = \frac{L}{R_{T_2}} \ln\left(\frac{V_{FP} - E_S + I_P R_S}{V'_V - E_S + I_V R_S}\right)$$

$$= \frac{300(10^{-6})}{183} \ln\left[\frac{.5 - .1 + 10^{-3}(100)}{.425 - .1 + .1(10^{-3})100}\right]$$

$$= .65\ \mu \text{ sec}$$

In the situation of Fig. 14.7(a) the diode is in stable state B, an ON condition. It can, however, be triggered from this point to the OFF condition. A negative pulse is required, and it must be able to decrease the current below the valley-point level. At point 3 the current would like to decrease to zero instantaneously. The inductor, of course, prevents this, and in attempting to maintain the current, the voltage shifts to point 4. Current will now increase until the peak point 1 is reached. The inductor again acts to maintain the current, the induced voltage switching the diode to point 2. From this point the current decreases gradually until stable point B is reached. The diode remains in this ON condition until a negative pulse again comes to trigger the device through the OFF transient.

The waveforms of interest are shown in Fig. 14.7(c). Note that the applied pulse triggers the diode from stable state B to point 4 with no time delay. From Fig. 14.7(c) we observe that the time required for the current

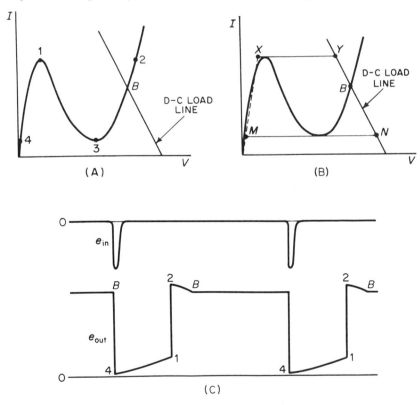

Fig. 14.7 ON state monostable tunnel diode. (A) Basic load-line situation. (B) Voltage values of interest in approximating the OFF pulse time. (C) Resultant triggered-pulse shape; e_{in} is the trigger pulse, e_{out} is the output waveform. Numbered points on output waveform correspond to numbers for abscissa voltage values in (A).

to decay from point 2 to point B is not associated with the OFF-time pulse width, points 4 to 1. The computation of OFF time requires the increment values of voltage between points XY and MN of Fig. 14.7(b). The basic conditions are such that

$$V_N = E_{S_2} - I_V R_S \tag{14.16}$$

$$V_M = I_V R_{D_1} \tag{14.17}$$

$$V_Y = E_{S_2} - I_P R_S \tag{14.18}$$

$$V_X = I_P R_{D_1} \tag{14.19}$$

The time for the diode to change from points 4 to 1, the OFF-time pulse width, is given by

$$t_{\text{off}} = \frac{L}{R_{T_1}} \ln \left(\frac{V_N - V_M}{V_Y - V_X} \right) \tag{14.20}$$

Substituting for the appropriate voltage values, we obtain

$$t_{\text{off}} = \frac{L}{R_{T_1}} \ln \left(\frac{E_{S_2} - I_V R_{T_1}}{E_{S_2} - I_P R_{T_1}} \right) \tag{14.21}$$

EXAMPLE. Assume that the diode characteristic of Fig. 14.8 is used in the circuit of the preceding example but now $E_S = .5$ v. The magnitudes of R_S and L are 100 ohms and 300 μh, respectively. Determine (a) the quiescent current (b) the magnitude of the current pulse necessary to trigger the device to the OFF state, and (c) the time duration of the OFF pulse.

(a) In order to draw the d-c load line, substitute a current value of 1.0 ma into Eq. (14.8) to obtain

$$V = E_S - I R_S$$

$$V = .5 - 1(10^{-3})100$$

$$= .4 \text{ v}$$

Draw a straight line between the coordinate points of 1.0 ma, .4 v, and 0 ma, 5 v. This is the d-c load line. This line intersects the diode curve at a current value of .41 ma.

(b) The current increment necessary to trigger the diode to the OFF state is the difference between the quiescent current and the valley current. This increment is $.41 - .1$ or .31 ma.

(c) In order to determine the OFF time, we must determine the quantities associated with the appropriate linearized region. By (14.2)

$$V'_P = .75 V_P = .75(.06) = .045 \text{ v}$$

By (14.3)

$$R_{D_1} = \frac{V'_P}{I_P} = \frac{.045}{10^{-3}} = 45 \ \Omega$$

By (14.4)

$$R_{T_1} = R_S + R_{D_1} = 100 + 45 = 145 \ \Omega$$

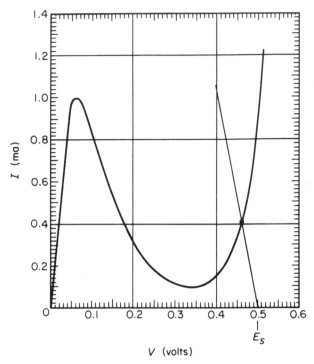

Fig. 14.8 Monostable example, ON quiescence; $E_S = 0.5$ v, $R_S = 100 \, \Omega$, $I_Q = 0.41$ ma.

By (14.21)

$$t_{\text{off}} = \frac{L}{R_{T_1}} \ln \left(\frac{E_{S_2} - I_V R_{T_1}}{E_{S_2} - I_P R_{T_1}} \right)$$

$$= \frac{300(10^{-6})}{145} \ln \left[\frac{.5 - .1(10^{-3})145}{.5 - 1(10^{-3})145} \right]$$

$$= .675 \, \mu \, \text{sec}$$

14.3. Bistable multivibrators.   In Sec. 14.1 we saw that in a monostable multivibrator, the OFF device must be *triggered* into the conduction state. Once ON, the time duration of conduction for the triggered device depended on an *RC* time constant. In many circuit applications it is important to have the conduction duration *trigger-dependent*. Thus the transistor in question starts to conduct when a trigger is applied, and ceases conduction only when a second trigger causes the second device to conduct, turning the transistor in question OFF.

A circuit useful in analyzing such a *bistable multivibrator* is shown in

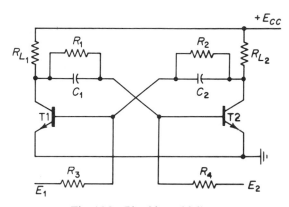

Fig. 14.9 Bistable multivibrator.

Fig. 14.9. For both coupling capacitors the bias resistor to supply voltage is omitted. Assume that T1 is ON and T2 is OFF. A positive trigger pulse E_2 will cause T2 to conduct. Capacitor C_2 switches through $-E_{CC}$ volts and in doing so causes T1 to turn OFF. Since C_2 cannot discharge, T1 will remain cut OFF and T2 will remain ON. Operation in these states will continue until a positive pulse E_1 causes T1 to turn ON. Capacitor C_1 switches through $-E_{CC}$ volts, causing T2 to turn OFF. Transistor T1 will remain ON and T2 OFF until the pulse E_2 is applied. The waveforms of interest are shown in Fig. 14.10. Notice that, depending on our reference, we can consider both positive and negative pulses as being generated. We will consider the use- fulness of the bistable circuit in counter applications in the next section.

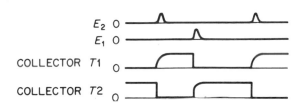

Fig. 14.10 Waveforms of interest in the bistable multivibrator of Fig. 14.9.

14.4. Counting circuits. We have seen that two separate input pulses are required to switch a transistor through one complete cycle in the bistable multivibrator. When the circuit is modified to be responsive to successive pulses from a *single* source, the circuit has potential in counter applications. The attainment of the desired operating condition is possible with the circuit

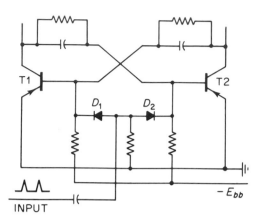

Fig. 14.11 Positive-pulse steering diodes for use in bistable multivibrator and single-pulse source.

of Fig. 14.11. This circuit is quite similar to the basic bistable circuit shown in Fig. 14.9. Included, however, are diodes D1 and D2. Since these diodes serve to direct successive input pulses to properly switch the transistors between states, they are called *steering diodes*. Consider the situation if T1 is conducting and T2 is not conducting. The forward-bias voltage that is permitting T1 to conduct appears also as a forward-bias voltage on D1. Thus D1 is slightly conducting and is in a low-impedance state. On the other hand, if T2 is not conducting, its base must be positive relative to the emitter of T2. This voltage serves to back-bias D2. Thus D2 is in a high-impedance state. When the input lead is now pulsed positively, the pulse chooses to flow in the low-impedance diode D1 rather than the high-impedance diode D2. When this pulse drives the base of T1 positive, T1 cuts OFF. As T1 cuts OFF, the collector and hence the capacitor switch through $-E_{cc}$ volts. This, of course, triggers T2 ON. Diode D2 reverts to a low-impedance condition while D1 reverts to a high-impedance state. The next time the input is positively pulsed, the pulse is steered through low-impedance D2 to trigger T2 from the ON to the OFF state. This in turn causes T1 to turn back ON. Note that the triggers pulse the ON transistor OFF and the secondary effect causes the OFF transistor to switch back ON. In the circuit configuration of Fig. 14.11 transistor switching was implemented as a function of *positive* trigger pulses. Hence the diodes as connected in Fig. 14.11 are called *positive-pulse steering diodes*.

A bistable circuit such as that of Fig. 14.11 can be made to respond to *negative* trigger pulses. Consider the circuitry shown in Fig. 14.12. Here the anodes of the steering diodes are connected to the bases of the tran-

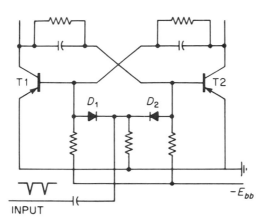

Fig. 14.12   Negative-pulse steering diodes for use in bistable multivibrator and single-pulse source.

sistors. Assuming T1 is conducting initially, we can expect D1 to be reverse-biased and D2 to be slightly forward-biased. If *positive* trigger pulses are applied, D2 goes to reverse-bias, and D1 continues reverse-bias. For this circuit, then, the positive trigger pulse does not affect the stable states of the transistors. If a negative pulse is now applied, diode D2 passes the pulse to the base of T2 and thus turns T2 ON. This, of course, turns T1 OFF. When T2 is ON and T1 is OFF, diode D1 is slightly forward-biased and D2 is reverse-biased. Thus, when another negative pulse comes along, T1 will switch from the OFF to the ON state and this in turn will cause T2 to turn OFF. Connected

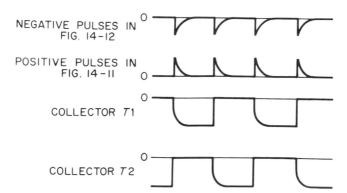

Fig. 14.13   Resultant collector waveforms in a bistable multivibrator when appropriate pulses are applied through steering diodes. Negative pulses for circuit of Fig. 14.12; positive pulses for circuit of Fig. 14.11.

as they are in a PNP transistor circuit, the diodes of Fig. 14.12 are called *negative-pulse steering diodes*. Please note that positive- and negative-pulse steering diodes do not switch the same stable NPN state that they do when connected to PNP devices.

The waveforms for the proper pulses in Figs. 14.11 and 14.12 are shown in Fig. 14.13. Note that a single pulse occurs in the output waveform for every two pulses applied at the input. Such a circuit is called a count-by-two circuit. A circuit of this sort is useful as a counter circuit in that a monitor of the number of output pulses provides an indication of the number of pulses occurring at the input.

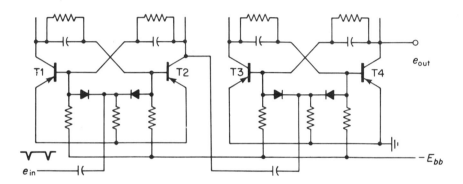

Fig. 14.14   Count-by-four circuit using bistable multivibrators.

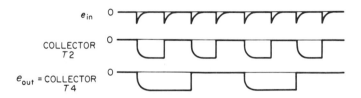

Fig. 14.15   Waveforms for a count-by-four circuit.

The circuits can be made more complex, as shown in Fig. 14.14. If the output of the first stage is used as a trigger pulse for a second bistable multivibrator, the composite becomes a count-by-*four* circuit. The waveforms for such a circuit are shown in Fig. 14.15.

14.5. Tunnel-diode counters.   A tunnel-diode load-line situation that results in two stable operating points is shown in Fig. 14.16(a). The circuit of Fig. 14.4 can be used. Here the d-c load, R_1, is greater than the negative

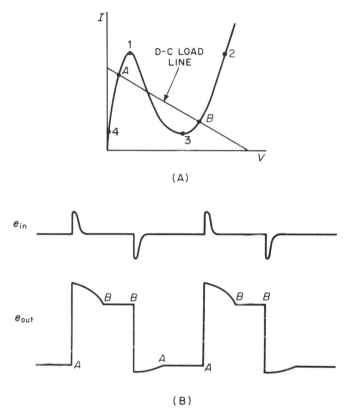

Fig. 14.16 Consideration of bistable tunnel-diode operation. (A) Load-line situation—circuit of Fig. 14.4. (B) Output waveform for appropriate triggers; e_{in} is trigger, e_{out} is output.

resistance of the diode. The value of d-c load, R_1, and supply voltage, E_s, are such that the d-c load line is positioned to intersect the diode characteristic at points A and B. Point A is an OFF state, whereas point B is an ON state. If the device is operating at point A, a positive pulse, sufficient to increase current above the peak point, will cause the device to switch to the ON state at point B. The device will remain in this state until a negative pulse, sufficient to decrease current below the valley value, will cause the device to switch back to the OFF state. The waveforms that result are shown in Fig. 14.16(b).

A circuit that incorporates bistable operation of tunnel diodes [1] and that responds to positive trigger pulses is shown in Fig. 14.17. In this circuit only one tunnel diode can be in the ON or high-voltage state at a given

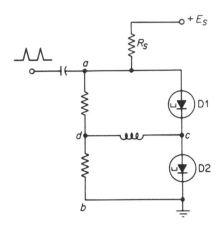

Fig. 14.17 Bistable tunnel-diode circuit which responds to unipolarity trigger pulses.

time. This condition is assured by controlling the supply voltage to a value less than that which will support both diodes in the ON state simultaneously. Assume, to begin with, that diode 1 is in the high-voltage, low-current state, while diode 2 is in the low-voltage, high-current state. The higher current that flows in diode 2 must be supported by a current flow through the inductor from circuit point d to circuit point c. If circuit point a is pulsed positively, the pulse will serve to switch diode 2 from an OFF to ON state. This means that the current through diode 2 reduces from a high to a low value. The inductor does not want to permit the current through it to reduce. The induced emf that results—circuit point d negative and circuit point c positive—serves as an in-circuit trigger causing diode 1 to switch from the ON to the OFF state. The resultant equilibrium situation finds

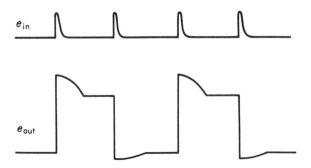

Fig. 14.18 Waveforms for circuit in Fig. 14.17; e_{in} is unipolarity trigger, e_{out} is output waveform.

current flowing in the inductor from circuit point c to circuit point d, with diode 2 in the high-voltage, low-current state and diode 1 in the low-voltage, high-current state. A second positive pulse at circuit point a causes diode 1 to return to the high-voltage state. The changing current in the inductor induces the voltage that switches diode 2 from the high-voltage to the low-voltage state.

The waveforms of interest are shown in Fig. 14.18. Notice that two input pulses are necessary to form one complete output pulse. Such a circuit can serve as a count-by-two circuit. If two such circuits were cascaded, we would have a count-by-four circuit. Note especially that in this tunnel-diode circuitry there is no need for the steering circuitry that was required for bistable multivibrators used as counters.

14.6. Logic-circuit fundamentals. In logic- or computer-circuit applications, the pulse circuits previously described must respond only to appropriate signals or combinations of signals. Switching circuits that provide the proper control to other functions of the circuit are called *gates*. Gates are the basic circuit blocks for the logic or computer realm. The two most common gate circuits are the AND gate and the OR gate. In an AND gate, a prescribed output condition (a pulse) can exist *only* if all the inputs to the gate simultaneously experience a prescribed pulse mode. In an OR gate, the prescribed output pulse can be obtained as long as a prescribed input-pulse mode appears at *any one* of the inputs.

Consider the diode circuit of Fig. 14.19. This is a basic AND-gate con-

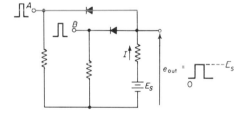

Fig. 14.19 Diode AND gate. Both inputs A and B must be pulsed simultaneously for an output pulse to occur.

figuration. As long as both diodes continue to conduct due to the applied bias E_S, the output voltage e_{out} is essentially zero. If a positive pulse appeared at each of the inputs A and B simultaneously, both diodes would be back-biased, current I would decrease to zero, and the circuit output would switch or pulse to a voltage level of E_S.

A single-transistor AND gate is shown in Fig. 14.20. The bias conditions are normally such that the transistor is full on, yielding a zero voltage output reference. The circuit resistors R_A and R_B are of such value that the transistor cuts off only when both inputs see a negative pulse. At such a time the output pulses to a $-E_{CC}$ value.

One form of an AND gate using two transistors is shown in Fig. 14.21.

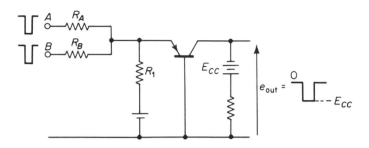

Fig. 14.20 Transistor AND gate. Transistor normally is conducting. When pulsed OFF an output pulse occurs.

During the time that both transistors are conducting, the output voltage is at a $-E_{cc}$ voltage level. If both bases are pulsed positively, the total current through R goes to zero and the output voltage increases to ground level.

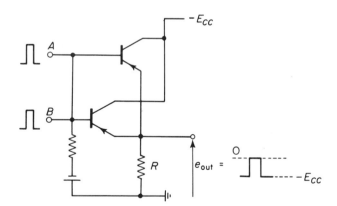

Fig. 14.21 Two-transistor AND gate. Transistors normally are conducting. When pulsed OFF an output pulse occurs.

The basic diode OR gate is shown in Fig. 14.22. Unless a positive pulse is applied to either input A or B, the output level remains at $-E_s$ relative to ground. When a positive pulse appears at either A or B, the appropriate diode is forward-biased. The current that results causes the output voltage to switch positively to pass from a $-E_s$ value to a zero value.

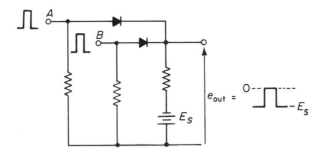

Fig. 14.22 Diode OR gate. A positive pulse at either A or B causes output to pulse from $-E_S$ to 0 volts.

A single-transistor OR gate is shown in Fig. 14.23. In this circuit the transistor is normally off because of the incomplete input-loop circuitry. The output voltage is normally at a $-E_{CC}$ level. When either input is positively pulsed, current flows in the transistor. This causes sufficient voltage drop in the load resistor so that the output voltage changes positively from a $-E_{CC}$ level to a zero level.

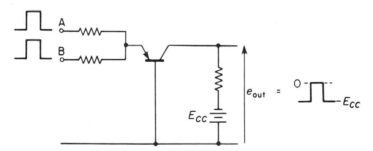

Fig. 14.23 Transistor OR gate. Transistor normally is OFF. A positive pulse at either input causes transistor to conduct and output to pulse to zero voltage.

Figure 14.24 shows an OR circuit that employs two transistors. This circuit is quite similar to the AND circuit of Fig. 14.21, except that the quiescent state of each transistor is nonconducting. The reference value of output voltage is zero. When negative pulses are applied to the input of either transistor, either will conduct, causing the output voltage level to change negatively from 0 to $-E_{cc}$ volts.

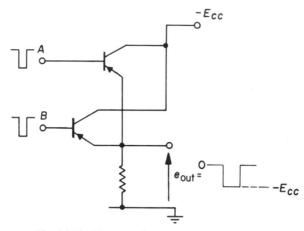

Fig. 14.24 Two-transistor OR gate. Transistors are normally OFF. A negative pulse at either base causes output to pulse from 0 to $-E_{cc}$ volts.

14.7. Summary. In this chapter we have discussed the operation of triggered pulse circuits. Circuits whose operation is trigger-dependent are of great value and can be used either as pulse amplifiers or as pulse-shaping vehicles. In addition, in most trigger circuits we can control the rate of occurrence of pulses and their time duration. We have discussed here the most common trigger circuits: the monostable and bistable multivibrator, and the monostable and bistable tunnel-diode circuit. The bistable circuit is further applicable as a counter, since one output pulse is formed for every pair of input pulses. We have also considered the basic circuit blocks of logic circuitry, the AND the OR gates. These circuits discern the input-pulse condition before generating an output pulse. Diodes and transistors both can be used in this type of circuit.

REFERENCES

1. W. F. Chow, "Tunnel Diode Digital Circuity," *IRE Transactions on Electronic Computers*, Vol. EC-9, September 1960, pp. 295–301.

SUGGESTED READING

1. *Transistors*, Program Manual by Federal Electric Corp. Staff. Englewood Cliffs, N.J.: Prentice-Hall, Inc., 1964.

2. K. Pullen, *Handbook of Transistor Circuit Design*. Englewood Cliffs, N.J.: Prentice-Hall, Inc., 1961.

3. F.Fitchen, *Transistor Circuit Analysis and Design.* Princeton, N.J.: D. Van Nostrand Co., 1960.

4. M. V. Joyce and K. K. Clarke, *Transistor Circuit Analysis.* Reading, Mass.: Addison-Wesley Publishing Co., 1961.

5. E. Wolfendale, *The Junction Transistor and Its Applications.* New York: The Macmillan Company, 1958.

6. S. S. Hakim, *Junction Transistor Circuit Analysis.* New York: John Wiley & Sons, 1962.

7. *General Electric Tunnel Diode Manual,* 1st ed., 1961.

PROBLEMS

1. Explain how a stable mode of operation exists in a monostable multivibrator.

2. Draw the waveforms for a monostable multivibrator that uses PNP devices.

3. Consider the tunnel-diode characteristic of Fig. 14.8. If $E_{S_2} - .65$ v, $R_S = 100$ Ω, and $L = 400$ μh, calculate the magnitude of the current pulse that switches the diode to the OFF state. Calculate also the time duration of the OFF pulse.

4. If, for Problem 3, $E_{S_1} = .12$ v, calculate the current pulse that turns the device ON, and the time duration of the ON pulse.

5. What happens to circuit operation if, for Problem 4, the supply voltage increases to .15 v?

6. Draw the schematic diagram and explain how positive-pulse steering diodes can be used with NPN devices in a bistable multivibrator.

7. Draw the waveforms for Problem 6.

8. Draw the schematic and explain the operation of negative-pulse steering diodes for NPN devices in a bistable multivibrator.

9. Explain with waveforms and block-diagram circuitry, a count-by-eight circuit.

10. Show how you would connect tunnel-diode circuits such as that in Fig. 14.17 to obtain a count-by-four circuit.

11. Explain the need for the hold-on emitter supply in the two-input type AND circuit of Fig. 14.20.

12. Draw waveforms for an NPN AND circuit connected as in Fig. 14.20.

13. Consider a circuit similar to the OR of Fig. 14.22. The supply is 9 v. The load resistor is 3 K. To what peak current should either diode be pulsed in order to achieve true OR action? Draw the waveforms.

15

POWER-SUPPLY

AND CONTROL CIRCUITS

In previous chapters we studied circuits that provided dynamic amplification of a-c signals over specific frequency ranges. In this chapter we direct our attention to *power-control circuits*. This is a broad classification covering, among other things, the conversion of low-frequency a-c power to d-c power and industrial applications such as phase controls and timing circuits. Appropriate circuits using the silicon-controlled rectifier are studied in this chapter also.

15.1. Basic power-supply considerations. Circuits that convert low frequency a-c power to d-c power are called *power supplies*. The semiconductor diodes used in power-supply circuits are called *rectifiers*. This categorization of devices implies that specification control is provided on parameters such as *peak inverse voltage, power rating, current*, and *surge current*.

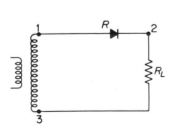

Consider the circuit of Fig. 15.1. This circuit was discussed qualitatively in Sec. 2.5. It is the simplest of power-supply circuits. The a-c voltage at the transformer secondary is labeled e_{13}. The peak value of this voltage is called V_m. When voltage e_{13} is positive, the rectifier conducts. If we as-

Fig. 15.1 Half-wave rectifier circuit.

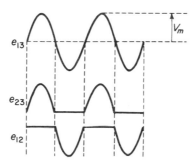

Fig. 15.2 Waveforms for source, load, and rectifier in a half-wave rectifier circuit.

sume that the forward drop in the rectifier is negligible, the voltage at the output, e_{23}, is a replica of the positive portions of e_{13}. Figure 15.2 shows the waveforms for the source, for the load, and for the rectifier itself. The rectifier voltage e_{12} is, of course, the difference between the supply and the load voltages. Since the rectifier drop is assumed equal to zero, the peak value of the load voltage is the same as the value for the supply voltage—that is, V_m. The average or d-c value of output voltage is

$$V_{\text{out(d-c)}} = \frac{V_m}{\pi} \tag{15.1}$$

The rms value of output voltage is

$$V_{\text{out(rms)}} = \frac{V_m}{2} \tag{15.2}$$

The d-c or rms current that flows in the output is related to the appropriate voltage and the load R_L. Thus

$$I_{\text{out(d-c)}} = \frac{V_{\text{out(d-c)}}}{R_L} \tag{15.3}$$

$$I_{\text{out(rms)}} = \frac{V_{\text{out(rms)}}}{R_L} \tag{15.4}$$

We now direct our attention to the rating or specification requirements on the rectifier itself. The waveform for voltage across the rectifier shows a reverse voltage with a peak value of V_m applied to the rectifier when it is not conducting. To assure that reverse voltage is not applied in sufficient magnitude to cause the rectifier to operate in its avalanche mode, a rating known as the *repetitive peak reverse voltage* is provided. By definition, the repetitive peak reverse voltage (PRV) for any given rectifier is the highest value of reverse voltage that can be applied recurrently without harmful effects due to avalanche conditions. As a minimum the PRV rating must exceed the peak value V_m of the transformer secondary sinusoid. In reality, rectifiers with repetitive PRV ratings more than adequate for the working voltage of the particular application are used. This prevents rectifier destruction as a result of uncontrolled or unsuppressed voltage surges that are apt to occur at relatively frequent intervals. The safety factor ranges from 2 to 5 times as a function of the presence and amount of suppression circuitry present. The short-term (less than 5-millisecond) *non* recurrent surge-voltage capability of a rectifier is indicated by the *transient peak reverse voltage rating*. This voltage rating is higher in magnitude than the repetitive RPV rating. Voltage ratings are related to operating waveforms in Fig. 15.3.

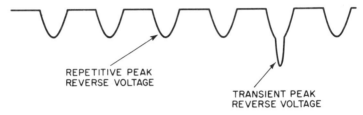

REPETITIVE PEAK
REVERSE VOLTAGE

TRANSIENT PEAK
REVERSE VOLTAGE

Fig. 15.3   Waveforms relating magnitude and frequency of occurrence of repetitive and transient peak reverse voltages for rectifier ratings.

As an indication of the power-handling ability of a rectifier, the *maximum allowable d-c output current* is always specified. This is the maximum permissible operating current that keeps the rectifier junction within its allowed temperature at a specified case or ambient temperature. Rectifier specification sheets normally provide derating curves for operation at other than the reference temperature. Surge currents will not be harmful if their time duration is short enough to keep the heating effect less than the maximum allowed level. The rating that relates the permissable pulse amplitude and duration is the so-called I^2t *rating*. The current I is an rms value and the time is seconds. The rating itself is a numerical constant. For convenience a graph of rms surge current versus pulse duration is often provided on the rectifier specification sheet. A sample of such a graph is shown in Fig. 15.4. An alternate method of expressing surge current capability is sometimes used: the *peak one-cycle surge current* rating. This, of course, is relatable to the I^2t rating. The peak one-cycle surge is the unique situation of a pulse duration equaling the time of a single rectifier conduction cycle. For 60-cps operation, the one-cycle surge corresponds to a time duration of 8.3 milliseconds. Current ratings are related to operating waveforms in Fig. 15.5.

The effectiveness of any rectifier circuit in converting a-c to d-c is

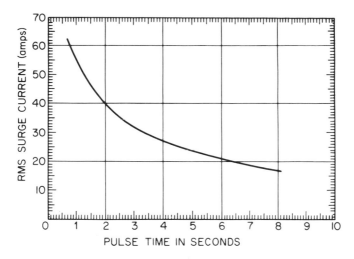

Fig. 15.4 The rms surge current versus pulse duration—based on I^2t rating.

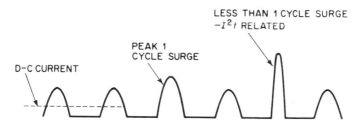

Fig. 15.5 Waveforms relate magnitude and duration of currents based on d-c, one-cycle surge, and I^2t ratings of a rectifier.

measured by *ripple factor*. Ripple factor is defined mathematically as the ratio of the effective value of a-c components in the output to the d-c value at the output. Thus

$$\text{ripple factor} = \frac{V_{\text{out(a-c)}}}{V_{\text{out(d-c)}}} \tag{15.5}$$

where $V_{\text{out(a-c)}}$ = effective value of the a-c components in the output
           $V_{\text{out(d-c)}}$ = average value at the output

The effective value of the a-c components in the output can be calculated if the rms and d-c of the total output waveform are known. Thus

$$V_{\text{out(a-c)}} = \sqrt{V_{\text{out(rms)}}^2 - V_{\text{out(d-c)}}^2} \tag{15.6}$$

Substituting Eq. (15.6) into (15.5), we obtain

$$\text{ripple factor} = \frac{(V_{\text{out(rms)}}^2 - V_{\text{out(d-c)}}^2)^{1/2}}{V_{\text{out(d-c)}}}$$

$$= \sqrt{\left(\frac{V_{\text{out(rms)}}}{V_{\text{out(d-c)}}}\right)^2 - 1} \qquad (15.7)$$

The smaller the numerical value of the ripple factor, the better the effectiveness of the rectifier circuit. For the half-wave rectifier circuit of Fig. 15.1, the numerical value of ripple factor is obtained by substituting Eqs. (15.1) and (15.2) into Eq. (15.7). Thus

$$\text{ripple factor} = \sqrt{\left(\frac{\pi}{2}\right)^2 - 1} = 1.21 \qquad (15.8)$$

The material in this section discloses the basic attributes in the design of a power-supply circuit: the d-c output voltage, d-c output current, and ripple factor. The ease with which the circuit objectives are obtained depends on the relative magnitudes of the a-c supply voltage and the ratings of the rectifier being considered. The half-wave rectifier is the simplest of rectifier circuits. More refined circuits are discussed in the sections that follow.

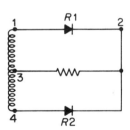

Fig. 15.6 Full-wave rectifier circuit.

15.2. Full-wave rectifier circuit. The full-wave rectifier circuit shown in Fig. 15.6 offers several advantages over the half-wave rectifier circuit. Assuming that the peak value of voltage e_{13} and e_{43} at the tap is V_m, the voltage e_{23} that is developed across the load is shown in Fig. 15.7. This is obtained by the diodes conducting alternately so as to provide essentially continual current flow in the load. The average or d-c value of output voltage is

$$V_{\text{out(d-c)}} = \frac{2V_m}{\pi} \qquad (15.9)$$

The rms voltage is

$$V_{\text{out(rms)}} = \frac{V_m}{\sqrt{2}} \qquad (15.10)$$

The d-c output voltage developed in the full-wave circuit is twice the output voltage of the half-wave circuit. The d-c working voltage for the rectifier is the same, however, in each circuit. The d-c and rms output currents for the full-wave circuit are

$$I_{\text{out(d-c)}} = \frac{2V_m}{\pi R_L} \qquad (15.11)$$

$$I_{\text{out(rms)}} = \frac{V_m}{\sqrt{2}\, R_L} \qquad (15.12)$$

For equal values of R_L the d-c load current in the full-wave circuit is twice the load current of the half-wave circuit. The d-c working-current level of the rectifier is the same in either circuit. Since the load voltage and current in the full-wave circuit are twice those of the half-wave circuit, it is evident that the full-wave circuit will develop four times the load power of the half-wave circuit.

In order to determine the repetitive PRV requirement for a rectifier in a full-wave circuit we can consider the loop equations for either loop 1231 or loop 12431. For loop 12431 we can write

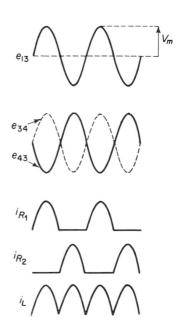

Fig. 15.7   Voltage and current waveforms for full-wave rectifier.

$$e_{12} + e_{24} + e_{43} + e_{31} = 0 \quad (15.13)$$

$$e_{12} = e_{42} + e_{34} + e_{13} \quad (15.14)$$

During the time that rectifier 2 is conducting, the drop e_{42} is considered negligible. Using the summation in Eq. (15.14), we find that the peak value of reverse voltage for rectifier 1 is the sum of the peak values of the sinusoids e_{34} and e_{12}. The repetitive PRV rating for a rectifier in a full-wave circuit is $2V_m$.

In order now to determine the ripple factor for the output voltage we substitute Eqs. (15.9) and (15.10) into (15.7). Thus

$$\text{ripple factor} = \sqrt{\left(\frac{\pi}{2\sqrt{2}}\right)^2 - 1} = .48 \quad (15.15)$$

Comparing statements (15.15) and (15.8) we observe the improved ripple factor for the full-wave circuit as compared to the half-wave circuit.

15.3. Example—full-wave rectifier.   Design the circuit that permits two 1N3569 rectifiers to operate at ratings in a full-wave rectifier circuit. Consider the primary to be 110-v 60-cps a-c. From the specification sheet of this device in the appendix we extract the following information:

$$\text{max repetitive PRV} = 100 \text{ v}$$
$$\text{max d-c current} = 3.5 \text{ amp}$$

Recalling that a rectifier must withstand a reverse voltage twice the magnitude of the end-to-tap voltage in a full-wave circuit, we know immediately that the maximum peak of voltage e_{13} (Fig. 15.6) is 50 v. Thus for this example $V_m = 50$ v. If we now designate the number of secondary turns between the tap and an end as n_t, we can say

$$\frac{n_p}{n_t} = \frac{110}{50} = 2.2$$

where n_p = primary turns
n_t = secondary turns to tap

The value of load resistor must be such that the average current in each rectifier does not exceed 3.5 amp. This is the same as restraining the d-c load current to 7.0 amp. From Eq. (15.11)

$$R_L = \frac{2V_m}{\pi I_{\text{out(d-c)}}} = \frac{2(50)}{\pi 7} = 4.55 \ \Omega$$

The d-c load power, incidentally, is

$$P_{L(\text{d-c})} = I_{\text{out(d-c)}}^2 R_L$$
$$= (7)^2(4.55) = 220 \ \text{w} \tag{15.16}$$

15.4. Bridge-rectifier circuit.   The circuit configuration of Fig. 15.8 is called a *bridge rectifier*. Electrically, this circuit yields the same results as the full-wave circuit of Fig. 15.6. During the time that voltage e_{14} is positive, rectifiers R1 and R2 conduct, as they see forward bias, while rectifiers R3 and R4 do not conduct, as they are reverse-biased. A pulse of current flows through R_L, making point 2 positive in relation to point 3. During the time that e_{14} is negative, rectifiers R3 and R4 become forward-biased while R1 and R2 become reverse-biased. The current through R3 and R4 passes through R_L from point 2 to point 3. Thus R_L experiences repetitive positive pulsations of voltage. The appropriate waveforms are shown in Fig. 15.9. The equations that were developed for the full-wave circuit apply to the bridge network. The only significant difference in circuits is that the series connection of rectifiers reduces the repetitive PRV rating per rectifier to V_m.

15.5. Capacitor input filter.   Often it is desirable to make the ripple factor very small, of the order of 1–10 per cent, with values of $V_{\text{out(d-c)}}$ a large per cent of V_m (greater than 99 per cent). To accomplish this, reactive elements are incorporated into the basic rectifier circuits already discussed. One form of improved power supply is the *capacitor-input filter*, sometimes called the *shunt capacitor filter*. The circuit is shown in Fig. 15.10. The basic concepts of circuit operation are explained with the help of Fig. 15.11.

Let the circuit be activated with the capacitor initially uncharged, at a

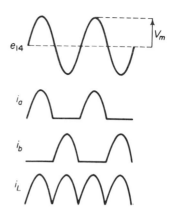

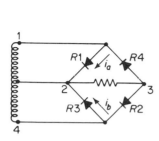

Fig. 15.8 Bridge rectifier—full wave.

Fig. 15.9 Voltage and current waveforms for full-wave bridge rectifier.

time noted as t_o. Rectifier current will flow, and for the time duration t_o to t_1 the load voltage e_{23} has the same value and form as the supply voltage e_{13}. At time t_1 the capacitor is, of course, fully charged to a voltage value V_m. After t_1 the supply voltage decreases from the peak value V_m. Since the capacitor does not discharge immediately, we see that beyond t_1 the cathode of the rectifier, point 2, is held more positive than the anode, point $1'$. This is a back-bias condition and the rectifier ceases to conduct. Load current continues to flow as the capacitor discharges into the load. The load voltage

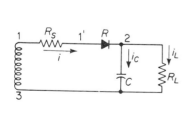

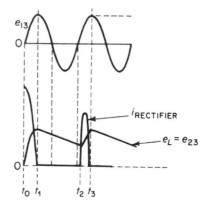

Fig. 15.10 Circuit diagram for capacitor-input filter.

Fig. 15.11 Waveforms for capacitor input filter. Note that the initial charge time $t_0 - t_1$ is greater than the recharge time $t_2 - t_3$.

is controlled by the capacitor until time t_2, where the supply voltage goes more positive than the existing voltage at the cathode end of the rectifier. The capacitor recharges to V_m at time t_3 and the cycle repeats. Note that the rectifier current flows only during the time intervals t_0 to t_1 and t_2 to t_3 to charge the capacitor.

As an approximation in calculating the d-c load voltage and ripple factor we assume that the capacitor discharges linearly at its initial rate from t_1 to t_2 and that the capacitor charge-time interval (t_0 to t_1 and t_2 to t_3) is zero. The load voltage can then be represented as the sawtooth of Fig. 15.12.

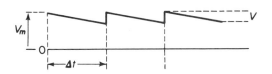

Fig. 15.12 Approximated waveform for load voltage in capacitor input filter.

The discharge of the capacitor for the sawtooth approximation is

$$e = V_m e^{-t/R_L C} \qquad (15.17)$$

For the time interval Δt in Fig. 15.12 we note

$$\Delta t = T = \frac{1}{f} \qquad (15.18)$$

and

$$V = \frac{V_m}{f R_L C} \qquad (15.19)$$

The d-c value of load voltage is given by

$$V_{\text{out(d-c)}} = V_m - \frac{V}{2} \qquad (15.20)$$

Substituting Eq. (15.19) into (15.20), we obtain

$$V_{\text{out(d-c)}} = V_m \left(1 - \frac{1}{2 f R_L C} \right) \qquad (15.21)$$

The Fourier analysis of the sawtooth waveform reveals that

$$V_{\text{a-c}} = \frac{V}{\sqrt{3}} \qquad (15.22)$$

where $V =$ sawtooth peak to peak
  $V_{\text{a-c}} =$ rms value of sawtooth

Substituting (15.19) into (15.22), we obtain

$$V_{a-c} = \frac{V_m}{\sqrt{3} \, fR_LC} \tag{15.23}$$

The ripple factor for the output voltage is obtained by substituting Eqs. (15.23) and (15.21) into Eq. (15.5):

$$\text{ripple} = \frac{V_{\text{out(a-c)}}}{V_{\text{out(d-c)}}} = R.F. \tag{15.5}$$

$$= \frac{\dfrac{V_m}{\sqrt{3} \, fR_LC}}{V_m \left(1 - \dfrac{1}{2fR_LC}\right)} \tag{15.24}$$

$$= \frac{1}{\sqrt{3} \, fR_LC - (\sqrt{3}/2)} \tag{15.25}$$

This equation can be rewritten to have the form

$$R_LC = \frac{1 + .865(R.F.)}{1.73f(R.F.)} \tag{15.26}$$

At this point we have knowledge of the supply voltage, d-c load voltage, ripple, and R_LC product. The ratio of d-c load voltage and d-c load current indicates the value of load resistance. Thus

$$I_{\text{out(d-c)}} = \frac{V_{\text{out(d-c)}}}{R_L} \tag{15.27}$$

When R_L and the R_LC product are known, the value of the capacitor, C, is determined. The value of the capacitor is vital in another way. As shown by Fig. 15.11, rectifier current flows only when the capacitor is charging. The worst-case charging condition occurs if the circuit is activated when the capacitor is completely discharged. To prevent an excessive starting surge current a small resistor R_S is added in series with the rectifier. The peak value of starting surge current is

$$i_{\text{surge}} = \frac{V_m}{R_S} \tag{15.28}$$

The time duration for the surge to occur is taken as

$$t_{\text{surge}} = R_SC \tag{15.29}$$

Generally a surge time of 1 millisecond is an optimum with which to work. Thus

$$R_S \cong \frac{1000}{C} \tag{15.30}$$

where R_S is in ohms and C is in microfarads.

The time duration which we define as t_{surge} is the time for any charging action of the capacitor. As Fig. 15.13 suggests, however, the peak of the normal cyclic charge current is considerably less than the peak of the starting

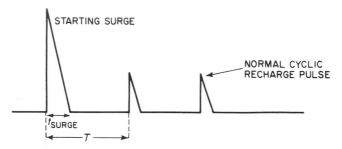

STARTING SURGE

NORMAL CYCLIC
RECHARGE PULSE

t_{SURGE}

T

Fig. 15.13 Appearance of starting and charging currents in rectifier when assumed to be clipped sawtooths.

surge current. This situation exists because the cyclic charging involves the load resistor R_L, whereas the starting surge involves R_S. The most severe current requirement of the rectifier is its ability to withstand the starting surge pulse. As a design criterion we require that the rms value of starting surge current be based on 1 cycle in Fig. 15.13. For 60-cps operation the time period T equals .0167 seconds. The Fourier analysis of a waveform such as that of Fig. 15.13 suggests that

$$I_{\text{rms}} = I_m \sqrt{\frac{t_{\text{surge}}}{3T}} \qquad (15.31)$$

Using a 1-millisecond value for t_{surge} and 16.7 milliseconds for T, a substitution of Eq. (15.28) yields

$$I_{\text{rms(surge)}} \cong \frac{V_m}{7R_S} \qquad (15.32)$$

This current value must, of course, be within the 1-msec surge rating of the rectifier being used. Under almost all design situations, a rectifier having a surge rating that satisfies the surge requirements of the circuit satisfies also the d-c current requirements of the circuit.

It has been derived elsewhere [1] that the peak value of recharging current is given by

$$I_{\text{peak}} = \frac{V_m}{R_L} \sqrt{1 + \omega^2 R_L^2 C^2} \qquad (15.33)$$

The average rectifier current becomes

$$I_{R(\text{d-c})} = \frac{V_m t_{\text{charge}}}{2TR_L} \sqrt{1 + (\omega R_L C)^2} \qquad (15.34)$$

The time to charge the capacitor is still given by $R_S C$ or 1 msec as a typical value. Substituting 1 msec for t_{charge} and 16.7 msec for T, we obtain

$$I_{R(\text{d-c})} = \frac{V_m}{33.4R_L} \sqrt{1 + (\omega R_L C)^2} \qquad (15.35)$$

The significant equations for a capacitor input filter are

$$V_{\text{out(d-c)}} = V_m \left(1 - \frac{1}{2fR_LC}\right) \tag{15.21}$$

$$I_{\text{out(d-c)}} = \frac{V_{\text{out(d-c)}}}{R_L} \tag{15.27}$$

$$R.F. = \frac{1}{\sqrt{3}\, fR_LC - .865} \tag{15.25}$$

$$R_LC = \frac{1 + .865(R.F.)}{1.73f(R.F.)} \tag{15.26}$$

$$R_S \cong \frac{1000}{C} \tag{15.30}$$

$$I_{\text{rms(surge)}} \cong \frac{V_m}{7R_S} \tag{15.32}$$

$$I_{R\text{(d-c)}} \cong \frac{V_m}{33.4R_L}\sqrt{1 + (\omega R_LC)^2} \tag{15.35}$$

The only significant compromise aspect of the design involves the relative values of C, R_S, and $I_{\text{rms(surge)}}$. Generally, the ratio of R_S to R_L should be of the order of .01 to assure good voltage regulation. In satisfying this rule of thumb the value of capacitance C or surge current may be not suitable. A rectifier with higher current rating is the answer.

15.6. Example: capacitor input filter. As an example of the application of the material in the preceding section, let us design a filter using a 1N3569 rectifier to yield a ripple factor of 10 per cent when a 30-ohm load resistor is used in conjunction with an 80-v peak, 60-cps transformer secondary voltage.

By Eq. (15.26)

$$R_L C = \frac{1 + .865(R.F.)}{1.73f(R.F.)}$$

$$= \frac{1 + .865(.10)}{1.73(60)(.10)}$$

$$= .1045$$

Since the load is 30 ohms,

$$C = \frac{.1045}{30} = 3500\ \mu f$$

By Eq. (15.30)

$$R_S \cong \frac{1000}{C}$$

$$= \frac{1000}{3500} = .29\ \Omega$$

Using a surge resistance value of .29 Ω and a peak voltage of 80, the rms surge current, by Eq. (15.32), is

$$I_{\text{rms(surge)}} = \frac{V_m}{7R_S}$$

$$= \frac{80}{7(.29)} = 39.5 \text{ amp}$$

Referring to the specification sheet of the 1N3569, we note that the allowed 1-msec surge current is 55 amp; thus we are well within the surge current requirements. The d-c current in the rectifier is given by Eq. (15.35); that is,

$$I_{R(\text{d-c})} = \frac{V_m}{33.4R_L} \sqrt{1 + (\omega R_L C)^2}$$

$$= \frac{80}{33.4(30)} \sqrt{1 + [2\pi(60)(.1045)]^2} = 3.12 \text{ amp}$$

This is seen to be within the 3.5-amp d-c current rating of the 1N3569.

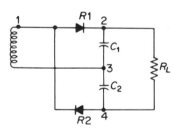

Fig. 15.14 Circuit diagram for voltage-doubler circuit.

15.7. Voltage-doubler circuit. A useful modification of the capacitor input filter is shown in Fig. 15.14. This circuit is called a *voltage-doubler circuit*. During the time when voltage e_{13} is positive, rectifier R1 conducts and capacitor C_1 is charged so that point 2 is positive relative to point 3. During the time that point 1 is negative relative to point 3, rectifier R2 conducts causing point 3 to be positive relative to point 4. The two capacitors are in series, however, relative to the load. Thus the load voltage is approximatly twice the output voltage of a single capacitor input filter.

15.8. Inductor input filters. In a capacitor input filter, the ripple and voltage regulation are poor when the load resistance is lowered in an already existing circuit. This is seen in Eq. (15.21). As R_L decreases, the d-c output voltage decreases. Thus ripple increases. Some degree of compensation for this condition is provided when inductors become a part of a filter network.

The basic inductor filter is the *inductor input filter* of Fig. 15.15. The function of the inductor may be shown with the help of Fig. 15.16. As the time constant L/R_L increases (R_L kept constant), we observe three specific effects. The time required for the circuit current to maximize becomes longer and longer, the time duration of current flow becomes longer and longer, and the peak value of circuit current becomes less and less. These effects are readily understood. The increasing inductance is more effective in opposing current increases and decreases. The reduction in peak current at high inductances is caused by the increase in circuit impedance. The inductor input circuit gives lowest ripple factor when the

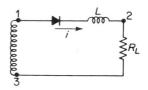

Fig. 15.15   Circuit of basic-inductor input filter.

load resistance is small, and the ratio of ωL to R high. This corresponds to a high-current, low-output-voltage operating mode, and is opposite to the capacitor input filter which gives its best ripple at a high output voltage.

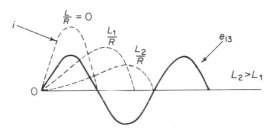

Fig. 15.16   Circuit current in inductor input filter as a function of L/R ratio.

Another filter circuit that contains an inductor is the *choke input filter* (Fig. 15.17). The mathematics of this circuit are complex and are not treated here; they are, however, covered in other publications. The basic design requirements are discussed in the *General Electric Rectifier Guide* [2]. The key mathematical expressions are

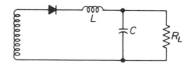

Fig. 15.17   Circuit of choke input filter.

$$L_c \geqslant \frac{R}{3\omega} \tag{15.36}$$

$$\omega^2 LC \geqslant .5 \tag{15.37}$$

The ripple factor obtainable for various values of $\omega^2 LC$ is shown in Fig. 15.18. The significance of the *critical inductance*, L_c, is that it is the smallest value of L that will maintain continual circuit current flow. The typical

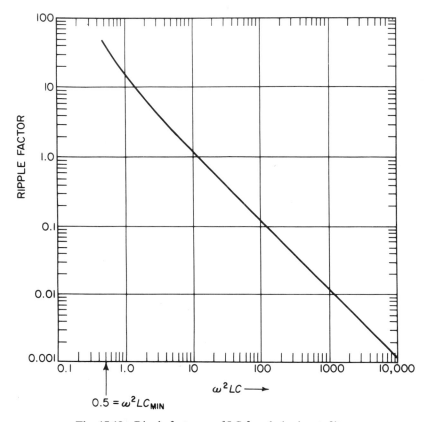

Fig. 15.18 Ripple factor vs $\omega^2 LC$ for choke input filter.

working-voltage situation at the output is

$$V_{\text{out(d-c)}} = .9V_m \tag{15.38}$$

Since the inductor is present as a series element, there is somewhat less concern for surge current protection.

15.9. Example: choke input filter. Specify the circuit components that are required to obtain a ripple factor of 10 per cent when a load of 100 ohms is to be properly handled in a choke input filter; $f = 60\,\text{cps}$.

By (15.36)

$$L_C \geqslant \frac{R}{3\omega}$$

$$\geqslant \frac{100}{3(2\pi 60)}$$

$$\geqslant .89 \text{ henries}$$

Let us use 1 henry as L. The magnitude of $\omega^2 LC$ is found from Fig. 15.18 to be about 100 for a ripple of 10 per cent. The magnitude of C is found as

$$C = \frac{100}{\omega^2 L}$$

$$- \frac{100}{14.2(10^4)(1)}$$

$$= 350 \ \mu\text{f}$$

This value of capacitance is reasonable.

15.10. Regulated power supplies.   Frequently it is desirable to provide supplementary circuitry in a power supply to assist in obtaining good voltage regulation. One basic form of regulator circuit is the *shunt voltage regulator* of Fig. 15.19. The key component in this circuit is the breakdown diode

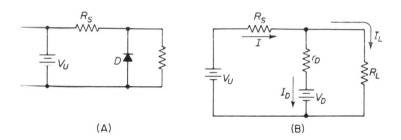

(A)   (B)

Fig. 15.19   (A) Basic circuit of shunt voltage regulator. (B) Equivalent circuit of breakdown diode incorporated into circuit.

D. The objective is to match the voltage-breakdown value of the diode with the desired regulated voltage value. Any change in the unregulated voltage V_U causes a change in total circuit current I. The current increment flows through the diode, the change in voltage appearing across the series resistor R_S. Generally the diode breakdown value is less than the desired regulated voltage by 2–4 per cent.

The circuit performance may be studied more closely with the help of Fig. 15.20. Curve A is the reverse characteristic of the breakdown diode. Curve B is the current-voltage plot for the load resistor R_L. Curve C is the composite characteristic of the diode and resistor R_L in parallel. Each coordinate point on curve C is the sum of the currents for each element for a given voltage, since the elements are in parallel. Curves D and E are possible load lines for the series resistor R_S. Curve D is drawn with an in-

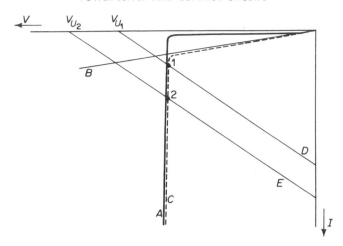

Fig. 15.20   Current-voltage characteristics for shunt regulator. (A) Breakdown diode. (B) Load resistor. (C) Composite of diode and load in parallel. (D) and (E) Possible load lines for R_S at different V_U.

tercept V_{U_1}, the smallest value of voltage to be regulated; curve E is for V_{U_2}, the largest value of voltage to be regulated. Intercept points 1 and 2 are the major factors in the circuit design. At any time

$$I = I_D + I_L \tag{15.39}$$

where I_D = diode current

$\quad\quad I_L$ = load current

$\quad\quad I$ = current from unregulated source

Notice from Fig. 15.20 that the current in the load, I_L, is essentially the same for both ordinate points, 1 and 2. The restriction for point 1 is that the value of diode current not be too small for regulation. The restriction at point 2 is that the diode current not be so large as to cause excessive power dissipation in the diode. The useful current range for voltage regulation is usually given on the specification sheet of the breakdown diode.

In order to design a regulator circuit, we first note the equivalent representation of the diode as noted in Fig. 15.19(b). The resistance r_D is the dynamic impedance of the breakdown region. The voltage source V_D is the breakdown value. Writing loop equations, we say

$$V_U = IR_S + I_D r_D + V_D \tag{15.40}$$

$$= IR_S + V_L \tag{15.41}$$

$$V_L = V_D + I_D r_D \tag{15.42}$$

$$= I_L R_L \tag{15.43}$$

Substituting Eq. (15.39) into (15.40) for I and solving for R_S, we obtain

$$R_S = \frac{V_U - I_D r_D - V_D}{I_D + I_L} \tag{15.44}$$

Solving Eqs. (15.42) and (15.43) for I_L and substituting into (15.44) for I_L, we get

$$R_S = \frac{V_U - V_D - I_D r_D}{I_D\left(1 + \frac{r_D}{R_L}\right) + \frac{V_D}{R_L}} \tag{15.45}$$

The minimum value of R_S that still keeps the diode within its power rating (I_D a maximum value) is determined by substituting the maximum values of R_L, V_U, and $I_{D(\max)}$. The maximum value of R_S that still allows the diode to regulate (I_D a minimum value) is determined by substituting the minimum values of R_L, V_U, and $I_{D(\min)}$.

In order to calculate the actual voltage-regulation value we first solve Eq. (15.40) for I_D.

$$I_D = \frac{V_U\,V_D - I_L R_S}{R_S + r_D} \tag{15.46}$$

Substitute (15.46) into (15.42) to get

$$V_L = V_D + r_D\left(\frac{V_U - V_D - I_L R_S}{r_D + R_S}\right)$$
$$= \frac{V_D R_S}{r_D + R_S} + \frac{V_U r_D}{r_D + R_S} - \frac{I_L r_D R_S}{r_D + R_S} \tag{15.47}$$

The voltage regulation, V.R., is defined as

$$V.R. = \frac{\Delta V_L}{\Delta V_U} \tag{15.48}$$

Taking the derivative of Eq. (15.47) with respect to V_U we get

$$V.R. = \frac{r_D}{r_D + R_S} \tag{15.49}$$

The major disadvantage of the basic shunt regulator of Fig. 15.19 is that breakdown diodes do *not* generally have a suitably large current range $I_{\max} - I_{\min}$ over which they can regulate. This situation is improved with the circuit of Fig. 15.21. In this circuit, the diode current is the base current of the transistor, and the diode breakdown voltage is serving as a clamp between the collector and base of the transistor. The emitter-base drop is small enough to be ignored, so that the regulated output voltage is still a function of V_D. The collector current of the transistor is

$$I_C \cong (1 + h_{FE})I_D \tag{15.50}$$

The useful current range of the diode in regulating the load voltage has been increased by a factor of $(1 + h_{FE})$.

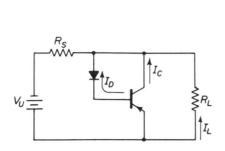

Fig. 15.21 Shunt voltage regulator with extended current-handling capability.

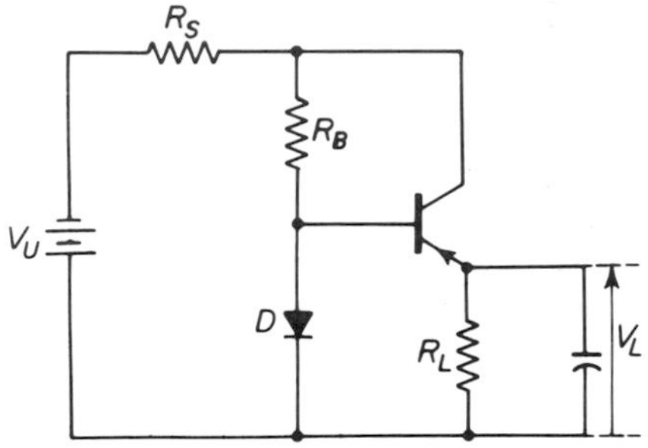

Fig. 15.22 Series voltage-regulator circuit.

The *series voltage regulator* of Fig. 15.22 is more efficient than the shunt regulators previously discussed. No shunt power losses exist. Rather, all of the useful source current flows directly through the load. Changes in the voltage drop across the transistor output compensate for the changes in the source voltage and thus a regulated output voltage is possible. Normally the bias resistor R_B is greater than the series resistance R_S. The transistor is biased such that the quiescent base-emitter voltage is V_D. When the load voltage V_L is less than V_D, the emitter is forward-biased and current flows. As soon as the load voltage reaches the desired value, the transistor is cut off.

15.11. Example: regulated supply.   Design a shunt regulator circuit so that an unregulated reference of 80 ± 5 v, is controlled to a V_L of 40 v for an R_L of 100 Ω. The breakdown diode has $V_D = 39$ v. Assume that the typical operating current of the diode, I_D, is 10 ma and $r_D = 3\ \Omega$.

By (15.43)

$$I_L = \frac{V_L}{R_L}$$

$$= \frac{40}{100} = 400 \text{ ma}$$

By (15.44)

$$R_S = \frac{V_U - V_D - I_D r_D}{I_D + I_L}$$

$$= \frac{80 - 39 - 10(10^{-3})3}{(10 + 400)10^{-3}}$$

$$= 100$$

The V.R. is given by (15.49):

$$V.R. = \frac{r_D}{r_D + R_S}$$
$$= \frac{3}{3 + 100} = .0291$$

Thus the plus or minus 5-volt change in the source is subdued to an increment of approximately 145 mv at the load.

15.12. Controlled-rectifier theory. The *controlled rectifier* is a four-layer device with many unique applications in the control of power in the industrial and commercial fields. Speaking generally, the device can be described as a high-power switch, which passes very high currents at a very low voltage level when it is switched to its conduction or ON state. Its construction and

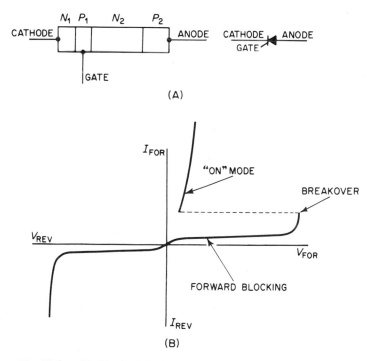

Fig. 15.23 (A) Physical depiction and circuit symbol for a controlled rectifier. (B) Open-gate characteristic of controlled rectifier.

circuit symbol are shown in Fig. 15.23(a). By comparison with the other regions, the N_2 region is very lightly doped and is physically long. The N_1 region is the most heavily doped, with the P_1 and P_2 at a lesser and approximately equal level. The current-voltage characteristic, which is obtained with a floating- or open-gate lead, is shown in Fig. 15.23(b).

To understand the current-voltage characteristic we must consider junction voltage and current behavior for various levels of forward bias. These are shown sequentially in Fig. 15.24. With no external voltage applied, a back-bias will exist across each junction [Fig. 15.24(a)]. For a fairly extensive region of forward bias the voltages are as shown in Fig. 15.24(b). Junctions N_1P_1 and N_2P_2 are forward-biased and junction P_1N_2 is reverse-biased. The

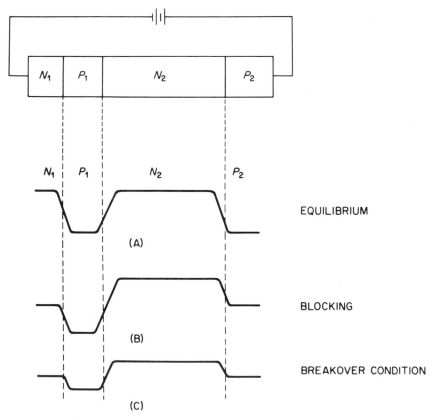

Fig. 15.24 Junction gradients for various levels of forward bias in a controlled rectifier. (A) Equilibrium. (B) Typical forward-bias level during blocking. (C) Knee and breakover condition.

length of N_2 and the reverse bias of P_1N_2 serve as a block between N_1 and P_2 interaction. At a sufficiently high level of bias (dependent on the construction of the device) we can anticipate the junction interaction leading to breakover.

The breakover mechanism is highly complicated. Our discussions here are somewhat idealized to provide general comprehension. We can assume some level of electron injection from N_1 to P_1. Some of these are carried via the reverse voltage to the N_2 region. Since these electrons (from N_1) have to diffuse through a long path before reaching P_2, we can assume for some brief period that the resistance of N_2 is lowered owing to an increase in total electron count. This causes the height of the reverse voltage between P_1 and N_2 to *decrease* and the forward-biasing between N_2 and P_2 to *increase*, which in turn stimulates added hole injection from P_2. Some of these holes combine with electrons in the N_2 region, but others travel to the P_1 region, where they encourage added electron injection from N_1. The injection of added electrons from N_1 will lead to an additional suppression of the voltage level of N_2 and more hole injection from P_2 into N_2. The monotonic sequence of events explains the knee in the blocking portion of the characteristic.

At some point the bias at P_1N_2 becomes a forward bias. At this point the four regions are forward-biased and the current will be high in value, limited only by the impedance of the external circuitry. However, the additive voltage between N_1 and P_2 is essentially that of a single forward-biased junction. We have, therefore, a high-current low-voltage mode of operation in the ON state. When steady-state levels of forward bias are applied to the gate, the device switches to the ON state at an anode voltage value less than that for an open-gate condition. Such a condition of forward bias at P_1 serves to increase the carrier level artificially in the device. Thus less injec-

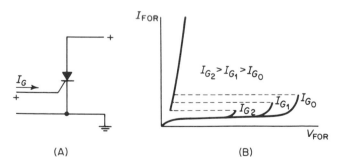

Fig. 15.25 (A) Circuit depiction showing gate input. (B) Anode characteristic for various gate currents.

tion must be stimulated by anode voltage. As the forward bias at the gate increases, the anode voltage level for ON switching decreases. Such a family of gate currents is shown in Fig. 15.25. In most circuit applications the controlled rectifier is triggered to the ON state by forward-bias pulses at the gate. We will treat this in other sections on controlled-rectifier applications.

In concluding our discussion of controlled-rectifier operation we should note that once the rectifier is turned on, it can be turned off only by removal of the anode voltage or by polarity reversal of the anode relative to the cathode.

15.13. D-C switching application for controlled rectifier. An example of the controlled rectifier in a d-c switching application is the flasher circuit of Fig. 15.26. This circuit is a modification of a circuit shown in the *General*

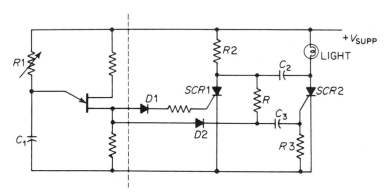

Fig. 15.26   Variable-frequency flasher circuit.

Electric Silicon Controlled Rectifier Manual [3]. The circuitry to the left of the dotted line is the familiar unijunction relaxation oscillator discussed in Sec. 13.7. The circuitry to the right of the dotted line is of immediate concern. The input at diodes D1 and D2 is a series of positive pulses. Consider for the moment that both controlled rectifiers are off. Diode D1, which is connected to the gate lead of SCR1, is much less reverse-biased than diode D2, which has essentially all of the supply voltage as a reverse-bias voltage. Thus the first positive output pulse of the unijunction circuit will act through D1 in preference to D2 to turn SCR1 on. When this occurs, capacitor C_2 is charged to supply voltage with the left side of C_2 minus with respect to the right-hand side. The next positive output pulse from the unijunction transistor can do nothing for SCR1. It does, however, act through D2, which is now only slightly reverse-biased to turn SCR2 on. When SCR2 turns on, its anode drops to essentially ground potential. The voltage across C2 is now applied directly to SCR1. Since the anode of SCR1 is now negative relative to its cathode, SCR1 turns off. During the time that SCR2 conducts, the charge on C_2 becomes minus on the right and plus on the left. At the diodes we see D2 very much reverse-biased and D1 only slightly reverse biased. The next pulse from the unijunction will turn SCR1 on and apply the voltage on C_2 to SCR2, shutting it off. During the time interval that SCR2 conducts, the lamp in the anode circuit of SCR2 is lit. Notice that the frequency at which the lamp lights is one-half the frequency of operation of the unijunction oscillator. The unijunction operation is controlled as expected by the time constant $R_1 C_1$. The controlled rectifier is especially suited for this application because it handles the high currents associated with the turn-on of the incandescent load lamp.

15.14. A-C phase-control application for controlled rectifier. A circuit demonstrating the use of the controlled rectifier as a power-control device is shown in Fig. 15.27(a). This circuit is extracted from the *General Electric Controlled Rectifier Manual* [4]. Here a breakdown diode, D1, is used in conjunction with a full-wave bridge to provide a clipped sine wave, voltage e_{11}. This is the voltage applied to the unijunction-controlled rectifier array. The waveforms are shown in Fig. 15.27(b). At time t_1 the supply voltage reaches the value necessary to cause diode D1 to break down. Since a fixed voltage is held across the unijunction circuit, capacitor C_1 starts to charge towards the peak value of e_{11}. At time t_2 the unijunction fires, pulsing the gate of the controlled rectifier, which also fires. In reverting to its low-voltage state, the SCR removes the breakdown diode from the circuit and permits current to flow through the load resistor for the remaining portion of the half-cycle. When the supply voltage reaches a zero value the SCR ceases to conduct. The same events occur in the next half-cycle, since the full-wave bridge supplies a unipolarity voltage to the SCR network. The direction of current flow does, however, change in the load resistor owing to its placement in series with the a-c supply voltage. If we want the load current to flow for a longer portion of the cycle, we reduce R_1 to permit C_1 to charge more quickly—that is, to make the time interval $t_0 - t_2$ smaller. If a lamp were used as the load, the brightness (or dimness) could be effectively controlled between full on and off. If semiconductor devices of suitable power-handling capability were incorporated, very effective speed control could be provided for electric drills and saws.

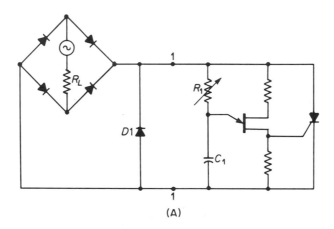

(A)

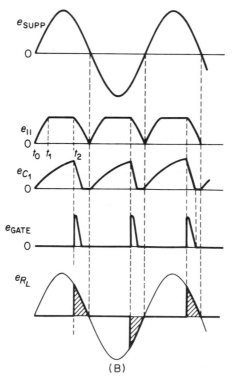

(B)

Fig. 15.27 (A) A-C phase-control circuit using a silicon-controlled rectifier. (B) Pertinent circuit waveforms.

15.15. Summary. The bulk of this chapter has dealt with power-supply circuitry. We have progressed from simple rectifier circuits to the design of capacitor and choke input filters and shunt and series voltage-regulator circuits. The concluding material dealt with controlled-rectifier theory and its application in static switching and phase-control circuits. The insight and understanding gained about the operation of the selected circuitry should bolster one's confidence in designing circuits to suit his own requirements.

REFERENCES

1. J. D. Ryder, *Electronic Fundamentals and Applications.* Englewood Cliffs, N.J.: Prentice-Hall, Inc., 1964, pp. 118 ff.

2. *General Electric Rectifier Guide*, 2nd ed., 1962, pp. 41 ff.

3. *General Electric Silicon Controlled Rectifier Manual*, 2nd ed., 1961, pp. 104–106.

4. *General Electric Silicon Controlled Rectifier Manual*, 2nd ed., 1961, pp. 115–117.

SUGGESTED READING

1. L. P. Hunter, *Handbook of Semiconductor Electronics*, 2nd ed. New York: McGraw-Hill Book Co., 1962.

2. R. A. Greiner, *Semiconductor Devices and Applications.* New York: McGraw-Hill Book Co., 1961.

3. *Handbook of Selected Semiconductor Circuits*, Bureau of Ships, Dept. of the Navy, NAVSHIPS 93484.

4. T. S. Gray, *Applied Electronics*, 2nd ed. New York: John Wiley & Sons, 1947.

5. *Westinghouse Silicon Controlled Rectifier Designers Handbook*, 1963.

PROBLEMS

1. Explain the difference between the repetitive peak reverse voltage rating and the transient peak reverse voltage rating in a rectifier.

2. Explain the significance of the I^2t rating of a rectifier.

3. Consider a 1N3569 rectifier in the circuit of Fig. 15.1. A circuit is to be designed for operation at 80 per cent levels of peak reverse voltage and I_{d-c} ratings. Calculate (a) the minimum value of load resistor and (b) the output power developed.

4. Using the derating factors of Problem 3, calculate the load resistor and output power for a pair of 1N3569 rectifiers in the full-wave circuit of Fig. 15.6.

5. In Sec. 15.2 it was mentioned that a full-wave circuit is capable of delivering

four times the load power of the half-wave circuit. Verify the conditions making this performance possible. Explain the results of Problems 3 and 4.

6. For the illustrative example in Sec. 15.6 determine the lowest ripple factor that is possible while still keeping the rectifier within its ratings. Which rating is the limitation, $I^2 t$ rating or d-c output-current rating?

7. Design a capacitor input filter using a 1N3569 rectifier to obtain a ripple factor of 8 per cent when a 20-ohm load resistor is used in conjunction with a 60-v peak 60-cps sine-wave source. Confirm that no current rating is exceeded.

8. Explain the operation of an inductor input filter.

9. Design a choke input filter to yield a ripple factor of 8 per cent when an 80-ohm load is used.

10. Explain the operation of a shunt voltage regulator using a breakdown diode.

11. A breakdown diode has a breakdown voltage value V_D of 29.5 v. It will regulate this voltage over a current range of 6–20 ma. Confirm the applicability of this diode in regulating an 80 ± 5 v source to a V. R. level of .02 at $V_L = 30$ v when $R_L = 100\ \Omega$. Assume $r_D = 3\ \Omega$. If the V. R. level of .02 is not attainable, calculate the V. R. that is possible.

12. Draw the waveforms for an SCR a-c phase control when the rms value of load voltage is large.

16

LABORATORY

EXPERIMENTS

Experiment 1: Diode characteristics and applications. In this experiment we study the characteristics of germanium and silicon diodes. An opportunity to use diodes in rectifier applications is also suggested.

Equipment

1 d-c power supply
1 a-c signal generator (audio)
1 multirange milliammeter
1 d-c vacuum-tube voltmeter
1 oscilloscope
1 100-K resistor
1 20-K resistor
1 47-K resistor
1 general-purpose germanium diode (1N64)
1 PNP audio transistor (germanium)
1 NPN silicon transistor

Procedure

Let us call the general-purpose germanium diode D1, the collector and base regions of the germanium audio transistor D2, the base and collector of the silicon device D3, and the base and emitter D4.

A. A circuit for measuring the reverse or back characteristic of a diode is shown in Fig. 16.1. For diodes D1, D2, and D3, vary the supply voltage so that V_{REV} increases in steps of about 1 v. For each value of V_{REV}, record

V_{REV} and I_{REV} on the data log. As the knee of a breakdown region is approached, adjustments of supply voltage should be predicated on controlled increases of current rather than V_{REV}. This minimizes the risk of running the junction into a destructive avalanche mode. Diode D4 is to be treated similarly to diodes D1, D2, and D3, keeping in mind that most emitter-base breakdowns in silicon devices are extremely sharp and occur between 6 and 8 volts.

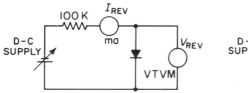
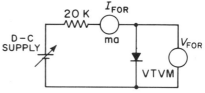

Fig. 16.1 Circuit for obtaining data to plot the reverse characteristic of a diode.

Fig. 16.2 Circuit for obtaining data to plot the forward characteristic of a diode.

B. A circuit for measuring the forward characteristic of a diode is shown in Fig. 16.2. For each diode vary the supply voltage so that I_{FOR} increases in steps of about 0.2 ma to a level of 3 ma. At each value of I_{FOR}, record I_{FOR} and V_{FOR} in the data log. The knee region of conduction may require extra data points.

C. As an application exercise connect each diode in the rectifier circuit of Fig. 16.3. Using D1 or D2, apply an a-c signal of about 20 volts peak-to-peak. Record the amplitude of the waveform across R. Then substitute D3 and D4 and record the waveforms for each.

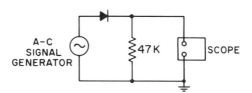

Fig. 16.3 Half-wave rectifier circuit to observe differences in back characteristics.

Data Processing

1. Plot the back characteristic of each diode.
2. Plot the forward characteristic of diodes D1, D3, and D4.
3. Comment on the differences in the forward characteristics of D1 and D3.

4. Comment on the differences in the forward characteristics of D3 and D4. [*Hint*: Consider the doping levels of emitter versus collector regions in a transistor.]
5. Explain the difference in rectified waveforms of D1 or D2 and D3 in step C.
6. Explain the waveform for D4 in the rectifier circuit.

Experiment 2: Transistor characteristics. This experiment provides the opportunity to obtain the basic transistor characteristics: the input characteristic and the output characteristic. Both the common-base and common-emitter connections are reviewed.

Equipment

2 d-c power supplies
2 decade resistance boxes
2 multirange milliammeters
1 10-MΩ potentiometer
1 10-KΩ potentiometer
PNP transistors
several 6-v lantern cells

Procedure

A. The circuit for measuring the common-base input characteristic is shown in Fig. 16.4. Note that the supply used for the collector circuit must have either a floating ground or the option to ground the positive terminal. As an alternative, the use of lantern cells to obtain this voltage may be desirable. For each of the conditions of $V_C = 0$, 5, and 15 volts, vary I_E and record I_E and V_E. Be sure to adjust R_C as required to maintain V_C at a constant value while I_E is changing. For the $V_C = 0$ condition, be sure to take data for two circuit conditions: an open-circuit collector ($V_{CO} = V_C$)

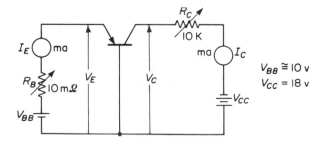

Fig. 16.4 Test circuit for common-base input and output characteristics.

and a shorted collector to base ($V_{CS} = V_C$). Do not permit the $V_C I_E$ product to exceed the power rating of the device being used.

B. To obtain data for the common-base output characteristic we again use the circuit connection in Fig. 16.4. For each of the I_E values of 1, 2, 3, and 5 ma, vary V_C, and record V_C and I_C. In order to explore the origin region, reverse the polarity of the collector supply and vary V_C in small increments until $I_C = 0$ for each of the I_E levels of 1, 2, 3, and 5 ma. Record V_C and I_C at each test point.

C. The common-emitter input characteristic can be explored with the circuit of Fig. 16.5. Lantern cells may be used for the supply voltages if

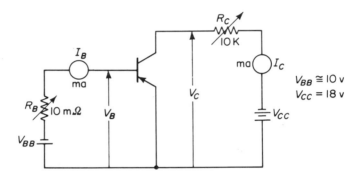

Fig. 16.5 Test circuit for common-emitter input and output characteristics.

desired. For each of the conditions of $V_C = 0$, 5, and 15 v, vary I_B and record I_B and V_B. Be sure to adjust R_C as required to maintain V_C at a constant value while I_B is changing. For the so-called zero-collector-voltage condition, take data for both an open-circuited and short-circuited condition. When taking data with collector voltage applied, be aware that at some value of V_B, current direction in the base will reverse. When this point is reached, use increments of reducing V_B as the controlling parameter rather than I_B.

D. The circuit of Fig. 16.5 can be used again to obtain data for the common-emitter output characteristic. For a range of I_B values (20 μa to 200 μa, for example) vary V_C and record V_C and I_C. The high value of I_B is determined by the current gain and the resultant value of I_C. Remember that the product of $I_E V_C$ or $I_C V_C$ should not be permitted to exceed the power rating of the device.

Data Processing

    1. Plot the common-base input characteristic from the data obtained.
    2. Plot the common-base output characteristic including the details of the origin exploration.

3. Plot the common-emitter input characteristic including the origin effects.
4. Plot the common-emitter output characteristic.
5. Why is the difference between an open and shorted collector less for the common-emitter input characteristic than it is for the common-base?
6. Calculate the approximate values of h_{FB}.
7. How might one determine values of I_{CER} for various values of R starting with circuits used in this experiment?

Experiment 3: D-C bias circuits. In this experiment, the salient aspects of various d-c bias circuits become apparent.

Equipment

1 d-c power supply
2 multirange milliammeters
1 vacuum-tube voltmeter
2 decade resistance boxes
1 10-MΩ potentiometer
assorted PNP devices

Procedure

A. The value of leakage, I_{CBO}, and current gain, h_{FE}, should be known for each device to be used in the subsequent bias experiments. The leakage I_{CBO} can be measured by placing each device in the circuit of Fig. 16.6(a). The value of current gain can be determined from data taken when each device is operating in the circuit of Fig. 16.6 (b). For each device, adjust R_B so that $I_C = 1$ ma. Record the corresponding values of I_B and V_{BE}. The value of h_{FE} is the ratio of I_C and I_B.

B. Complete the circuit of Fig. 16.7 by selecting R_B to make a midrange device (of those measured) operate at a collector current of 1 ma. Refer

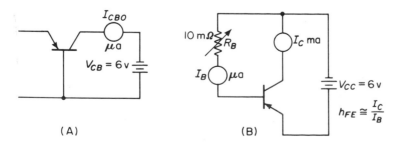

Fig. 16.6 (A) Circuit for measuring I_{CBO}. (B) Circuit for measuring h_{FE}.

to Sec. 6.2 for a review of fixed-bias-current circuits. The appropriate equations are

$$I_C = (1 + h_{FE})I_{CBO} + h_{FE}I_B$$

$$R_B = \frac{V_{CC} - V_{BE}}{I_B}$$

After the value of R_B is determined and the circuit of Fig. 16.7 completed, record the values of collector current and base current for each device when it is placed into the circuit.

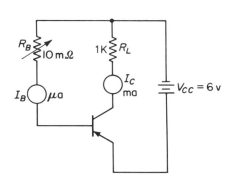

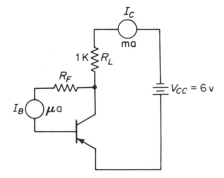

Fig. 16.7 Fixed-bias current circuit. For lab purposes (experiment 3 part B) adjust R_B so mid h_{FE} device operates at $I_C = 1$ ma.

Fig. 16.8 Current-feedback bias circuit in lab experiment (part C). This circuit should be designed so that a mid h_{FE} unit (of those measured) should draw an I_C of 1 ma.

C. Complete the circuit of Fig. 16.8 by selecting R_F so that the same mid-range unit used in part B operates at a collector current of 1 ma. Refer to Sec. 6.3 for a review of current-feedback bias circuitry. The appropriate design equations are

$$I_C = h_{FE}I_B + (1 + h_{FE})I_{CBO}$$

$$V_C = V_{CC} - (I_C + I_B)R_L$$

$$I_B = \frac{V_C - V_{BE}}{R_F}$$

When the circuit of Fig. 16.8 is completed, record the values of collector current and base current for each device when it is placed into the circuit.

D. Repeat step C for a circuit where $R_L = 3$ K.

E. As an expedited way of checking the voltage-feedback circuitry, consider the circuit in Fig. 16.9. For the mid-range device previously used, adjust R_M and R_N simultaneously so that $I_C = 1$ ma. Let R_N be of the order of 2 K. For each device, record the value of collector current.

F. Repeat step E, but use R_N of the order of 5–6 K.

Data Processing

1. Calculate the current gain of each transistor.

2. Plot collector current versus current gain for each device as used in steps C and D. Comment on the difference in performance.

3. Comment on the behavior of base current in steps C or D.

4. Explain the difference in performance in steps E and F.

5. Plot collector current versus current gain for steps B, D, and E.

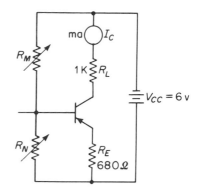

Fig. 16.9 Voltage-feedback bias circuit in lab experiment (part E). Adjust R_M so that a mid h_{FE} unit has an $I_C = 1$ ma with R_N in the order of 2 K.

Experiment 4: Class A audio amplifiers. Some of the important features of Class A transformer-coupled audio circuits are studied in this experiment.

Equipment

1 oscilloscope
1 a-c signal generator (audio)
1 d-c power supply
1 power load box
1 100-Ω resistor, $\frac{1}{4}$ watt
2 decade resistor boxes
1 5-μf coupling capacitor
1 100-μf decoupling capacitor
1 milliammeter
1 Class A audio output transformer (500 Ω/3.2 Ω)
several audio output transistors (2N270, 2N241A)

Procedure

A. Connect the circuit shown Fig. 16.10. Adjust R_M and R_N so that as the a-c signal (400 cycles) increases, clipping occurs at both peaks of the output waveform simultaneously. Record R_M and R_N. Reduce the a-c signal to zero and record the quiescent level of current in the emitter. If a load box is not available, a resistive load can be connected to the transformer. The scope or a VTVM can be used to indicate rms voltage across the load.

B. Increase the a-c drive gradually until power output saturates. Record I and P_{rms} for each point.

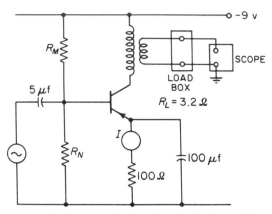

Fig. 16.10 Class A transformer-coupled audio amplifier.

C. Decrease the quiescent current to 70 per cent of the value in part A. Record the waveform after distortion first occurs.

D. Increase the quiescent current to 120 per cent of the value in part A. Record the waveform after distortion first occurs.

Data Processing

1. Calculate efficiency for each data point taken step A. Plot efficiency versus P_{rms}.
2. Explain the results of step C.
3. Explain the results of step D.
4. What is the maximum ideal rms power for the circuit?

Experiment 5: Class AB audio amplifiers. In this experiment the behavior of Class AB push-pull audio amplifiers is studied.

Equipment

1 oscilloscope
1 a-c power supply (audio)
1 d-c power supply
1 power load box
1 2.2-ohm resistor, $\frac{1}{4}$ watt
1 100-ohm resistor, $\frac{1}{4}$ watt
1 decade resistor box
1 d-c milliammeter
1 Class AB audio output transformer, 200-ohm C.T./3.2 ohm

1 driver transformer 2 K/5 K C.T.
several audio transistors (2N270, 2N241A)

Procedure

A. Connect the circuit of Fig. 16.11. A 3.2-ohm resistor may be used as a load if a load box is not available. A scope or a VTVM may be used to measure rms voltage across the load. With a moderate signal applied, adjust the bleeder resistor R_2 to a value that causes crossover distortion and then decrease R_2 until crossover does not occur. Remove the a-c signal and record the quiescent battery current for both devices and for each device individually.

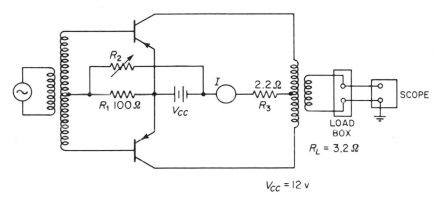

Fig. 16.11 Class AB push-pull audio amplifier.

B. Vary the a-c signal so that power output increases in uniform steps (to the point where clipping occurs at each power-output value). Record the total battery current and the a-c voltage across one-half of the primary of the output transformer at each power-output level.

C. At any arbitrary level of output power observe the total waveform across R_3

D. At any arbitrary level of output power reduce the value of supply voltage and observe the effects on the output waveform.

Data Processing

1. Explain the function of R_2 adjustment in controlling the amount of crossover distortion.
2. Using the data of step B, plot output power and battery power versus peak value of voltage across one-half of the primary winding.

3. Using the data of step C, comment on the relative current-gain values of the transistors being used.
4. How do the quiescent-current values for each device compare with respect to the relative current gains of the devices?
5. Comment on the observations of step D.

Experiment 6: Frequency response in a cascade amplifier.   This experiment provides the opportunity to study a cascade amplifier and its frequency response both with and without feedback.

Equipment

1 Class AB audio output transformer, 200-ohm C.T./3.2 ohm
1 Class AB driver transformer, 2 K/5 K C.T.
1 oscilloscope
1 a-c signal generator (audio)
1 d-c power supply
1 power load box
1 100-Ω resistor, $\frac{1}{4}$ watt
1 4.7-K resistor, $\frac{1}{4}$ watt
2 decade resistor boxes
1 1-K resistor
1 8-μf coupling capacitor
1 100-K resistor
1 .22-μf capacitor
3 audio PNP transistors (2N270, 2N241A)

Procedure

A. Connect the circuit of Fig. 16.12. To adjust the quiescent point of the Class AB stage connect the signal generator to the primary of the driver transformer (driver transistor out of the circuit). Then adjust R_1 so that no crossover occurs. In setting the quiescent point of the driver transistor reconnect the driver circuit and apply an a-c signal through C_1. R_2 should be adjusted so that at maximum power in the output, the waveform distortion is controlled by the output pair and *not* the driver.

B. Set the signal level at 400 cps to obtain about 100 mw in the load. Vary f down to about 80 cps and up to about 10 Kc. At each frequency record P_{out}, e_{in}, and the open-circuit generator voltage e_o.

C. Without changing the generator setting add a 100-K feedback resistor between the base of the driver and that side the output secondary which does not cause regeneration. Repeat the data of step B.

D. Change the feedback network to the 100-K and .22-μf capacitor in series. Repeat step C.

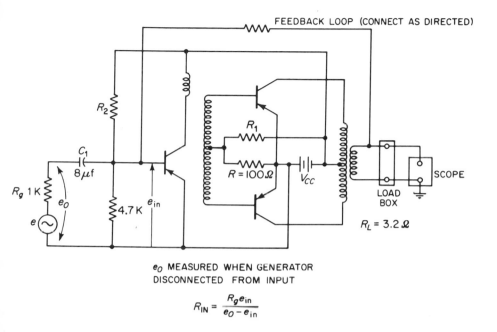

Fig. 16.12   Cascade stage—to study performance variation with frequency.

Data Processing

1. Using the data of step B, plot power gain versus frequency. The input power can be calculated by

$$P_{in} = \frac{e_{in}^2}{R_{in}}$$

where

$$R_{in} = \frac{R_g e_{in}}{e_o - e_{in}}$$

2. Using the data of step C, plot power gain versus frequency.
3. Plot power gain versus frequency for step D.
4. Comment on the performance for each connection.
5. Discuss the output-waveform situation that would occur if the quiescent current of the driver were set (a) too high, (b) too low.

Experiment 7: Unijunction relaxation oscillators.   In this experiment we study the operation of the unijunction transistor.

Equipment

    1 oscilloscope
    1 d-c supply
    1 10-MΩ potentiometer
    1 .47-μf capacitor
    1 100-Ω resistor, $\frac{1}{4}$ watt
    1 33-Ω resistor, $\frac{1}{4}$ watt
    several unijunction transistors (such as 2N1671)
    1 15-K resistor

Procedure

    A. Complete the circuit of Fig. 16.13 and set R_1 equal to 15 K. Vary V_{BB} from 8 v to 24 v. For each value of V_{BB} use a scope across C to observe the corresponding values of V_P and V_V. Record V_{BB}, V_P, and V_V.

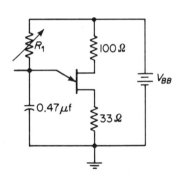

    B. Repeat the variation of V_{BB} from 8 v to 24 v, but record now the value of V_{OB_1} for each V_{BB}.

    C. Set V_{BB} to 20 v, and increase R_1 until the circuit no longer oscillates. Record the value of R_1.

    D. Leaving V_{BB} set at 20 v, reduce R_1 until the circuit no longer oscillates. Record the value of R_1.

Data Processing

Fig. 16.13 Unijunction transistor relaxation oscillator.

    1. From the data of step A, calculate the standoff ratio η for each value of V_{BB}.

    2. From the data of step B, make a chart of diode impedance R_E versus peak emitter current I_E.

    3. What is the minimum frequency of oscillation? What is the value of peak current?

    4. What is the maximum frequency of oscillation? What is the value of valley current?

    Experiment 8: Tunnel diodes. In this experiment we study the application of tunnel diodes in sinusoidal and relaxation oscillator circuits.

Equipment

    1 d-c supply

1 oscilloscope
1 decade resistance box
1 100-Ω resistor
1 .8-mfd capacitor
1 1.7-mfd capacitor
1 10-mh inductor
1 1-ma I_P tunnel diode

Procedure

A. Connect the circuit of Fig. 16.14. Adjust the decade-box value until free-running oscillations are obtained. Note and record the peak-to-peak amplitude of the waveform and whether it varies as the operating point is varied by changes in supply voltage.

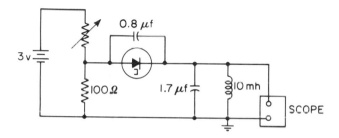

Fig. 16.14   Tunnel-diode sinusoidal oscillator.

B. Note how the waveform distortion varies as the operating point varies within the negative-resistance region.

C. Connect the circuit of Fig. 16.15. This circuit should yield waveforms for the relaxation oscillator studied in Sec. 13.9 when it is biased in the negative-resistance region. Note and record the peak-to-peak amplitude of the waveform.

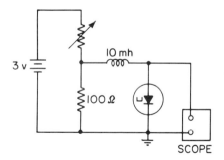

Fig. 16.15   Tunnel-diode relaxation oscillator.

D. Note the waveform at the lowest and highest values of supply voltage, respectively, that permit free-running oscillations. Note in passing the "lock-up" voltage level at the extremities of the free-running region.

Data Processing

1. Compare the voltage amplitudes of the waveforms in steps A and C. Explain why they differ.
2. Explain the distortion variation as the operating point is varied within the negative-resistance region in step B.
3. Calculate the frequency of operation of the circuit of Fig. 16.14.
4. Explain the waveform variation noted in step D as voltage is varied.
5. Calculate the frequency of oscillation for the circuit in Fig. 15.15 when the E_s value is .3 volts.

Experiment 9: Multivibrators. The basic attributes of multivibrator operation are studied in this experiment.

Equipment

2 oscilloscopes
2 decade resistor boxes
2 .22-μf capacitors
1 d-c supply
2 general-purpose NPN silicon transistors
2 45-K resistors
1 3-v cell
1 100-K resistor

Procedure

A. Connect the circuit shown in Fig. 16.16. Initially the decades used as R_1 and R_4 can be set to about 2 kilohms.

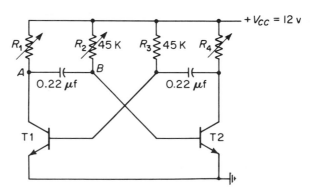

Fig. 16.16   Astable or free-running multivibrator.

B. Observe and record the waveforms at the collector of T1 (point *A*) and the base of T2 (point *B*)

C. Vary R_1 to observe how the leading edge of the off portion of the waveform at *A* varies.

D. Now vary R_2 and observe how the frequency of operation is affected.

E. Revise the circuit of Fig. 16.16 to that shown in Fig. 16.17.

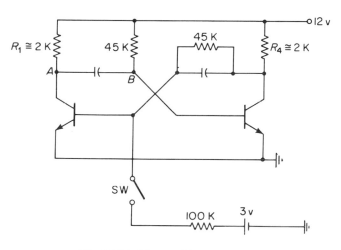

Fig. 16.17   Monostable multivibrator.

F. With the pulse switch open, connect the collector supply. Observe the stable operation of the circuit.

G. Now apply a pulse of current manually. Observe and record the waveforms at points *A* and *B*.

Data Processing

1. Explain the operation of an astable multivibrator. Refer to the waveforms of step B, and comment on applicability in the explanation of circuit operation.
2. Explain the observations of step C.
3. What is happening in step D?
4. Calculate the frequency of operation when R_1 and R_4 equal 2 K and R_2 and R_3 equal 45 K.
5. Explain the operation of the circuit used in steps F and G.

APPENDIX

PNP

GERMANIUM TYPES
2N1413
2N1414
2N1415

Computer-Industrial TRANSISTORS

The General Electric types 2N1413, 2N1414 and 2N1415 are intended for those industrial audio amplifiers and low frequency switching applications where cost is of prime importance. All units are hermetically sealed and are subjected to 100 hours of high temperature bake as well as a hermeticity test, thus assuring reliable performance under adverse environmental conditions. Efficient thermal characteristics are assured by welding the transistor base to the case.

absolute maximum ratings: (25°C)

Voltages

Collector to Base	V_{CBO}	—35 volts
Collector to Emitter	V_{CER} ($R_{BE} \leqq 10K$)	—25 volts
Emitter to Base	V_{EBO}	—10 volts

Collector Current

	I_{CM}	—200 ma

Temperatures

Storage	T_{STG}	—65°C to +85 °C
Operating	T_J	+85 °C

Total Transistor Dissipation*

	P_T	200 mw

*Derate 3.33 mw/°C increase in ambient temperature above 25°C.

DIMENSIONS WITHIN JEDEC OUTLINE TO-5

370 MAX 360 MIN
335 MAX 325 MIN
.100 MIN (NOTE 1)
.260 MAX .215 MIN
1.5 MIN
.210 MAX .190 MIN
3 LEADS .017 + .002 − .001 (NOTE 3)
THIS LEAD GROUNDED TO HOUSING
90°
45 ± 3°
.040 MAX .029 MIN (NOTE 2)
.031 ± .003

NOTE 1: This zone is controlled for automatic handling. The variation in actual diameter within this zone shall not exceed .010.

NOTE 2: Measured from max. diameter of the actual device.

NOTE 3: The specified lead diameter applies in the zone between .050 and .250 from the base seat. Between .250 and .5 maximum of .021 diameter is held. Outside of these zones the lead diameter is not controlled. Leads may be inserted, without damage, in .031 holes while transistor enters .371 hole concentric with lead hole circle.

APPROX WEIGHT: .05 OZ
ALL DIMENSIONS IN INCHES

electrical characteristics: (25°C)

SMALL SIGNAL CHARACTERISTICS

(Unless otherwise specified $V_C = -5V$ common base; $I_E = +1ma$; $f = 1000$ cps)

Characteristic	Symbol	2N1413			2N1414			2N1415			Units
		Min.	Typ.	Max.	Min.	Typ.	Max.	Min.	Typ.	Max.	
Output Admittance (Input AC Open Circuited)	h_{ob}	.1	.65	1.3	.1	.62	1.2	.1	.55	1.0	μmhos
Input Impedance (Output AC Short Circuited)	h_{1b}	26	29	36	26	29	35	26	29	33	ohms
Reverse Voltage Transfer Ratio (Input AC Open Circuited)	h_{rb}	1	4.8	10	1	5.2	11	1	5.7	12	$\times 10^{-4}$
Forward Current Transfer Ratio (Common Emitter; Output AC Short Circuited)	h_{fe}	20	30	41	30	44	64	44	64	88	
Frequency Cutoff	f_{hfb}	0.8	3.2		1.0	3.6		1.3	4.0		mc
Output Capacity (f = 1mc; Input AC Open Circuited)	C_{ob}		26	40		26	40		26	40	$\mu\mu$f
Noise Figure (f = 1 kc; BW = 1 cycle)	NF		6			6			6		db

D-C CHARACTERISTICS

Forward Current Gain (Common Emitter, I_C/I_B)

Characteristic	Symbol	2N1413			2N1414			2N1415			Units
		Min.	Typ.	Max.	Min.	Typ.	Max.	Min.	Typ.	Max.	
($V_{CE} = -1v$; $I_C = -20ma$)	h_{FE}	25	36	42	34	52	65	53	73	90	
($V_{CE} = -1v$; $I_C = -100ma$)	h_{FE}	23			30			47			
Collector Saturation Voltage ($I_C = -20ma$; I_B as indicated)	$V_{CE(SAT)}$ @ $I_B =$		-.070 -2.0			-.075 -1.33			-.080 -1.0		volts ma
Base Input Voltage, Common Emitter ($V_{CB} = -1v$; $I_C = -20ma$)	V_{BE}		-.255			-.243			-.230		volts
Collector Cutoff Current ($V_{CBO} = -30v$)	I_{CO}		-6	-12		-6	-12		-6	-12	μa
Emitter Cutoff Current ($V_{EBO} = -10v$)	I_{EO}		-4	-10		-4	-10		-4	-10	μa
Collector to Emitter Voltage ($R_{BE} \leqq 10K$ ohms; $I_C = -.6ma$)	V_{CER}	-25			-25			-25			volts
Reach-Through Voltage	V_{RT}	-25			-25			-25			volts

SMALL SIGNAL
CHARACTERISTICS

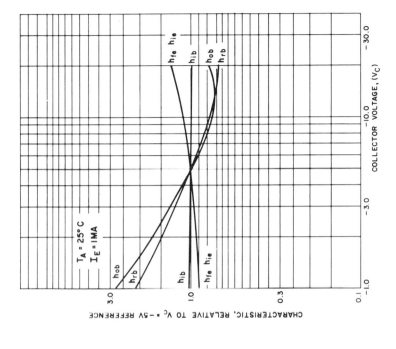

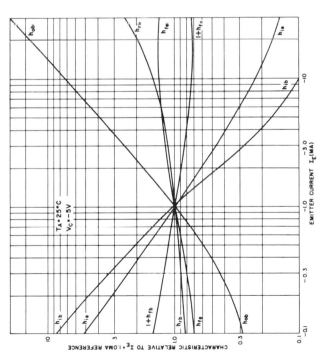

TYPES 2N1413, 2N1414, 2N1415

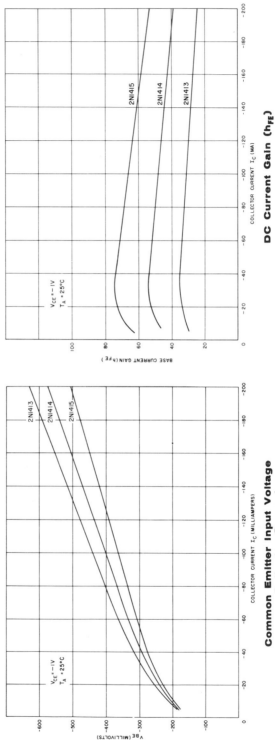

DC Current Gain (h_FE) vs. Collector Current

Common Emitter Input Voltage vs. Collector Current

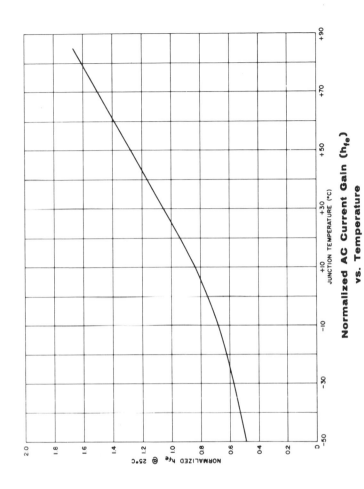

Normalized AC Current Gain (h_fe)
vs. Temperature

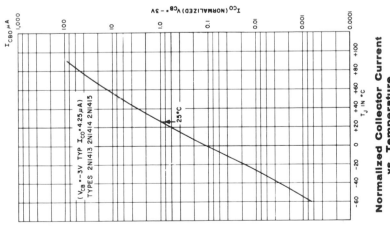

Normalized Collector Current
vs. Temperature

SILICON TYPES

2N1671 2N1671A 2N1671B

Computer-Industrial TRANSISTORS

WITH FIXED-BED CONSTRUCTION

The General Electric Silicon Unijunction Transistor is a three terminal device having a stable "N" type negative resistance characteristic over a wide temperature range. A stable peak point voltage, a low peak point current, and a high pulse current rating make this device useful in oscillators, timing circuits, trigger circuits and pulse generators where it can serve the purpose of two conventional silicon or germanium transistors.

The 2N1671 is intended for general purpose industrial applications where circuit economy is of primary importance. The 2N1671A is intended for industrial use in firing circuits for Silicon Controlled Rectifiers and other applications where a guaranteed minimum pulse amplitude is required. The 2N1671B is intended for applications where a low emitter leakage current and a low peak point emitter current (trigger current) are required.

These transistors feature Fixed-Bed Construction and are hermetically sealed in a welded case. All leads are electrically isolated from the case.

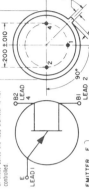

NOTE 1: This zone is controlled for automatic handling. The variation in actual diameter within this zone shall not exceed .010.

NOTE 2: Measured from max. diameter of the actual device.

NOTE 3: The specified lead diameter applies in the zone between .050 and .250 from the base seat. Between .250 and 1.5 maximum of .021 diameter is held. Outside of these zones the lead diameter is not controlled.

EMITTER   E   LEAD 1
BASE ONE   B1   GOLD LEADS
BASE TWO   B2

absolute maximum ratings (25°C)

RMS Power Dissipation	450	mw[1]
RMS Emitter Current	50	ma
Peak Emitter Current[2]	2	amperes
Emitter Reverse Voltage	30	volts
Interbase Voltage	35	volts
Operating Temperature Range	−65°C to +140°C	
Storage Temperature Range	−65°C to +150°C	

442

electrical characteristics (25°C)

PARAMETER	SYMBOL	NOTE	2N1671 MIN.	2N1671 MAX.	2N1671A MIN.	2N1671A MAX.	2N1671B MIN.	2N1671B MAX.	UNITS
Intrinsic Standoff Ratio ($V_{BB} = 10v$)	η	3	0.47	0.62	0.47	0.62	0.47	0.62	
Interbase Resistance ($V_{BB} = 3V$, $I_E = 0$)	R_{BBO}	4	4.7	9.1	4.7	9.1	4.7	9.1	$K\Omega$
Emitter Saturation Voltage ($V_{BB} = 10V$, $I_E = 50ma$)	$V_E(SAT)$			5		5		5	volts
Modulated Interbase Current ($V_{BB} = 10V$, $I_E = 50ma$)	$I_{B2}(MOD)$		6.8	22	6.8	22	6.8	22	ma
Emitter Reverse Current ($V_{B2E} = 30V$, $I_{B1} = 0$)	I_{EO}	Fig. 6		12		12		0.2	μa
Peak Point Emitter Current ($V_{BB} = 25V$)	I_p	Fig. 8		25		25		6	μa
Valley Point Current ($V_{BB} = 20V$, $R_{B2} = 100\Omega$)	I_v	Fig. 9	8		8		8		ma
Base-One Peak Pulse Voltage	V_{OB1}	5	3.0		3.0		3.0		volts

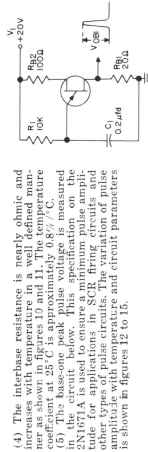

NOTES:

(1) Derate 3.9 MW/°C increase in ambient temperature (Thermal resistance to case $=0.16$°C/MW.)

(2) Capacitor discharge—10μfd or less, 30 volts or less—Total interbase power dissipation must be limited by external circuitry.

(3) The intrinsic standoff ratio, η, is essentially constant with temperature and interbase voltage. η is defined by the equation:

$$V_p = \eta V_{BB} + \frac{200}{T_J}$$

Where V_p=Peak point emitter voltage
V_{BB}=interbase voltage
T_J=Junction Temperature (Degrees Kelvin)

(4) The interbase resistance is nearly ohmic and increases with temperature in a well defined manner as shown in figures 10 and 11. The temperature coefficient at 25°C is approximately 0.8%/°C.

(5) The base-one peak pulse voltage is measured in the circuit below. This specification on the 2N1671A is used to ensure a minimum pulse amplitude for applications in SCR firing circuits and other types of pulse circuits. The variation of pulse amplitude with temperature and circuit parameters is shown in figures 12 to 15.

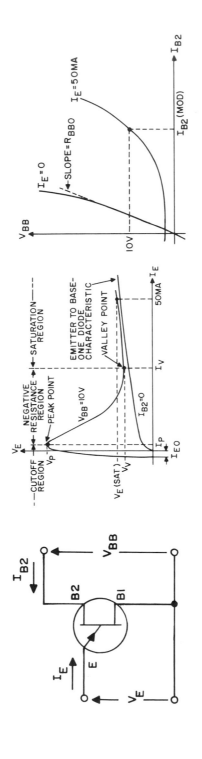

FIG. 3

Static interbase characteristic curves showing important parameters and measurement points.

FIG. 2

Static Emitter Characteristic curves showing important parameters and measurement points (exaggerated to show details).

FIG. 1

Unijunction Transistor Symbol with Nomenclature used for voltage and currents.

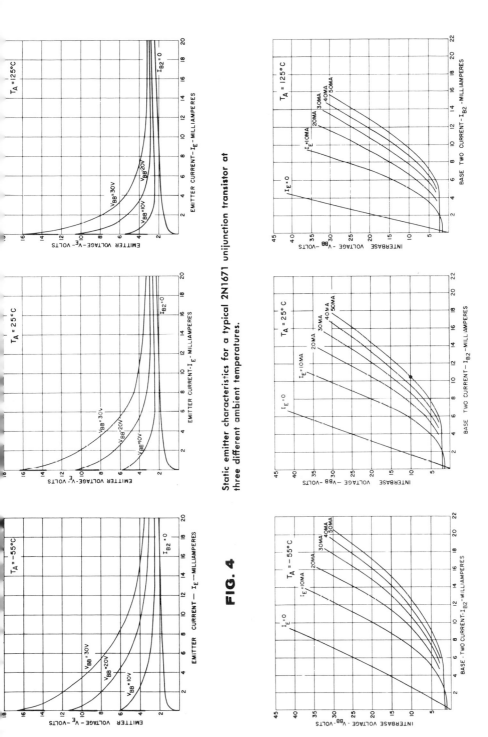

Static emitter characteristics for a typical 2N1671 unijunction transistor at three different ambient temperatures.

FIG. 4

Static interbase characteristics for a typical 2N1671 unijunction transistor at three different ambient temperatures.

FIG. 5

445

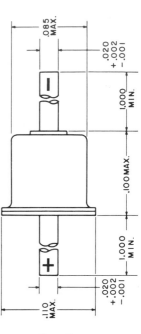

Computer–Industrial TUNNEL DIODES

GERMANIUM TYPES TD1-5 / TD1A-5A

The General Electric TD1 through TD5 and TD1A through TD5A are Germanium Tunnel Diodes offering peak currents of 1.0, 2.2, 4.7, 10, and 22 ma. These devices, which make use of the quantum mechanical tunneling phenomenon to obtain a negative conductance characteristic, are designed for low level switching and small signal applications at very high frequencies. All "A" version parameters are closely controlled for use in critical applications such as level detection, frequency converters, etc. These devices are housed in General Electric's new hermetically sealed subminiature axial package.

FEATURES:

▲ V_{FS} Specified for more accurate designing of load lines

▲ Low capacitance

▲ Fast speed

AXIAL DIODE OUTLINE

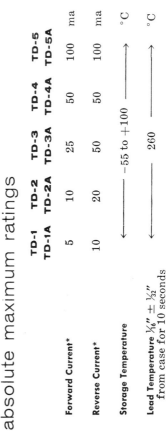

ALL DIMENSIONS IN INCHES.
DIMENSIONS ARE REFERENCE UNLESS TOLERANCED.

absolute maximum ratings

	TD-1 TD-1A	TD-2 TD-2A	TD-3 TD-3A	TD-4 TD-4A	TD-5 TD-5A	
Forward Current*	5	10	25	50	100	ma
Reverse Current*	10	20	50	50	100	ma
Storage Temperature			−55 to +100 →→			°C
Lead Temperature $\frac{1}{16}'' \pm \frac{1}{32}''$ from case for 10 seconds			260 →→			°C

*Derate maximum currents 1% per °C ambient temperature above 25°C.

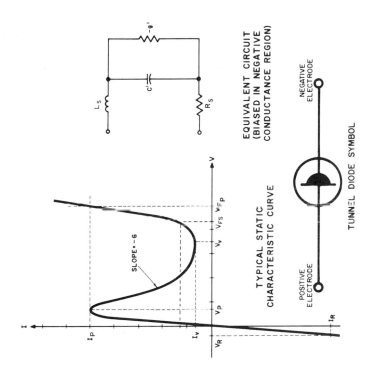

SLOPE = -G

TYPICAL STATIC
CHARACTERISTIC CURVE

EQUIVALENT CIRCUIT
(BIASED IN NEGATIVE
CONDUCTANCE REGION)

TUNNEL DIODE SYMBOL

POSITIVE
ELECTRODE

NEGATIVE
ELECTRODE

electrical characteristics:

STATIC CHARACTERISTICS

		TD-1			TD-1A			TD-2			TD-2A		
		Min.	Typ.	Max.	Min.	Typ.	Max.	Min.	Typ.	Max.	Min.	Typ.	Max.
Peak Point Current	I_P	0.9	1.0	1.1	0.975	1.000	1.025	2.0	2.2	2.4	2.15	2.20	2.25
Valley Point Current	I_V		0.12	0.18	.075	.095	.140		0.29	0.48	.165	.210	.310
Peak Point Voltage	V_P		65		58	65	72		65		58	65	72
Valley Point Voltage	V_V		350		315	355	395		350		315	355	395
Reverse Voltage ($I_R = I_P$ typ.)	V_R			40		20	40			40		20	40
Forward Voltage ($I_F = I_P$ typ.)	V_{FP}		500		475	510	535		500		475	510	535
($I_F = .25\ I_P$ typ.)	V_{FS}*				410	450					410	450	

DYNAMIC CHARACTERISTICS

		TD-1			TD-1A			TD-2			TD-2A		
		Min.	Typ.	Max.	Min.	Typ.	Max.	Min.	Typ.	Max.	Min.	Typ.	Max.
Total Series Inductance	L_S		0.5			0.5			0.5			0.5	
Total Series Resistance	R_S		1.5	4.0		1.7	4.0		1.0	3.0		1.1	3.0
Valley Point Terminal Capacitance	C		5	10		3.5	5.0		10	25		7.0	10.0
Max. Negative Terminal Conductance	$-G$		8		7.5	8.5	9.5		18		16	19	22
Resistive Cutoff Frequency	f_{ro}		2.3			3.2			2.2			3.0	
Self-Resonant Frequency	f_{xo}		3.2			3.8			2.2			2.7	
Frequency of Oscillation	F_{osc}**		3.2			3.8			2.2			2.7	
Rise Time	t_r***		1.7			1.7			1.6			1.6	

*V_{FS} is defined as the value of forward voltage at a forward current of one quarter the typical peak current.
**The frequency of oscillation (under short circuit conditions) for steady state large signal sinusoidal oscillation is given by equation (3) which is the maximum frequency attainable without capacitance compensation.

***Switching speed with constant current drive. $t_r \approx \dfrac{V_{FP} - V_P}{I_P - I_V}\, C$

	TD-3			TD-3A			TD-4			TD-4A			TD-5			TD-5A			
	Min.	Typ.	Max.	Min.	Typ.	Max.	Min.	Typ.	Max.	Min.	Typ.	Max.	Min.	Typ.	Max.	Min.	Typ.	Max.	
	4.2	4.7	5.2	4.58	4.70	4.82	9.0	10.0	11.0	9.75	10.00	10.25	20	22	24	21.5	22	22.5	ma
		0.60	1.04	.350	.45	.60		1.3	2.2	.75	.95	1.40		2.9	4.8	1.65	2.10	3.10	ma
		65		58	65	72		65		58	65	72		65		58	65	72	mv
		350		315	355	395		350		315	355	395		350		315	355	395	mv
			40		20	40			40		20	40			40		20	40	mv
		500		475	510	535		500		475	510	535		500		475	510	575	mv
				410	450					410	450					410	450		
		0.5			0.5			0.5			0.5			0.5			0.5		nh
		.50	2.0		.52	2.0		.30	1.5		.36	1.5		.20	1.0		.22	1.0	ohms
		25	50		13	25		50	90		27	50		90	150		55	100	pf
		40		36	41	46	75	80		75	85	95		180		160	190	220	10^{-3} mho
		1.8			3.4			1.6			2.8			1.6			2.6		KMC
		1.4			1.9			.97			1.3			.67			.78		KMC
		1.4			2.0			1.0			1.4			.74			.95		KMC
		1.4			1.4			1.3			1.3			1.2			1.2		nsec

$$f_{ro} = \frac{|g'|}{2\pi C'} \sqrt{\frac{1}{R_S |g'|} - 1} \qquad (1)$$

$$f_{xo} = \frac{1}{2\pi} \sqrt{\frac{1}{L_S C'} - \left(\frac{|g'|}{C'}\right)^2} \qquad (2)$$

$$f_{osc} = \frac{1}{2\pi} \sqrt{\frac{1}{L_S C} - \left(\frac{R_T}{L}\right)^2} \qquad (3)$$

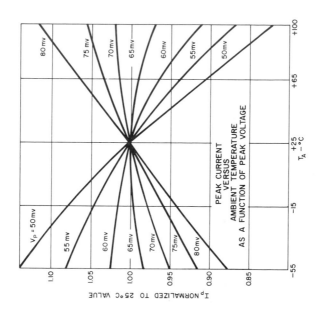

PEAK CURRENT
VERSUS
AMBIENT TEMPERATURE
AS A FUNCTION OF PEAK VOLTAGE

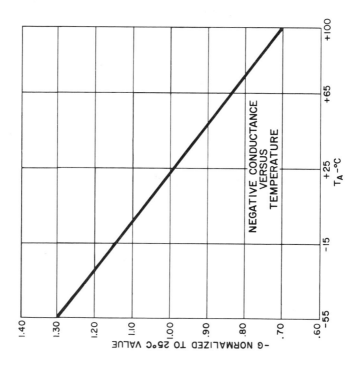

NEGATIVE CONDUCTANCE
VERSUS
TEMPERATURE

450

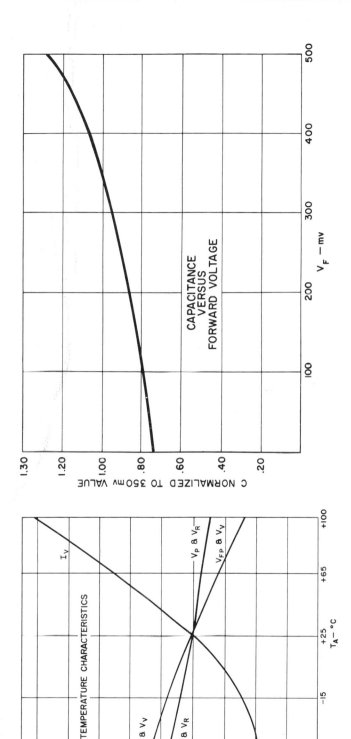

CAPACITANCE
VERSUS
FORWARD VOLTAGE

V_F — mv

C NORMALIZED TO 350mv VALUE

TEMPERATURE CHARACTERISTICS

I_V

V_P & V_R

V_{FP} & V_V

V_{FP} & V_V

V_P & V_R

I_V

T_A — °C

V_P, V_V, V_{FP}, V_R AND I_V NORMALIZED TO 25°C VALUE

rectifier

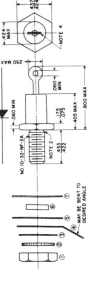

140.43 2/62

SERIES
1N3569—1N3574

SILICON
MEDIUM CURRENT RECTIFIER
3.50 A Up to 600 V

The 1N3569-74 series stud mounted device in the popular DO-4 package is designed especially for reliability and long life. This series is especially desirable in industrial applications that require high surge capabilities. In addition to this feature, the 1N3569-74 units have:

- Hermetically Sealed Housing
- Transient PRV Rating
- Low Forward Drop
- Operating Temperature up to 165°C

OUTLINE DRAWING

NOTES
1 UNIT MUST NOT BE DAMAGED BY TORQUE OF 15 IN LB APPLIED TO 10-32-NF-28 NUT ASSEMBLED ON THREAD.
2 DIA OF UNTHREADED PORTION .189 MAX AND .169 MIN.
3. COMPLETE THREADS TO EXTEND TO WITHIN 2 1/2 THREADS OF HEAD.
4 ANGULAR ORIENTATION OF THIS TERMINAL IS UNDEFINED.
5 MAXIMUM PITCH DIAMETER OF PLATED THREADS SHALL BE BASIC PITCH DIAMETER (.1697) REFERENCE SCREW THREAD STANDARD FOR FEDERAL SERVICES 1957 HANDBOOK H28 1957 PI.

COMPLIES WITH EIA REGISTERED OUTLINE DO-4

APPROX WEIGHT = .15 OZ

① 10-32 BRASS NI PL HEX NUT
② LOCK WASHER (EXT) STEEL NI PL
③ FLAT WASHER 7/16" OD .004 THK
④ TERMINAL .010 THK COPPER TIN PL
⑤ MICA WASHER .005 THK
⑥ TEFLON WASHER .032 WALL THK
⑦ MICA WASHER .005 THK

452

RATINGS AND SPECIFICATIONS
60 cps Resistive or Inductive Load

	1N3569	1N3570	1N3571	1N3572	1N3573	1N3574	
**Maximum Allowable Transient Peak Reverse Voltage (non-recurrent, 5 millisecond duration)	150	275	400	525	650	775	V
Maximum Allowable Repetitive Peak Reverse Voltage (PRV)	100	200	300	400	500	600	V
Maximum Allowable RMS Voltage	70	140	210	280	350	420	V
Maximum Allowable DC Blocking Voltage	100	200	300	400	500	600	V
*Maximum Allowable DC Output Current							
at 85°C Stud Temperature			3.50				Amps
at 150°C Stud Temperature			1.25				Amps
**Maximum Allowable Peak One Cycle Surge Current (60 cps single phase, non-recurrent) —See Fig. 5			35				Amps
**Minimum I²t Rating (non-recurrent) —See Fig. 6			3				Amp² sec
Maximum Full Load Voltage Drop (full cycle average at rated load) 150°C Ambient			0.5				V
Maximum Reverse Current (full cycle average at rated voltage) 150°C Ambient			0.4				ma
Maximum Operating Temperature			−65°C to +165°C				
Maximum Storage Temperature			−65°C to +175°C				
Thermal Characteristics							
Typical Thermal Impedance: Junction to Stud			10°C/W				

Notes: *For current ratings on fins and at other stud temperatures, see Figures 1 and 2. Stud temperature refers to temperature on outside flat of hex.

  **Rectifier must return to normal thermal equilibrium before reapplication of these overloads.

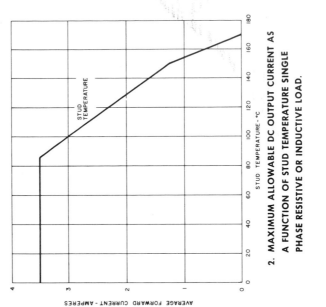

STUD TEMPERATURE

AVERAGE FORWARD CURRENT - AMPERES

STUD TEMPERATURE - °C

2. MAXIMUM ALLOWABLE DC OUTPUT CURRENT AS A FUNCTION OF STUD TEMPERATURE SINGLE PHASE RESISTIVE OR INDUCTIVE LOAD.

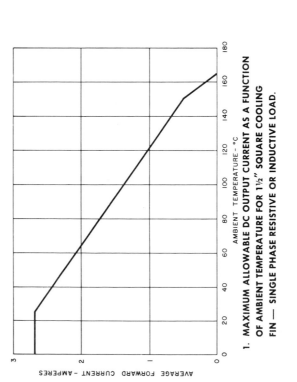

AVERAGE FORWARD CURRENT - AMPERES

AMBIENT TEMPERATURE - °C

1. MAXIMUM ALLOWABLE DC OUTPUT CURRENT AS A FUNCTION OF AMBIENT TEMPERATURE FOR 1½" SQUARE COOLING FIN — SINGLE PHASE RESISTIVE OR INDUCTIVE LOAD.

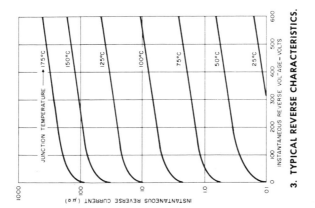

3. TYPICAL REVERSE CHARACTERISTICS.

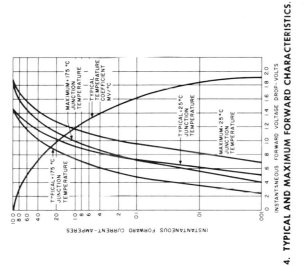

4. TYPICAL AND MAXIMUM FORWARD CHARACTERISTICS.

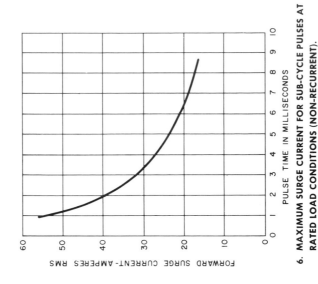

6. MAXIMUM SURGE CURRENT FOR SUB-CYCLE PULSES AT RATED LOAD CONDITIONS (NON-RECURRENT). CURVE USED IN CALCULATION OF I^2t.

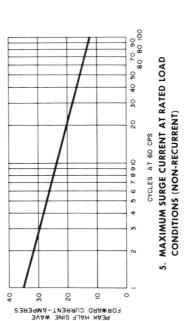

5. MAXIMUM SURGE CURRENT AT RATED LOAD CONDITIONS (NON-RECURRENT)

456

INDEX